With best wishes [illegible]
friend of The S[illegible]

J. Roger Hollingsworth

Creating a Tradition of Biomedical Research

Contributions to the History of The Rockefeller University

Edited by
Darwin H. Stapleton

THE ROCKEFELLER UNIVERSITY PRESS
NEW YORK

The Rockefeller University Press
New York

Library of Congress Cataloging-in-Publication Data

Creating a tradition of biomedical research : contributions to the history of the Rockefeller University / edited by Darwin H. Stapleton.
p. cm.
Includes bibliographical references and index.
ISBN 0-87470-061-2 (hardcover)
1. Rockefeller University--History. 2. Medicine, Experimental--New York (State)--New York--History--20th century. I. Stapleton, Darwin H.
R747.R69C74 2004
610'.7207471--dc22
2004019356

ISBN: 0-87470-061-2

Contents

Acknowledgments

This volume results from the Rockefeller University's centennial observance of 2000–2001. Dr. Torsten Wiesel, president of the University during the initial planning of the observance, generously agreed to a program of special grants-in-aid for scholarly research on the history of the University. The conference, which drew on research inspired by those grants, was supported by the subsequent president, Arnold Levine, and Executive Vice President Alice Lustig. Continued support from the University's Office of the President has made completion of this project possible. Others at the University whose collaboration was essential included Vice President for Finance John Harrigan, Assistant Vice President Robin Maloney, Dr. Elizabeth Hanson, and University Librarian Patricia Mackey and other members of the library staff.

At the Rockefeller University Press, Executive Director Michael Held provided the patience and commitment necessary for the publication of this historical volume. Suzanne Runyan, Rob O'Donnell, and Erinn Grady each generously contributed their time and skills. Every chapter has benefited from the consistent, capable, and resourceful editorial work of Aisha Caruth.

Many of the staff of the Rockefeller Archive Center played critical roles in the development of this volume. Camilla Harris managed all aspects of the November 13–14, 2000 conference, "Creating a Tradition of Biomedical Research," at the Rockefeller University; she also was responsible for the early organization and formatting of the essays. Norine Goodnough later took over management of this volume, and her assistance was instrumental in bringing it to completion. Chief Archivist Lee R. Hiltzik and Senior Archivist Renée Mastrocco cheerfully, efficiently, and accurately assisted with the research that underpins all of the chapters in this volume, and also responded to frequent queries during the editorial phase. They, along with Chief Archivists Erwin Levold and Thomas Rosenbaum, and Assistant Director Kenneth W. Rose, provided insightful commentary and editorial support when needed. As usual, Donna Stapleton made numerous contributions to the entire enterprise, serving as a sounding board, vetter of ideas, and a volunteer staff member.

I am grateful to Johns Hopkins University Press for giving permission to republish Bert Hansen's article in the *Bulletin of the History of Medicine* as chapter three of this volume. I also extend my thanks and deep appreciation to each author for participating in this effort to provide new perspectives on the history of the Rockefeller University.

Although this volume originated in the Rockefeller University's centennial observance, and has received the University's financial support, the selection of the contributors and the editorial responsibility for this volume have been mine. The views and judgments of the authors are theirs alone, and do not the represent the official views or judgments of the Rockefeller University.

Darwin H. Stapleton

Creating a Tradition of Biomedical Research

Contributions to the History of The Rockefeller University

Part I: Context

Chapter 1

The Rockefeller (University) Effect: A Phenomenon in Biomedical Science

Darwin H. Stapleton

Rockefeller Archive Center, The Rockefeller University, Sleepy Hollow, NY

At least since Francis Bacon depicted the ideal scientific institution in *The New Atlantis* (1626), Western literature has envisioned an island as the quintessential location for the pursuit of unfettered scientific research. In fact, in Sinclair Lewis's *Arrowsmith* (1925), the fictional McGurk Institute—modeled after the Rockefeller Institute for Medical Research in New York City—was referred to as a "Grecian isle," even though its location was in the heart of bustling Manhattan.[1]

The Rockefeller University, founded as the Rockefeller Institute for Medical Research (RIMR) in 1901, has approached the image of the ideal research institution portrayed by Bacon and Lewis, and is often described as an oasis of learning. However, its life history is best understood if it is viewed not as a walled-off sanctuary, but as a continuing symposium open to other individuals and institutions. The two most important sets of connections for The Rockefeller have been those that have bound it to a network of Rockefeller-related institutions, and those that have linked it to other worldwide biomedical research institutions. These connections [illegible] uenced the lives and careers of biomedical researchers throughout the world, and have [illegible] what might be termed as the "Rockefeller effect." A consideration of those influences is [illegible] to this volume's collection of essays on the history of the Rockefeller University.

[illegible] is important to recognize that the university's connections to ideas, people, and institu[illegible] nd its effect on them, have much to do with the shaping of the twentieth century and [illegible] ablishing an agenda for biomedical research in the twenty-first century. They place [illegible] ller University near the center of such important currents as the globalization of scien[illegible] ication and knowledge; the integration of science, medicine, and technology; and the [illegible] s of market capitalism, government, and educational institutions. In particular, the [illegible] ion of philanthropy and research at the university has served as a magnet for highly [illegible] d, highly imaginative, seekers of change.[2] Thirty years ago Kenneth Clark, in a sweeping [illegible] w of the rise of Western civilization, argued that it was a measure of science's high esteem [illegible] dern life that the most capable people are drawn to it and judged by their contributions, [illegible] ss of cultural and national origins.[3] Certainly Rogers Hollingsworth's essay in this [illegible] demonstrates that generation after generation of outstanding researchers have come [illegible] Rockefeller University from all over the globe. To understand the milieu that has drawn and sustained them, we need to look not only at the scientific core of the institution but also its setting and interrelationships.

Rockefeller Philanthropy

John D. Rockefeller Sr., who founded RIMR, was raised in a Baptist household in which the idea of tithing to the church was firmly instilled. For example, his first personal account book, begun at sixteen after receiving his first salary, listed donations to his church, missionary causes, and the poor.[4] This practice of giving continued throughout his life at a rate that met the biblical goal of the tithe, and then exceeded it when he began to donate large sums to establish or support organizations.[5]

It is important to understand that Rockefeller's Christianity was stamped with the evangelical passions of upstate New York and northern Ohio that not only promoted a heavenly reward but also a belief in the potential perfectibility of humans on Earth. Both Rockefeller and his wife, Laura Spelman Rockefeller, were raised in households that supported the abolition of slavery even before the American Civil War. In their married life, they were committed to such causes as controlling or prohibiting the use of alcoholic beverages, saving orphaned or delinquent children, wholesome recreation, and aid to African Americans.[6] Thus, Rockefeller's philanthropic acts were intended not just to relieve suffering, but were made explicitly to provide for human improvement. His habit of carefully considering or even investigating every potential recipient was an attempt to ensure that his money would be used wisely to achieve long-term goals.

Although Rockefeller was not alone in this style of giving, over the years his philanthropy included two elements that were unusual. First, he had more money to give than any of his predecessors. The success of Rockefeller's Standard Oil corporation in the 1880s made him very wealthy; after the turn of the century, he became the richest man in the United States—exceeding even Andrew Carnegie's fortune by a substantial margin.[7] Second, Rockefeller's genius in creating the modern corporate business form was paralleled only by his skill in shaping nonprofit entities or what he famously called "the business of benevolence."[8] He was remarkably successful in creating long-lived organizations in both sectors.

The factors in Rockefeller's organizational genius that are easiest to isolate are planning and delegation. In fact, his strategic thinking could be compared to a great general or admiral, who studied the field of engagement with great care, made every preparation for failures as well as successes, who kept the long-range goals always in mind, and who trusted his personally chosen field officers to make appropriate tactical judgments.[9] In the most recent Rockefeller biography, Chernow noted that Rockefeller "believed there was a time to think and a time to act. He brooded over problems and quietly matured plans over extended periods. Once he had made up his mind, however, he was no longer troubled by doubts and pursued his vision with undeviating faith."[10]

Equipped with this steely mind and indomitable purpose, Rockefeller was a major figure in reshaping the role of philanthropy in American life. Although Andrew Carnegie, Margaret Olivia Sage, and a few others were also pioneers in systematic philanthropy, it could be argued that Rockefeller set a standard for the disposition of industrial wealth that has not since had its equal in either scale or long-term effects.[11] Guided by experts and advisers, and always adhering to his core belief that education and health were fundamental to the improvement of humankind, Rockefeller focused on creating organizations that would alleviate the root causes of human problems.[12] In retrospect, it is clear that he fundamentally affected the course of the twentieth century by founding, or taking a major role in founding, Spelman College in 1884 (the first higher education institution for African American women in the United States); the University of Chicago in 1884 (one of the earliest post-graduate institutions in the United States); RIMR in 1901 (the first biomedical research institute in the United States); the General Education Board in 1902 (by far the largest philanthropic organization dedicated to the improvement of education in the American South); the Rockefeller Foundation in 1913 (the largest global philanthropy of the first half of the twentieth century); the International Health Board in 1913 (dedicated to worldwide public health, and successor to the short-lived Rockefeller Sanitary Commission for the Eradication of Hookworm Disease); and the Laura Spelman Rockefeller Memorial in 1918 (the first large-scale philanthropy dedicated to support of the social sciences).[13] He capped this sequence of acts, which transferred half of his wealth to charity, by giving virtually all the rest of his fortune to his son, John D. Rockefeller Jr., who continued his father's tradition of creating institutions as a means of perpetuating philanthropic goals.[14]

Founding the RIMR

Nowhere is Rockefeller's style more evident than in the founding of RIMR. Because he held a deep interest in health, Rockefeller made significant gifts to medical colleges and research hospitals.[15] When at the turn of the century his philanthropic adviser Frederick Gates, and Rockefeller's son, Junior, approached him with a vision of building a substantial medical research organization, the elder Rockefeller was receptive but demanded a thorough consideration of its possible functions, goals, and form. It took nearly a year to satisfy him, and for a few years after its founding he kept a tight leash on the RIMR budget.[16]

Rockefeller did not interfere in the least with the researchers or their research even though, as Bert Hansen's article demonstrates, medical research was a new and only recently respectable idea. He allowed his son and Gates to monitor and report, and the first director, Simon Flexner, to administer the new organization without restraint. As in his business life, Rockefeller was content to have well-chosen leaders carry out his projects. In this case, it was a two-pronged design including the creation of a laboratory-centered institute searching for new ways to attack disease while at the same time nurturing a generation of young investigators who would travel throughout the United States and the world with cutting-edge research agendas. Flexner, whose style of leadership matched Rockefeller's inclinations, was an exemplar of the modern laboratory director.[17] Bernard Unti's contribution to this collection shows that he had excellent public relations skills as well.

The second prong of the design is less appreciated than the first one. The desire to have RIMR serve as a wellspring of biomedical research for the entire globe is reflected in the trustees' early decision to initiate a grant-giving program, an effort that continued for fifteen years.[18] Small grants to researchers in the United States and Europe not only nurtured scientific medicine when the link between science and medicine was still a fragile one but also helped establish relationships between RIMR and a wide range of laboratories.[19] From the beginning, the RIMR needed well-trained young researchers to carry out the imaginative agendas of the laboratory heads recruited by Flexner, and it was important to know where leading research was occurring.

Simon and Abraham Flexner

RIMR's connections with other researchers and research programs were facilitated by its close relationships with the other Rockefeller philanthropies, primarily the Rockefeller Foundation.[20] Simon Flexner was the most obvious embodiment of these relationships. He served as a trustee of the Rockefeller Foundation for over fifteen years (1913–1929), often sitting at the center of discussions dealing with medical and scientific questions. Robert Kohler has noted that Flexner's "endorsement in any [Foundation] matter could be decisive."[21] In 1915, Flexner was made a trustee of the China Medical Board, a spin-off from the Foundation, and in that same year he was one of the board's commissioners who visited medical and research institutions in Japan and Korea before undertaking an extensive review of Chinese hospitals and medical schools. In 1916, he was elected a trustee of the Peking Union Medical College (created by the China Medical Board), and later went to its opening ceremonies in Beijing in 1921.[22] He also was a trustee of the International Health Board from its inception in 1913 until its merger with the Rockefeller Foundation in 1928.

In terms of his influence on Rockefeller philanthropy in general, it should be noted that Flexner was a personal friend of John D. Rockefeller Jr., the chairman of the Rockefeller Foundation and creator of the International Education Board. In fact, Flexner and his wife Helen often visited Rockefeller Jr. and his wife Abby, and spent summers near the Rockefellers at Seal Harbor, Maine.[23] On several occasions, Flexner assisted the Rockefeller family by arranging for RIMR hospital physicians to accompany them on their travels or by providing consultations on medical conditions.[24]

Another relationship of importance to the course of Rockefeller philanthropy was Simon's closeness to his brother Abraham Flexner who, drawing substantially on his brother's views and experience, wrote a monumentally influential report on medical education in the United States and Canada (1910) for the Carnegie Foundation for the Advancement of Teaching.[25] Soon after, Abraham became an officer of the General Education Board and was the central figure in creating its new program of aid to medical schools; a few years later, he also became an officer of the Rockefeller Foundation. In 1930, Abraham Flexner became the founding director of the Institute for Advanced Study, whose leading scientists often traveled to RIMR in the 1930s and 1940s.

The Institute and the Foundation

All of the RIMR's directors after Simon Flexner, through Frederick Seitz (1968–1978), simultaneously served as trustees of the Rockefeller Foundation. These interconnects fostered certain direct relationships that lasted for over fifty years. After the United States's entry into World War I, for example, the Foundation established on RIMR's campus a War Demonstration Hospital for the improvement of surgical techniques to repair battle wounds. Headed by RIMR's Nobel Prize-winning Alexis Carrel, whose innovations are described in this volume by Shelley McKellar, the hospital gave specialized training to dozens of military surgeons and doctors, and in the process acquainted them with RIMR.

At about the same time the International Health Board, which collaborated closely with the Rockefeller Foundation, began to investigate the possibilities of a global anti–yellow fever campaign. As Aya Takahashi notes in her essay, RIMR researcher Hideyo Noguchi was quickly drawn into this project, leading a Foundation-supported research team to Guayaquil, Ecuador in 1918 to establish a temporary laboratory with a goal of identifying a microbial cause of yellow fever. For the same purpose, he later traveled to Mexico, Peru, and Brazil at the behest of the Foundation, and died—a martyr to scientific medicine—on a Foundation yellow fever expedition to West Africa.[26]

In 1929, the Foundation decided to place a virus research laboratory on the RIMR campus, and staffed it with outstanding figures like Max Theiler, who received a Nobel Prize in 1950 for developing a vaccine for yellow fever. This laboratory, though completely funded by the

Foundation and operating under its direction, was integrated with the operations of RIMR at a number of levels. Its staff used the facilities of the RIMR, including its library and the dining room—famous for its scientific interactions. The virus laboratory was the site for the development of important instrumentation, such as the ultracentrifuge and the electron microscope, which were shared with RIMR.[27] There was also a certain exchange of staff: for example, Frank Horsfall, an epidemiologist, moved from the virus laboratory to the Institute in 1941; and Jordi Casals, an immunologist, went from the Institute to the virus laboratory in the 1952.[28] Until the virus laboratory was relocated to Yale University in 1964, it was deeply interwoven with the life of the Institute.[29]

During the quarter century heyday of global Rockefeller philanthropic support of the natural and medical sciences, about 1925–1950, the RIMR also served as a major destination for Rockefeller-supported scientific tours of the United States.[30] Beginning with the fellowship programs of the short-lived International Education Board—founded by John D. Rockefeller Jr. in 1923, and merged with the Rockefeller Foundation in 1928—and the International Health Board, and continuing through the 1930s and 1940s, the Institute (being in the port city where ocean liners from Europe most often discharged their passengers) was often the first stop for overseas recipients of what were unofficially known as "Rockefeller traveling fellowships."[31] RIMR hosted dozens of such visitors for periods of a few days to several months. Sometimes they were merely brief observers, but often they received substantial instruction in particular laboratory procedures, and occasionally they joined a laboratory's staff, participating in its research program.[32] In the records of visitors who came under the auspices of other Rockefeller organizations one may read such remarks as: "Rockefeller Institute Dr. Carrel arranged for B. to see techniques used in the cultivation of tissues" (Arthur Neville Burkett, Australia, 1924), and "C.'s experience at [the RIMR's Princeton, New Jersey laboratories] is all that he has dreamed of. He is taking up a new line of work there, namely a problem of Kunkel's on the transmission of plant viruses. . . ." (Alvaro Santos Costa, Brazil, 1942–1943).[33]

Such visitors both spread the research gospel of the Institute, and brought to it word of the latest developments elsewhere. For some of these visitors, the Institute was not just a stop along the way, but a primary destination. As Elizabeth Hanson noted

> In the first half of the [twentieth] century, before formal postdoctoral training became routine, a stint at the Institute became almost a prerequisite—although an unofficial one—for young scientists pursuing a research career [in biomedical science]. The concentration of renowned researchers, and opportunities for short-term research appointments, drew a steady stream of fresh ideas and scientific expertise to the Institute.[34]

Many of those researchers were physicians, and their commitment to research and education led them to positions of leadership in U.S. medical schools, and throughout the world. For example, Dr. John Auer received a medical degree from Johns Hopkins in 1902, and then conducted research at RIMR from 1903 to 1921 (less two years as an instructor at Harvard). He moved to the St. Louis University (Missouri) School of Medicine, where for twenty-seven years he was a professor of pharmacology and later the director of that department.[35]

Certainly the Institute's intended role as a postgraduate teaching and training institution often served the purposes of the Rockefeller Foundation. A small, but consistent, number of its fellowships were essentially educational stipends intended to substantially upgrade a fellow's knowledge and skills, and often to equip them to take positions with Rockefeller Foundation-funded institutions in medicine and public health. Although many fellows who received this kind of support were sent to traditional graduate programs at Johns Hopkins, Cornell, Harvard, Chicago, and other leading schools, a steady stream came to RIMR. This program contributed substantially to the international cast of RIMR, bringing Chinese, Latin American, and European researchers to the laboratories beginning in the 1910s.[36] In the 1950s and 1960s, when the Rockefeller Foundation was consciously involved in improving race relations, the fellowship program brought outstanding African American researchers to the campus.[37]

There was also a modest reverse flow of RIMR staff who temporarily went to Rockefeller-related institutions. Most notably, Alfred E. Cohn, Henry Houghton, Ann G. Kuttner, Louise Pearce, Carl Ten Broeck, and Donald Van Slyke went to the Peking Union Medical College—opened in 1921 under the auspices of the Rockefeller Foundation's China Medical Board.[38] While engaged in their mission to found a tradition of scientific medical education in China by teaching Chinese students, they served as evaluators for the Foundation's fellowship program, recommending especially promising young investigators who were sent to RIMR.[39] The first, Dr. Edgar Chen, arrived in 1918.

A more complex kind of diffusion of RIMR expertise, illustrated by the career of Dr. Edmund V. Cowdry, also occurred under the reach of the Foundation but in collaboration with RIMR. Cowdry received a PhD in anatomy from the University of Chicago (1913), and taught first there, and then at Johns Hopkins. In 1917, he took an appointment at the Peking Union Medical College, and then went to RIMR from 1921 to 1928 as an Associate Member. He moved to Washington University (St. Louis, Missouri) in 1928, and in the 1930s he received Rockefeller Foundation funding for his cytology laboratory. Although he served on the Rockefeller Foundation Yellow Fever Commission, he remained at Washington University until retirement. Cowdry's career, thoroughly and remarkably shaped by a trajectory through Rockefeller-related institutions, was the epitome of the Rockefeller effect on many other biomedical researchers of his generation. Often the molding of a life in science by Rockefeller appointments, fellowships, and grants is not fully revealed by scientists' biographies and autobiographies, which tend to depict careers as a fabric of research problems. But for hundreds of scientists, including some of the women discussed in Elizabeth Hanson's essay, the Rockefeller effect was substantial.

Other Connections and Networks

The Rockefeller University, throughout its hundred years, has had strong connections with many organizations in addition to the Rockefeller Foundation and its allied philanthropies. The directors and presidents of the University themselves had significant outside relationships. Flexner had connections with German laboratories both from his medical studies there in 1891 and his post-appointment travels, which also took him to the Pasteur Institute in Paris, in 1903–1904.[40] Among others, he established a friendship with Paul Ehrlich, the great immunologist, and arranged for him a gift of $10,000 from John D. Rockefeller Sr. when Ehrlich's Institute at Frankfurt had a funding shortage.[41] Participating in the Rockefeller Foundation's mission to east Asia in 1915 gave Flexner a set of contacts there.

As Abigail O'Sullivan describes it in her contribution, Flexner's successors Herbert Gasser and Detlev Bronk had strong affiliations with British neurophysiology laboratories that resulted in campus visits and student migrations. Bronk and later Frederick Seitz were presidents of the U.S. National Academy of Sciences, which brought them into a vast web of American scientists; Seitz was an adviser to the Republic of China on Taiwan.[42] Joshua Lederberg, David Baltimore, and Torsten Wiesel, presidents in the 1970s, 1980s, and 1990s, respectively, served on numerous corporate, philanthropic, and government boards and commissions. Arnold Levine was at two leading biomedical research institutions (the State University of New York at Stony Brook and Princeton University) before coming to the Rockefeller University in 1998–2002.

The faculty of the university have equally important connections to scientific organizations and networks. In the early years, there were affiliations with the Naples (Italy) Zoological Station and the Woods Hole (Massachusetts) Marine Biological Station, sites not only of research but also of symposia where cutting-edge research was discussed and critiqued.[43] In the latter part of the century, faculty had collaborative relationships, or visiting appointments, at biomedical foci such as Cold Spring Harbor Laboratory (New York), the Salk Institute (California), and the Weizmann Institute (Israel). For over a half-century, Rockefeller faculty have collaborated with researchers at the Memorial Sloan-Kettering Cancer Center, and the New York Presbyterian Hospital–Cornell University Medical Center, which are adjacent to the University's campus in New York City. In 1956, The Population Council—an organization created by John D. Rockefeller 3rd in 1952—established laboratories at the University (now called the Center for Biomedical Research), and its faculty have worked closely with a number of University faculty. In 1986, the University became an affiliate of the Howard Hughes Medical Institute (HHMI), a foundation that appoints and funds biomedical researchers who perform their work at existing centers. By 2001, there were eleven HHMI investigators at the University, tenured faculty who once a year present their research to other HHMI researchers gathered from all over the United States.

Combined with the ebb and flow of researchers and graduate students (since the graduate program began in 1955) who have come to the University, and who have left to join other institutions, or even to found them,[44] the multi-faceted connections of the faculty and administration have given the University an important set of linkages to the global biomedical research community.

Conclusion

The history of the first century of the Rockefeller University is a record of connectivity—of both persons and institutions—and effects, that give it global significance. Just as the city of New York from inception has been an international crossroads for people and ideas,[45] the University has been part of a global network. Geographically on an island, it never has been isolated in its roles in the philanthropic and scientific communities.

Each of the following essays, in addition to revealing a particular aspect of the history of the Rockefeller University, in some way connects it to the scientific currents and social fabric of the twentieth century. This volume responds to the call of the distinguished historian of medicine and science, Charles Rosenberg, who asked fellow historians to locate research institutions within "the developing ecology of knowledge."[46] What follows recounts some of the extraordinary achievements that have occurred on that small space on the east side of Manhattan, while reminding us that those achievements were linked to the world. To paraphrase a famous passage in a poem by John Donne: Rockefeller has not been an island, entire of itself; it has been a piece of the continent, and a part of the globe.

Endnotes

1. Sinclair Lewis, *Arrowsmith* (New York, 1941), 290; Francis Bacon, *New Atlantis* (Los Angeles, CA, 1985).
2. Abraham Flexner, *Medical Education: A Comparative Study* (New York, 1925), 293. In a review of American and European medical research institutions in 1925, Flexner argued that they were places where "workers and teachers from every corner of the compass are brought into close and stimulating contact."
3. Kenneth Clark, *Civilisation: A Personal View* (London, 1971), 35.
4. John D. Rockefeller, Sr., ledger A, series F, Record Group 1, Rockefeller Family Archives, Rockefeller Archive Center, Sleepy Hollow, New York (hereafter RAC). The Rockefeller Archive Center is a division of the Rockefeller University.
5. John Ensor Harr and Peter J. Johnson, *The Rockefeller Century* (New York, 1988), 22, 60–2.
6. Ibid. 16–17, 25; Kenneth W. Rose, "John D. Rockefeller's Philanthropy and Problems in Fundraising at Cleveland's Floating Bethel Mission and the Home for Aged Colored People," *Ohio History* 108 (1999): 145–61; Darwin H. Stapleton, "Religion, Reform, Race (and Rockefeller): Cleveland History Viewed through the Lens of Philanthropy," in *From All Sides: Philanthropy in the Western Reserve*, ed. Gladys Haddad (Cleveland, OH, 1995), 20–9.
7. Michael Klepper and Robert Gunther, "The American Heritage 40," in *American Heritage* (1998) October: 56–7.
8. Two eminent historians of business refer to "Rockefeller's managerial genius," Thomas C. Cochran and William Miller, *The Age of Enterprise: A Social History of Industrial America*. Rev. ed. (New York, 1962), 144. See also Alfred D. Chandler, *The Visible Hand: The Managerial Revolution in American Business* (Cambridge, MA, 1977), 321–26, 418–24; and Robert H. Bremner, *American Philanthropy* (Chicago, 1960), 117.
9. Ron Chernow, *Titan: The Life of John D. Rockefeller Sr.* (New York, 1998), 223–4, 228–9. Chernow's biography, the most recent, builds on a series of studies of Rockefeller that begin with the muckraking books on the Standard Oil empire of a hundred years ago. The standard biography for nearly a half-century was Allan Nevins, *Study in Power: John D. Rockefeller, Industrialist and Philanthropist*, 2 vols. (New York, 1953).
10. Chernow, *Titan* (n. 9 above), 230.
11. Brief entrées into the goals of American foundations and philanthropy in the twentieth century include: Barry D. Karl and Stanley N. Katz, "The American Private Philanthropic Foundations and the Public Sphere, 1890–1930," *Minerva* 19 (Summer 1981): 236–70; and Barry D. Karl, "Foundations and Public Policy," in *Encyclopedia of the United States in the Twentieth Century*, ed. Stanley I. Kutler, Robert Dallek, David A. Hollinger, and Thomas K. McCraw. (New York, 1996), 1:491–512.
12. John D. Rockefeller Sr., *Random Reminiscences of Men and Events* (Tarrytown, NY, 1984), 95. When he had amassed sufficient resources to do so, Rockefeller's philanthropic strategy focused entirely on long-term attempts to remedy the causes of human misery rather than the short-term amelioration of problems. In 1909, he remarked that "to help the sick and distressed appeals to the kindhearted always, but to help the investigator who is striving successfully to attack the causes which bring about sickness and distress does not so strongly attract the giver of money."
13. For a discussion of the early years of several of these institutions see Kenneth W. Rose and Darwin H. Stapleton, "Toward a 'Universal Heritage': Education and the Development of Rockefeller Philanthropy, 1884–1913," *Teachers College Record* 93 (Spring 1992): 536–55.
14. Joseph, W. Ernst, ed., *"Dear Father"/"Dear Son": Correspondence of John D. Rockefeller and John D. Rockefeller, Jr.* (New York, 1994), 67–8.
15. Kenneth W. Rose, comp., *A Guide to John D. Rockefeller's Charities Index Cards*. Rev. ed. (Sleepy Hollow, NY, 1998) lists gifts totaling $5,000 or more for five hospitals and dispensaries, and smaller gifts to over a dozen other hospitals in the years up to 1902.
16. The standard history of the first fifty years of the Rockefeller University is George Corner. *A History of*

the Rockefeller Institute, 1901–1953 (New York, 1964). Elizabeth Hanson has recently surveyed the University's first century in *Achievements: A Century of Science for the Benefit of Humankind, 1901–2001* (New York, 2000). For the founding of the Rockefeller Institute for Medical Research see also Howard S. Berliner, *A System of Scientific Medicine: Philanthropic Foundations in the Flexner Era* (New York, 1985), 53–91; and Robert S. Morison, "Frederick T. Gates and The Rockefeller Institute for Medical Research," in *Trends in Biomedical Research, 1901–1976.* Proceedings of the Second Rockefeller Archive Center Conference, December 10, 1976 (North Tarrytown, NY, 1977), 3–11.

17. The only book-length study of Flexner claims that "The Kaiser Wilhelm Institute in Berlin was directly modeled on Flexner's organization of the Rockefeller Institute." John Thomas Flexner, *An American Saga: The Story of Helen Thomas and Simon Flexner* (New York, 1993), 441. Nathan Reingold, a leading observer of American science, argued that Flexner's leadership model was so influential that "when the federal government expanded its role in medicine [after World War II], the National Institutes of Health clearly showed the imprint of his achievements." See Nathan Reingold, ed., *Science in America: A Documentary History, 1900–1939* (Chicago, 1981), 169.
18. Corner, *History of Rockefeller* (n. 16 above), 44–6.
19. Ibid., 44–6, summarizes the grant program and its significance, but a thorough study of the program is needed.
20. It is worth noting that for the four years after the Rockefeller Foundation was created in 1913, up to $2,000,000 a year was set aside for purposes to be designated by John D. Rockefeller Sr. According to the Foundation's published annual reports, from 1914 to 1917 over $2,900,000 was given to the Rockefeller Institute for Medical Research (RIMR) as founder's designations, and during the years 1915–1919, the Foundation gave RIMR an additional $4,700,000 for endowment and research.
21. Robert E. Kohler, *Partners in Science: Foundations and Natural Scientists, 1900–1945* (Chicago, 1991), 55, 56, 78 (quote), 88, 97, 126, 138, 140, 143–4, 237, 291–4; Reingold, *Science in America,* 221, 340–44.
22. John Z. Bowers, *Western Medicine in a Chinese Palace: Peking Union Medical College, 1917–1951* (New York, 1972), 44, 48–56.
23. "Simon Flexner, 1909–1957," folder 453, box 61, Friends and Services series, RG 2, Office of the Messrs. Rockefeller, Rockefeller Family Archives, RAC; Bernice Kert, *Abby Aldrich Rockefeller: The Woman in the Family* (New York, 1993), 130.
24. For example, Dr. Ralph H. Boots accompanied John D. Rockefeller Jr.'s family on a summer trip to Europe in 1923, and Dr. William S. Tillett went along on travels through the western United States in 1924: John D. Rockefeller Jr. to Simon Flexner, 7 August 1923, and Simon Flexner to John D. Rockefeller Jr., 19 September 1924, John D. Rockefeller Jr. folder, reel 99, Simon Flexner Papers (microfilm of originals at the American Philosophical Society), RAC.
25. Abraham Flexner. *Medical Education in the United States and Canada* (New York, 1910).
26. Corner, *History of Rockefeller* (n. 16 above), 189–94.
27. Ibid., 184–85; 22 September 1936, Warren Weaver diary, RG 12.1, Rockefeller Foundation Archives, RAC. The first electron microscope used by Institute staff, 1943–1945, was located at the offices of the Interchemical Company on the west side of Manhattan; in 1944, the virus laboratory purchased a microscope specifically to share with the Institute. See Carol L. Moberg, "The Electron Microscope Enters the Realm of the Intact Cell," *Journal of Experimental Medicine* 181 (March 1995): 831–7; J. H. Bauer, memorandum on electron microscope, 3 November 1943, folder 83, box 10, series 100, RG 100, Rockefeller Foundation Archives, RAC.
28. Corner, *History of Rockefeller* (n. 16 above), 387, 466.
29. An introduction to the history of the virus laboratory is provided by Wilbur G. Downs, "The Rockefeller Foundation Virus Program: 1951–1971 with Update to 1981" *Annual Review of Medicine* 33 (1982): 1–29.
30. Among other descriptions of Rockefeller philanthropic influence on the development of the natural and medical sciences, see Robert E. Kohler, *Partners in Science: Natural Scientists and Foundations* (Chicago, 1991); and Pnina G. Abir-Am, "The Strategy of Large versus Small Scale Investments, 1930–1960: The Rockefeller Foundation's International Network of Protein Research Projects," in *American Foundations and Large-Scale Research: Construction and Transfer of Knowledge*, ed. Giuliana Gemelli (Bologna, 2001), 71–90.

31. The standard history of the International Education Board is George W. Gray. *Education on an International Scale: A History of the International Education Board, 1923–1938* (New York, 1941). See also a recent study, Reinhard Siegmund-Schultze, "Support by Rockefeller's International Education Board for the Cooperation of Physics and Mathematics at Göttingen and Paris in the 1920s and 1930s," in *American Foundations and Large-Scale Research: Construction and Transfer of Knowledge*, ed. Giuliana Gemelli (Bologna, 2001), 51–67; and John Farley, *To Cast Out Disease: A History of the International Health Board* (New York, 2003).
32. For example, Ludwik Louis Chrobak of the Jagellonian University in Cracow, Poland joined W. G. Wyckoff's laboratory at the Institute for studies of x-ray crystallography in 1931–1932: fellowship recorder card for Chrobak, Natural Sciences Division, Rockefeller Foundation Archives, RAC.
33. Fellowship recorder cards for Arthur Neville Burkett. Australia, Division of Medical Education, and Alvaro Santos Costa, Brazil, Natural Sciences Division, Rockefeller Foundation Archives, RAC.
34. Hanson, *Achievements: Century of Science*, 41.
35. Jules Hirsch, "The Role of Clinical Investigation in Medicine: Historical Perspectives from Rockefeller University," *Perspectives in Biology and Medicine* 41 (Autumn 1997): 117; "Dr. John Auer, 73, is Dead," *New York Times*, 2 May 1948, p. 76.
36. Although few historians have commented on the significance of the fellowship programs of the Rockefeller philanthropies. the following articles are suggestive: Stanley Coben, "The Scientific Establishment and the Transmission of Quantum Mechanics to the United States, 1919–1932," *American Historical Review* 76 (1971): 442–66; Laurence A. Schneider, "Genetics in Republican China," in *Science and Medicine in Twentieth-Century China: Research and Education*, eds. John Z. Bowers, J. William Hess, and Nathan Sivin (Ann Arbor, MI, 1988), 3–29; Marcos Cueto, "The Rockefeller Foundation's Medical Policy and Scientific Research in Latin America: The Case of Physiology," in *Social Studies of Science* 20 (1990): 229–54
37. See Charles W. Johnson Sr., *The Spirit of a Place Called Meharry: The Strength of its Past to Shape its Future* (Franklin, TN, 2000), 132–7. I thank Quentin Jones, archivist at Meharry Medical College, for this reference. See also the fellowship recorder card for Charles William Johnson, Rockefeller Foundation Archives, RAC, which notes that half-way into Johnson's first fellowship year (1957–1958), "Dr. Merrill Chase [of the RIMR] called to inquire about a second year for [Johnson]. He is very much pleased with [Johnson] and feels that a second year would be very important to completing his training." Chase's request was approved, and Johnson remained.
38. Corner, *History of Rockefeller* (n. 16 above), 57; Homer F. Swift to E. C. Smith, 12 June 1937, folder 30, box 17, RG 450.1, Rockefeller University Archives, RAC. I am grateful to archivist Renée Mastrocco for locating this letter.
39. Mary Brown Bullock noted that before 1937, 55% of Peking Union Medical College graduates studied abroad, and that "for the most part, these graduates studied in the United States at Johns Hopkins, Harvard, and the Rockefeller Institute on grants from the China Medical Board." See Mary Brown Bullock, *An American Transplant: The Rockefeller Foundation and Peking Union Medical College* (Berkeley, CA, 1980), 126.
40. Corner, *History of Rockefeller* (n. 16 above), 58. Board of Director's minutes, 29 May 1909, 9 October 1909, RG 110.2, Rockefeller University Archives, RAC.
41. Flexner's correspondence with Ehrlich suggests that they may not actually have met during that trip to Europe: Paul Ehrlich to Simon Flexner, 18 December 1903, 13 January 1904, 9 June 1904, 25 July 1904, reel 32, RAC microfilm of Rockefeller Institute for Medical Research series, Simon Flexner Papers, American Philosophical Society, Philadelphia, PA (hereafter APS). Note that Flexner and Hideyo Noguchi later exchanged research material with Ehrlich and that Noguchi subsequently visited his laboratory: Simon Flexner to Paul Ehrlich, 8 December 1911, 20 October 1912, Hideyo Noguch to Paul Ehrlich, 5 July 1912, and Paul Ehrlich to Simon Flexner, 2 October 1913, reel 32, APS, RAC microfilm. For John D. Rockefeller Sr.'s gift see Board of Directors' Minutes, 29 May 1909, 9 October 1909, RG 110.2, Rockefeller University Archives, RAC.
42. Darwin H. Stapleton, "Frederick Seitz," in *Notable Twentieth-Century Scientists* (Detroit, 1995), 1810–2.
43. Board of Scientific Directors' Minutes, 21 January 1911, 25 April 1911, 3 June 1911, RG 110.2, Rockefeller University Archives, RAC; Simon Flexner to Reinhard Dohrn, 11 July 1924, reel 29, Simon

Flexner Papers, APS (This letter is mislocated in the "Doerr" file.); "List of Investigators, Marine Biological Laboratory, Summer of 1923," attached to Frank R. Lillie to Simon Flexner, 13 July 1923, reel 65, Simon Flexner Papers, APS; Corner, *History of Rockefeller* (n. 16 above), 77–8, 367.

44. Corner, *History of Rockefeller*, 283; Hanson, *Achievements: Century of Science*, 25. A list of staff who have left Rockefeller to found, or to serve as the head of other labs or institutions, would be quite lengthy. Recent examples include Purnell Choppin, who became president of the Howard Hughes Medical Institute in 1986, and Anthony Cerami, who was the founding president of the Picower Institute for Medical Research in 1991.
45. A recent work that argues this point is Ric Burns, James Sanders, and Lisa Ades, eds., *New York* (New York, 1999).
46. Charles Rosenberg, "Toward an Ecology of Knowledge: On Discipline, Context, and History," in *The Organization of Knowledge in Modern America, 1860–1920*, ed. Alexandra Oleson and John Voss (Baltimore, 1979), 452.

Chapter 2

Institutionalizing Excellence in Biomedical Research: The Case of The Rockefeller University

J. Rogers Hollingsworth

Professor of History and Sociology, University of Wisconsin–Madison, Madison, WI

Introduction

The goal of this essay is to explain why more major discoveries occurred in biomedical science at Rockefeller University than at any other research organization during the twentieth century. Why would this small organization in New York City—unknown to millions of Americans—have performed better on this criterion than such renowned organizations as Harvard, Yale, and Stanford universities in the United States; Cambridge and Oxford universities in Britain; and the Pasteur Institute in Paris? And why is Rockefeller credited with more major breakthroughs in biomedical science than all the German Kaiser-Wilhelm and Max-Planck Institutes combined? (See Appendix I for a definition of major breakthroughs in biomedical science and Appendix II for Rockefeller scientists who made major breakthroughs.)

There is no single answer to such a complex problem. To address it requires a theoretical framework to explain how the structure, culture, and leadership patterns of research organizations interact with their changing environment so that they can continuously have radical innovations; in this case major discoveries in biomedical science.[1] Several themes in the recent literature on organizations and radical innovations are relevant if we are to understand what occurs in a research organization over a long period of time. First, it is important to comprehend how changes in the environment of an organization influence changes in the organization itself. Second, if an organization is to make radical breakthroughs time and time again, it needs to be ambidextrous in its internal operations: both taking the necessary incremental steps so that strategy, structure, leadership, and personnel are linked to one another in a fairly harmonious fashion on a day to day basis; and having leadership with the capacity to take the radical or revolutionary steps to look beyond the present so that the organization can quickly adapt to significant changes in the environment. Throughout the twentieth century Rockefeller University has been ambidextrous and highly adaptive to its environment, often pursuing both incremental and radical changes simultaneously.

An organization accustomed to delicately balancing its components cannot lightly alter them, lest its operating system be endangered. Change in organizational strategy, structure, and leadership styles is often unwelcome, even resisted, inasmuch as it requires moving away from norms, habits, and conventions that previously had been effective. In fact, much of the success of the University over the last century in making major breakthroughs occurred because of its ability to carry out these dual activities: to maintain its established practices at high levels of performance and to look beyond the immediate future to make radical changes in its practices.

The achievements of Rockefeller are uncharacteristic of research organizations across the globe. Most organizations tend to experience a great deal of inertia, generally failing to make radical changes as environments change. Even organizations that have performed well have a tendency to congeal in self-congratulation, to idealize their own practices to such an extent that they do not adequately modify themselves in response to environmental change.

But research organizations that successfully adapt to their changing environment, and in the process make fundamental breakthroughs across long periods of time, have particular structural attributes. A recent study of research organizations in Britain, France, Germany, and the United States demonstrates that major discoveries throughout the twentieth century tended to occur in an organizational setting in which there was a high degree of interaction among scientists in diverse fields, and a high degree of flexibility in the organizational structure allowing it to adapt quickly to new trends in science. Over time, biomedical knowledge has become increasingly more complex (involving both multiple fields of knowledge and greater depth), but if research organizations are to make major discoveries, it is imperative for them to incorporate scientific diversity and depth in such a way that scientists can interact with intensity and frequency across diverse fields. However, as research organizations add greater scientific diversity and depth, it is important that these parts remain well-integrated and not isolated from one another; otherwise, there will not be the requisite horizontal communication with frequent and intense multidiscipline interaction.[2]

Increases in scientific diversity and depth, if not properly managed, can ultimately limit the capacity of a research organization to make major discoveries. As research organizations increase in diversity and depth, there is a tendency for them to become larger, more differentiated, less integrated, and less flexible. These changes in turn are usually accompanied with increases in hierarchical coordination, bureaucracy, and organizational rigidity with negative consequences for scientific research and discovery.

Successful research organizations credited with several major discoveries have had a distinctive style of leadership, that is, leaders who have had (1) a strategic vision for integrating diverse areas and for providing focused research; (2) an ability to facilitate obtaining funding; (3) a capacity to facilitate the provision of rigorous criticism of science but within a nurturing environment; and (4) an ability to recruit sufficiently diverse personnel so that research groups are constantly aware of significant problems. Leaders who exhibit all of these qualities also have tended to be so well versed in the past accomplishments of their organizations that they have a high capacity to articulate their cultures. At the same time, they have tended to be versatile in those areas of science just emerging on the horizon, giving them a good sense of the direction in which the organization should move. In short, the distinguished leader is one who cannot only bring about dovetailing between the existing culture and competence of the research organization and new fields of science, be sensitive to the traditions of the organization, and be highly supportive of what the organization is doing in the short-term, but also be a visionary and risk-taker capable of moving researchers into unknown areas. As long as a research organization is relatively small, it is feasible for the very rare and talented individual to have the ambidexterity to play these seemingly contradictory roles. However, as the organization increases in size and complexity, it becomes ever more difficult for a single individual to embody all of these traits.

The discussion that follows develops these themes. It focuses on the changes within the Rockefeller University in response to changes in its environment, and on the strategy, structure, leadership, and personnel of the organization as it has attempted to adapt to alterations in twentieth century science.

There was no steady state in any of these trends. The leaders of Rockefeller have not always correctly understood and responded to the changes in the external environment. They have not always anticipated the major institutional and scientific patterns of change, nor has the organization always had the same level of excellence in its flow of ongoing work. Nevertheless, the University has been more successful in meeting all of the aforementioned challenges than any other research organization, and this is the key to understanding why it has performed so well in having so many major breakthroughs in biomedical science.

Institutionalizing a Culture of Excellence

To understand the origins of the Rockefeller Institute for Medical Research, we need to recognize that in the latter part of the nineteenth century, the United States lagged far behind the frontiers of biomedical science as they existed in Europe, especially in Germany. Throughout the nineteenth century, the United States lacked high standards in biomedical science and did not provide high-quality training for young scientists and physicians. Most medical schools had few if any laboratories, they were rarely affiliated with hospitals or universities, and their capital outlays were generally quite small.[3] Of course, some schools were better than others, and a few Americans made contributions to medical knowledge; but overall even the best medical schools and centers for research in the United States were inadequate. Among the best were those of the University of Pennsylvania, the University of Michigan, and Harvard, Yale, and Columbia universities. Although by 1900 they were progressing in basic science research, the training and research at each of these schools fell far short of the best medical advances of the time. Germany had become the center for scientific medicine in the late nineteenth century, and more than 15,000 Americans went there between 1870 and 1914 to study the medical sciences. In the history of American biomedical science, few things are of greater importance than the traveling of this generation of Americans to Germany, especially in the 1870s and 1880s. They brought back what they found, and it was these European institutions and ideas that ultimately revolutionized science and clinical medicine in the United States.[4]

All of this must be set in the context of the major institutional changes taking place in the United States during the last half of the nineteenth century. There was literally a transformation in the American economy, which produced unprecedented wealth in America. John D. Rockefeller Sr., the wealthiest of all Americans and one of the great entrepreneurs of American capitalism, believed that his capacity to make money was ". . . a gift from God . . . to be developed and used to the best of our ability for the good of mankind. I believe my duty is to make money and still more money and to use the money I make for the good of my fellow man according to the dictates of my conscience."[5] To assist in his philanthropic activities, Rockefeller Sr. chose Frederick T. Gates, a Baptist minister, who quickly immersed himself in understanding Rockefeller's business and philanthropic affairs.

In 1897, Gates submitted a proposal to Rockefeller in which he argued that although various departments of natural sciences had been generously endowed in various American universities, medicine, because of the commercial orientation of medical schools, had not been well supported. As a result, medical research was in a poor condition in America, usually conducted by practitioners who could, at best, steal a short time from their private practices. He argued that medicine could hardly hope to become a science until research was properly endowed and dedicated scientists were permitted to have uninterrupted study and investigation, completely independent of clinical practice. To achieve these ends, he proposed the establishment of a research institute. With John D. Rockefeller Jr., a new graduate of Brown University, Gates developed a wonderful working relationship in managing Rockefeller philanthropic affairs in general, and more specifically, in the development of a biomedical research institute.[6]

As both men quickly realized that they needed the advice of people with a rich knowledge of medical science, they gathered a distinguished group. Rockefeller Jr. consulted with his family physician, Dr. Emmett Holt, renowned pediatrician and author of the leading textbook on pediatrics; Christian Herter, a well-known scientific investigator who had established his own private laboratory in New York City for his research in biochemistry, pharmacology, and bacteriology; William H. Welch, the dean of the Johns Hopkins Medical School; Hermann M. Biggs, head of the Division of Bacteriology of the New York City Department of Health; T. Mitchell Prudden, professor of pathology at the Columbia University College of Physicians and Surgeons (who had known Welch since their student days in Germany in the 1870s); and Theobald Smith of the Harvard Medical School, the leading American bacteriologist of the day and a former student of Welch. Welch suggested the addition of his former student at Johns Hopkins, Simon Flexner—then professor of pathology at the University of Pennsylvania. And in 1901, these people became members of the board of directors of the Rockefeller Institute for Medical Research.[7]

Each had training in pathology, and each believed that the best strategy at the time for attacking disease was by using the tools of bacteriology. Each also thought that it was only a matter of time before physiology and chemistry would have to be integrated with bacteriology in order to advance knowledge of diseases. Despite common elements in their scientific backgrounds, the group represented diversity in experience, which in the long-term was to prove valuable to the Rockefeller Institute. Herter had extensive experience in research and in clinical practice; Holt in hospital clinical practice; Biggs and Smith had backgrounds in public laboratories; and Smith, Welch, Prudden, and Flexner were researchers in university medical schools. From the very beginning, there was an extremely high level of trust among these men, and this was extremely important in understanding the early success of the Institute.

Perhaps the most important contributor to the success of the Rockefeller Institute was William H. Welch, who had already been instrumental in establishing Hopkins as the premier medical school in North America. The more Welch reflected on the idea of an institute, the more he was intrigued by its potential, so when he was pressed by Rockefeller Jr., Gates, and the small group of scientific advisers, he agreed to serve as president of the new institute's board, a position he held for thirty-two years. The choice of Welch as president is indicative of the capacity of the Rockefellers to recruit excellent people to implement their programs. Some have argued that Welch had more influence in developing the biomedical sciences in the United States than anyone else in American history. In addition to serving for more than three decades as president of the Board of the Rockefeller Institute, he served as president of the American Association for the Advancement of Science, the National Academy of Sciences, the American Medical Association, the Association of American Physicians. In addition, he was a member of the Board of Trustees of the Hooper Foundation for Medical Research at the University of California, San Francisco, one of the key individuals in establishing the National Research Council, and a member of the Board of Trustees of the Carnegie Institution in Washington (1906–1934) and Chairman of its Executive Committee from 1909 to 1916. As a key figure in these organizations, Welch had frequent and more contact with the elite in all fields of American science than anyone else.[8] The Rockefellers could not have made a better choice than Welch to steer the initial board of the Rockefeller Institute. He had an excellent comprehension of the direction in which biomedical science was moving, high visibility and legitimacy in American science, and outstanding judgment about the type of scientists and the specific scientists whom the Institute should recruit.

One critical decision was what kind of organization Rockefeller Institute should be. Because of their academic backgrounds, Welch, Prudden, Flexner, and the other scientific advisers tended to think the new organization should be linked to an existing university. However, the Rockefellers and Gates were insistent that there be no formal link with a university. The idea of the Rockefeller organization, as conceived by the Rockefellers and Gates—laymen who had become sensitive to the shortcomings of the existing medical establishment—was that biomedical knowledge could not be substantially advanced until an organization existed with proper endowment, and with qualified scientists with adequate salaries, independent of both private medical practice and university teaching, devoting full time to research.[9]

Welch proposed Simon Flexner to be the first director. Here, too, a better choice could hardly have been made. Flexner, the fourth of five children, was born to Jewish parents in Louisville, Kentucky and grew up in semi-poverty, after his father died prematurely. Shortly after receiving a medical degree from a local school in Louisville, he went to Johns Hopkins—but not as a regular medical student—where he became associated with Welch. Quickly, the breadth of his education increased. He went to Europe in 1892 and studied in some of the great laboratories and later worked in the laboratory of Jacques Loeb at Woods Hole. Slowly, Flexner was integrating medical and biological science, so that by the time he became the director of the Rockefeller Institute he had demonstrated that he was a creative and productive scientist, capable of absorbing and integrating new and complex ideas, and with the capacity to develop and implement new research programs and to operate on many fronts at once.[10]

Flexner's Vision

As the first director, Simon Flexner left an indelible mark on the Institute. As a result of his achievements and efforts, the expectation developed among the trustees of the Rockefeller organization that it should be headed by an individual who had a strategic vision for integrating scientific diversity, who could create an organizational environment that blended criticism and nurturing, who had the capacity to recruit personnel alert to significant problems and able to solve them, and the ability to secure funds. Not all subsequent heads of Rockefeller lived up to the leadership standards that Flexner epitomized, but these are the ideals by which successive leaders have been evaluated.

Although the Koch Institute in Berlin and the Pasteur Institute in Paris were founded around great scientists and their research, the Rockefeller organization under Flexner's leadership became a new kind of research organization that from its beginning emphasized diversity in the biomedical sciences. Instead of being focused on a specific area of science, the Institute pursued research in multiple areas of the biomedical sciences. Biomedical science was changing very rapidly by the time the Rockefeller Institute was established. Because bacteriology had become closely linked with pathology, and both fields were becoming more closely related to discoveries in organic and physical chemistry, as well as physics, a broad conception of biomedical science was the guiding philosophy of the Institute from the beginning. As Flexner internalized a great deal of scientific diversity, perhaps it was almost intuitive on his part that he would recruit a staff that reflected a good bit of scientific diversity.

The recruiting of a high level staff proved to be very difficult. Most senior professors in leading American medical schools viewed the Rockefeller Institute as a high risk "up-start," and they were unwilling to leave the security of their permanent positions. Most young people, hoping for careers at established universities, also viewed the Institute with some suspicion. For some years, there had been vicious attacks in the press by Henry Demarest Lloyd, Ida Tarbell, and others against "Rockefeller money" and the Standard Oil Trust, and by the time of planning for the Institute much of the nation's press was hostile to the Rockefellers.

Many medical practitioners perceived the scientific agenda of the Institute as an assault on their legitimacy, and indeed, the dominant tone of the medical profession of New York City was quite hostile to basic biomedical research.[11] Young scientists were frequently warned to stay clear of the Institute. Both Peyton Rous, a future Nobel laureate from the Institute, and Jacques Loeb, one of the most important scientists in the history of the Institute, had initial reservations about going there because they feared they might not have freedom to conduct their research.[12]

Flexner thought it necessary to recruit at least a few experienced scientists, not only young people. Because senior university professors were unavailable, many tended to view initial scientific staff he gathered as a "motley group."[13] Most had outstanding ability, but were uninvolved with established American universities and academic disciplines, which proved to be a blessing in disguise. For the most part, the earliest appointments were opportunistic and personalistic in nature. Flexner placed considerable emphasis on recruiting scientists whose origins were in different cultural areas and who worked in different scientific areas (e.g., Alexis Carrel from France; Karl Landsteiner from Austria; Hideyo Noguchi from Japan; Phoebus Levene and Samuel Meltzer from Russia; and Jacques Loeb, Leonor Michaelis, and Max Bergmann from Germany). Several were of Jewish origin in an era of strong antisemitism. Almost every one of these scientists internalized cultural diversity in his own cognitive makeup, which increased the potential for crossing scientific disciplines. Feeling an affinity for others who crossed academic discipline boundaries, the early appointed scientists established and reinforced a culture based on broad, interdisciplinary approaches to scientific problems.

From the beginning, the Institute did not organize the production of knowledge around academic disciplines, which was the usual practice in major universities. In organizations in which academic disciplines were dominant for organizing and coordinating the production of knowledge, there was a tendency to recruit specialists in disciplines, scientists who by definition internalized less scientific diversity (and often, less cultural diversity). The distinctive Rockefeller recruitment of scientists socialized in several cultures, subsystems, disciplines, or working environments meant the presence of a staff with more potential to acquire new styles of thought and scientific competence. From the outset, the Institute was a place where there was a willingness of scientists to participate in multiple scientific worlds simultaneously, fostering the cross-fertilization of ideas and the opportunity for communication across diverse fields of research. These conditions facilitated the development of the hybridization of ideas that over time leads to scientific creativity, sudden insights, and the opening of novel pathways to difficult problems.

As a research organization, the Institute had several distinct advantages over most teaching institutions. Most teaching organizations attempt to present an entire field of knowledge to their students and find it awkward to neglect certain subfields. They tend to recruit people not so much because of their research excellence but because of the necessity to cover a particular area of knowledge. Unlike a university, a research institute has no obligation to cover an entire field of knowledge, and it can be very opportunistic in terms of the fields on which research is undertaken. It can neglect or pursue fields, can recruit scientists solely on the basis of their ability to attack selected problems, and it has the flexibility to move into new areas with considerable rapidity. Moreover, the Rockefeller Institute had the luxury of being able to recruit scientists of excellence even if they had limited ability to speak English or could not teach.[14]

Over many years, a generous endowment by the Rockefellers has created excellent working conditions for scientific research. Several other institutes founded at about the same time were also very well endowed: the Phipps Institute in Philadelphia, established by the steel magnate Henry Phipps; the Memorial Institute for Infectious Diseases in Chicago, funded by Harold McCormick, a son-in-law of John D. Rockefeller Sr.; and the Carnegie Institution in Washington, endowed by Andrew Carnegie. However, the history of the Rockefeller Institute, viewed in a comparative perspective, suggests that although financial resources are necessary for outstanding research, they are less important than having the right strategy, structure, personnel, and leadership. An organization must be able to do excellent work on a day-to-day basis, but at the same time must be willing to reorient itself on a continual basis in anticipation of scientific change.

The Rockefeller Institute, with its laboratory structure, was sufficiently ambidextrous so that it was able to adapt quickly to its environment; i.e., to move in new directions at the same time that it was carrying on more established lines of research. One of the most important resources for a research organization if it is to continue making major discoveries is the quality of its leadership—a variable that many organizational sociologists give scant attention. Over the years, Rockefeller has had several directors (later presidents) who were capable of interacting in a meaningful way with its scientists and who personally knew the leading biomedical scientists of the world. Of the eight directors or presidents since the founding of the Rockefeller Institute, six made major discoveries in biomedical science, and the two who made no major biomedical discoveries (Detlev Bronk and Fred Seitz) were distinguished scientists who had been presidents of the National Academy of Sciences. Four of the eight were Nobel laureates in physiology or medicine.[15]

Originally, a single Board of Directors designed and implemented plans for the development of the new institute; but in 1910, Welch, who had been president of the Board of Directors, became president of the Board of Scientific Directors, and due in part to the prestige he lent the Institute, some of America's leading biomedical scientists subsequently agreed to serve on the Board of Scientific Directors. Over time, board members included future Nobel laureates Vincent du Vigneaud, Herbert Gasser, and George Whipple; and three other scientists who made major breakthroughs in biomedical science Walter B. Cannon of Harvard, Ross Harrison of Yale, and Theobald Smith of Harvard (discussed earlier). In addition, Bronk, then president of the Johns Hopkins University, and James B. Conant, president of Harvard, served on the Board.

Governance of the Institute

The board was responsible for the appointment of the scientific staff and for the establishment of general policies concerning the scientific investigations, and it did much to keep the research organization performing optimally. The director of the Institute (Flexner) was appointed by the Scientific Directors and was in intimate contact with the scientific staff. Beginning in 1910, there was also a Board of Trustees that had oversight over the financial affairs of the Institute. The distinctive role of the Board of Scientific Directors, combined with the skills of Flexner and his successor Herbert Gasser, facilitated the recruitment of some of the most innovative scientists assembled to that time. Permanent appointments had to be approved by both boards, although the director appointed nonpermanent members of the staff, determined their rank, and fixed their salaries. Flexner personally interviewed every scientist, even those who were at the Institute for only a single year, before any appointment was made.

The original Board of Trustees consisted of John D. Rockefeller Jr., Gates, and their lawyer Starr J. Murphy. Welch and Flexner served on both the Board of Trustees and the Board of Scientific Directors, providing communication between the two boards. The existence of two boards lasted until 1953, when the two were merged into a single Board of Trustees. Since then, the Rockefeller organization has not had a separate board of world-class scientists making the final decisions about personnel. The quality of recruitment, while continuing to be high, has not had the same degree of extraordinary consistency as during the time when the Institute had a Board of Scientific Directors with distinguished scientists intimately involved in making staff appointments and overseeing the scientific research of the Institute. The Board of Scientific Directors met three or four times a year and focused in great detail on the quality of Rockefeller appointments. Since 1953, there have been scientists on the Board of Trustees, but they have never exercised the same degree of oversight on the organization's appointments as when there was a separate board for scientific affairs.

At the Institute, permanent scientists were called members and had indefinite appointments corresponding to professorial appointments in American universities. The next highest title was associate member, a three-year appointment renewable for three more years. In general, after a second term, associate members either were appointed as members or were expected to resign. Associates were appointed for two years, and assistants and fellows for one. Eligible for reappointment, scientists in the lower ranks left the Institute or rose to higher rank after three to five years. Like the Kaiser-Wilhelm or Max-Planck Institutes, which later had similar promotion policies, the Rockefeller Institute provided advanced training for what became the elite of biomedical scientists in America. The process of appointment as a member was extremely rigorous. Not all senior scientists received their initial appointments at that level. For example, in 1934, 46 percent of senior scientists had initially been appointed to the rank of member, whereas 54 percent had been promoted from a lower rank. Members rarely left: only one resigned by the mid-1930s, and even he returned.

Although the Board of Scientific Directors was responsible for the scientific policies of the Institute, the research problems under investigation were chosen by individual scientists. Members and their associates and assistants made up laboratory groups that were organized into divisions. Funds for scientific investigations were allocated to laboratories and administered by the head of the laboratory, though budgets were of course modified from time to time by special action of the Board of Scientific Directors.

The meetings of the Board of Scientific Directors were held quarterly, and for these meetings, the head of each laboratory or division submitted a technical scientific report. Discussion of the reports became the most important item of business at the meetings. The reports played an important role in communicating to the board what was going on in the Institute. Members of the Board of Scientific Directors generally attended all meetings, and they read the reports carefully. Some members of the board made a habit of consistently visiting various laboratories, not in the spirit of monitoring but because of their genuine interest in the Institute's research. An important incentive to be a board member was the opportunity to be informed about the Institute's research activities.[16]

Reflections of Flexner

During the first three decades of the Institute, its overall governance and operating procedures were reflections of Flexner's philosophy, ideals, personal mannerisms, and scientific style. The insistence after 1910 that every laboratory prepare periodic scientific reports for the Board of Scientific Directors was due in part to Flexner's insatiable appetite for learning. As the Institute developed, these reports reflected some of the latest trends in science, and provided opportunities for Flexner and the directors to consider what the Institute might do next. Although Flexner had been primarily interested in infectious diseases during the 1890s when he was at Johns Hopkins, by the time of Jacques Loeb's appointment to the Institute (1909), Flexner's cognitive framework had significantly expanded to encompass a very broad view of biomedical science. He increasingly believed that biomedical sciences must rely primarily on chemistry, physics, and biology, and that investigations had to be based on the methods of those fields. This change was due in part to the fact that the Institute provided a rich learning environment. Flexner held the view that most scientific knowledge is interrelated. For him, all forms of life were "related organically and . . . united physiologically and pathologically." In the pursuit of knowledge, there should be no disciplinary boundaries separating the study of different forms of life, though there had to be separate laboratories for purposes of "economy of action."[17]

Flexner also was very much aware that knowledge changes very rapidly in the global world of science, and he believed that if a biomedical institute was continuously to absorb and integrate new knowledge, there had to be an intimate commingling of investigators in various fields of science, even if in the short term some fields of biomedical science appeared unrelated to others.[18] He believed that the range and scope of the Institute should provide considerable scientific diversity. Moreover, the internal organization should be highly flexible so that it could quickly adapt to new knowledge. For Flexner, the culture within the Rockefeller Institute should be such that scientists would be willing to communicate and cooperate with each other. Such a strategy meant that each scientist should internalize extensive scientific diversity, and should be able to communicate with every other scientist. Indeed, scientific diversity and ability to communicate with others on the scientific staff were prerequisites for recruitment. Because so many of the scientists were fluent in multiple languages, foreign scientific publications were frequently discussed by the staff, and scientists from abroad were eager to visit the Institute and to discuss research of mutual interest.

Flexner was aware that scientists who had the kind of scientific diversity that he wanted to recruit were in short supply. His strategy was that the Institute over time should train a number of its own staff, and during his directorship, the Rockefeller Institute became one of the world's leading centers of training for young postdoctoral biomedical scientists. This meant carefully recruiting able young people and providing them with excellent opportunities to grow scientifically. Although the overwhelming majority departed after a few years of training, Flexner retained the most exceptional. This obviously meant that members were constantly attentive to the strengths and weaknesses of younger staff. Although only one in twenty was retained, by 1950 almost one-half of those with permanent Institute appointments had risen through the ranks.

Flexner's correspondence demonstrates that he was enormously attentive to the well-being of young investigators. Even if they failed in particular investigations, he would encourage and console them and give them new opportunities. When a depressed young investigator told him that he had accomplished nothing worthy of publication, Flexner warmly consoled him by remarking, "Nothing? . . . you don't seem to realize that to have nothing is to have something."[19] Flexner was wise enough to know that for the young people coming to the Institute, it was one of the great experiences of their lives, and he encouraged his senior colleagues to make certain that this was the case. Even if Flexner did not retain a young scientist, he frequently paid the investigator a salary for a year after his departure as an incentive for another academic institution to recruit the person. This kind of practice let young people know that if they went to the Rockefeller Institute, they would have an excellent opportunity to have a position upon exiting, and this did much to keep a steady stream of able young scientists.

Over time, hundreds of young people passed through the Institute and went on to be prominent biomedical scientists. Flexner was highly committed to upgrading the quality of America's universities and medical schools, and believed that one of the major contributions of the Institute was its development of young investigators and teachers for universities and medical schools. He was very proud that by the early 1920s, the leading American universities in the country eagerly sought the Institute's young investigators.[20]

With so many scientists passing through the Institute, some errors in judgment were made. Not everyone retained was of world-class distinction, but probably no other research organization in the world had such a high proportion of the scientific staff eminent in biomedical science. Still, the Institute encouraged a few scientists to depart whom it should have kept. One such scientist was Michael Heidelberger, whose exceptional qualities kept him at the Institute for a very long period (1912–1927, except for a short period during World War I). Eventually, Heidelberger was encouraged by Flexner to leave for fear that he was not getting sufficient recognition for his many achievements that were invariably co-authored with a senior scientist. In the words of Elvin Kabat, Heidelberger was a "Leonardo da Vinci–type Renaissance man . . . who became the father of quantitative immunochemistry."[21]

As director, Flexner also worked to maintain close research communication with members of the original Board of Directors and the subsequent Board of Scientific Directors and the Board of Trustees, and this was important in promoting cohesion and trust among those governing the Institute. Flexner and Christian Herter became intimate friends, and their families visited one another's homes. The Flexners and the Herters had summer houses at Seal Harbor, Maine, and one of Flexner's sons married one of Herter's daughters. With Hermann Biggs, Theobald Smith, and Emmett Holt, Flexner's relations were somewhat formal, though they became closer over time. He was especially respectful of Smith's scientific knowledge, and he wrote a book with Holt on dysentery among infants.[22] Among the trustees, Flexner developed a very warm relationship with Gates, and the Flexners frequently visited the Gates' home in New Jersey and their summer house on Lake George, New York. Over time, he also developed a close relationship with Rockefeller Jr. As Mrs. Flexner and Mrs. Rockefeller liked each other, the Flexners frequently joined the Rockefellers at their New York City residence and were invited from time to time to the family estate at Pocantico Hills.

More than anyone else, Flexner institutionalized a culture of excellence within the Institute. Throughout his directorship, he did not become a full-time administrator, but continued to work in the laboratory.[23] Within the Institute, he was usually too busy to engage in small talk. He set very high standards not only for himself but also for everyone around him. In some respects, he was a bundle of contradictions. He could be extraordinarily charming, but if he believed the situation called for it, he could be coldly blunt. He tended to be extremely instrumental in his dealings with the scientific staff. He was willing to be very harsh with individuals if he believed this was the most effective way of getting "the most out of a man and was best for his development."[24] On the other hand, he worked tirelessly to establish a nurturing environment in the Institute. Overall, he was a very considerate and affectionate individual. He kept in touch with the lives of most everyone in the Institute, and all staff—scientific or otherwise—usually received birthday or wedding anniversary cards. He was solicitous of the needs of the nurses, secretaries, porters, laboratory helpers, keepers of animals—all of the unheralded people essential for a high-quality research organization. When they encountered family emergencies, he would help them cope with the problem—financially if necessary.[25]

Salaries and Assessments

On the other hand, there is evidence that during the Flexner years, the Institute was often conservative—if not outright stingy—with regard to salaries. In part, this practice stemmed from Flexner's fear that universities would accuse the Rockefeller Institute of stealing faculty by paying inflated salaries, and this did not happen. Rather, it was the universities that from time to time attempted to lure Rockefeller members away with extremely high salaries. Because he was solicitous about the welfare of American universities, Flexner was determined to keep Institute salaries within the range of American salaries at high-quality universities.[26] However, for research expenses within the Institute, the situation was different: Institute scientists received generous research funding from the director in comparison with the leading universities in America.

Funding for research was administered by Flexner in a somewhat personal style. Even so, the decision-making process about funding research within the Institute was in some respects more effective than what currently exists in most contemporary American funding agencies. Flexner had a great deal of information about the research potential of almost everyone in the Institute, and he and his colleagues were in an excellent position to make well-informed decisions about what was high risk and low risk research, and who had the abilities to conduct high risk, long-term projects and who did not. They were well positioned to monitor investments in scientific research, as a result of periodic scientific reports and their ability to discuss and advise about the progress of specific research projects. Moreover, having the *Journal of Experimental Medicine*, and other high-quality journals, edited at the Rockefeller Institute provided the director with a great deal of information about papers produced at the Institute. In sum, the Institute strategy for funding science was highly flexible because of the large amount of information possessed by those making scientific investment decisions.[27]

A New Department at Princeton

From the very beginning, the culture of the Institute was entrepreneurial and high risk oriented. Flexner regarded trivial and unimportant research with contempt. He had no objection if labs were unproductive for lengthy periods of time, as long as they were addressing important problems. He would wait a long time before concluding that a young scientist was not suitable for the Institute. Mindful of the weakness of his own early education, he took the view that one of the missions of the Institute was to provide research training for young postdoctoral researchers.[28] And because of the Institute's rich scientific diversity and the excellent internal communication among the scientific staff, he frequently encouraged scientists to move into totally new fields of research. On one such occasion, he informed a young scientist who was moving to a new problem that it would take at least two years to begin to understand the parameters of his new problem. "I will not expect anything of you until after that," he said. Flexner's ability to identify, and to fund new areas of research—as with the work of Peyton Rous—was emblematic of the Institute's capability to anticipate new directions, even radically different directions, and move towards them rapidly.

On almost all occasions, Flexner was available as both an intellectual and scientific resource. Often, he went out of his way to inform young investigators that they needed an assistant and that he would provide the funding.[29] At the height of the Depression, when Tom Rivers told Flexner that he needed extra funding for his research (though he did not specify the amount), "without batting an eye" Flexner provided $10,000, a great deal of money at the time.[30] On the other hand, Flexner did not hesitate to be stern—even with a senior member—if he believed the person was not being prudent with the resources provided by the Institute.[31]

Gates and the two Rockefellers did much to set the tone for the research strategy of the Institute. From the beginning, they told the original Board of Directors that they expected no short-term utilitarianism or results. Indeed, Gates and the Rockefellers had early concluded that no important discoveries were likely to result from the Institute. Their major hope was that the Institute would conduct high-quality research, be a training ground for young investigators, and serve as an example for other philanthropists. Research on important problems, even if long periods of incubation were necessary, was encouraged at the outset.[32] Thus, without pressure to produce results in the short term, Flexner could encourage his staff to think "big," to take risks, but to be aware that rigorous standards of excellence would be the criteria by which all results would be assessed.

From the beginning, Welch, Flexner, and others on the Board of Scientific Directors had advocated a research program on animal pathology, in part because certain diseases are transmitted from animals to humans. An unanticipated event in 1913, the widespread outbreak of hog cholera, brought the matter to the fore. After studying the epidemic, Flexner and Theobald Smith proposed that the Institute create a full-scale department of animal pathology, to which the board agreed. Smith was asked to head the new department and the decision was made to locate the department in the Princeton, New Jersey area. In 1917, the Institute's Department of Animal Pathology opened with a state-of-the-art facility, with a faculty that grew to be an integrated scientific community, with research and social life tightly intertwined.[33]

The new department at Princeton was almost the equivalent of establishing a new institute. Although organizationally under the direction of Flexner, the department's day-to-day operations, most staff appointments, and local policies were under the direction of Smith. The Princeton department had scientific leadership with a vision of how to address "do-able," major problems, with the capacity to identify scientific talent from diverse fields, and to integrate this scientific diversity in a rigorous, but nurturing environment. As well, the Princeton site had scientific diversity, depth, and integration, and a high-quality staff. Significantly, several major discoveries did occur in the Princeton branch of the Rockefeller Institute, breakthroughs that resulted in Theobald Smith's being awarded a Copley Medal and John Northrop and Wendell Stanley receiving Nobel Prizes in Chemistry for separate research conducted in the Princeton laboratories between 1917 and 1937. However, these recognitions are only a part of the story of the Princeton department.

Smith was a very cautious director of research, and unlike Flexner, averse to risk. Thus, he added relatively few staff who were unrelated to his immediate research interests. Because Flexner exercised scientific oversight over the Princeton department, he was able to counterbalance Smith's conservative tendencies, with fortuitous consequences for the Princeton program. This was seen most dramatically in the career of John Northrop, one of the most innovative scientists during the first forty years of the Institute. Flexner arranged for Northrop to move to the Princeton site in 1926, even though Northrop clearly did not focus on animal diseases.

Flexner's moving Northrop to Princeton contributed to a creative research program culminating with Northrop's being awarded a Nobel Prize for Chemistry in 1946. At the Rockefeller Institute, Northrop had worked closely with Jacques Loeb, who taught him how to design complex experiments in order to answer important well-focused questions. Loeb also influenced Northrop to be interested in the colloidal properties of proteins and to work on pepsin and trypsin. Northrop was a creative and highly productive scientist with a magnetic personality, and over the years he attracted several first-rate scientists to his lab.[34] Using solubility measurement, ultracentrifuge analysis, and electrophoresis, Northrop and his colleagues demonstrated that pepsin is a pure enzyme, thus challenging the then-dominant views of Richard Willstätter that enzymes were carriers of other molecules that give them specificity. As a result of the work of Northrop's lab as well as that in the Institute's New York labs, Rockefeller investigators "led the world" in enzymology by the early 1930s.[35]

By the time of Smith's retirement (1930), Flexner had decided that the Institute should have a program in plant pathology, also located at Princeton. He believed that a program on plant disease, especially plant viral diseases, would be of enormous benefit to the Institute.[36] One of the nation's leading plant pathologists, Louis O. Kunkel was appointed to head a program in plant pathology, with a mandate to study plant diseases caused by bacteria, fungi, and viruses. Kunkel decided to concentrate on tobacco mosaic virus (TMV), and he recruited a diverse group of talented young scientists (including Wendell Stanley) who could work on most aspects of the biology of TMV.

Stanley's training had made him a promising investigator in physiological chemistry, but he was devoid of training about viruses. At the time Stanley began his work, no one had previously isolated a virus. Stanley assumed that viruses were proteins, and in the small Princeton environment, he quickly became very familiar with the work of Northrop's lab, which had demonstrated that enzymes were crystallizable and were, in fact, proteins. Stanley then set out to discover if viruses could be purified by methods similar to those used by the Northrop group.[37] After several years of hard work and more than 100 chemical reagents later, Stanley reported that he had isolated a "protein" virus, and after further purification had obtained highly infectious needle-like crystals. In a 1935 paper, he reported that he had "strong evidence that the crystalline protein herein described is either pure or is a solid solution of proteins."[38] According to George Corner, "No discovery made at the Rockefeller Institute, before or since, created such astonishment throughout the scientific world as this."[39] Immediately, Stanley became a national celebrity. For many, he was raising fundamental problems about life, just as Jacques Loeb had earlier done at the Institute. Because Stanley's 1935 paper attracted so much attention in the popular media, it naturally stimulated great interest in the scientific community, and criticism was not long in coming. From Britain, researchers reported that TMV was not a pure protein as reported by Stanley but contained approximately six percent nucleic acid (RNA) and that it was a nucleoprotein. Why had Stanley missed the RNA?

Over the years, Stanley received severe criticism both for missing the RNA in his paper and for not recognizing that the "crystals" were paracrystalline in nature.[40] But when Stanley began his research in 1932, the true nature of viruses was still a mystery. It had not been established whether they were inorganic, hydrocarbon, carbohydrate, lipid, or protein. No one had isolated them as such. Though Stanley's 1935 paper had shortcomings, it was a major step forward in the field of virology. Later, with input from Thé Svedberg, Stanley was able to extend his work and publish a portrait of the rod-shaped TMV. By 1946, largely due to Stanley's initiatives, work on the concentration and purification of different viruses was proceeding in several laboratories, and over a dozen viruses had been obtained in a highly purified form—primarily by the techniques of high speed centrifugation.

Having a distinguished program established at Princeton—a program initially focused on animals and then incorporating research on plants—not only brought new kudos to Rockefeller scientists, but brought to the fore whole new lines of inquiry. To some extent, the local circumstances at Princeton mimicked the New York example of intense and frequent communication among scientists of very diverse interests, although internal disagreements were also a part of the Princeton locale. In establishing an off-site program, the Rockefeller Institute took a gamble, acting somewhat precipitously in choosing the Princeton location.

Journals at the Institute

The Institute also took the lead in enhancing scientific excellence in America by editing and publishing journals. By developing journals of the highest quality and encouraging the staff to publish in them, the leadership of the Institute further emphasized its independence from the existing institutional environment. The *Journal of Experimental Medicine* (founded by Welch) was the first journal to be edited at the Institute. Flexner became the editor in 1904, and in addition to all his other responsibilities, he served as the chief editor for fifteen years, though assisted at the outset (1904–1910) by Eugene Opie. Eventually, he asked Peyton Rous in 1921 to be co-editor, and Rous essentially functioned as the editor for the next thirty-six years, though Flexner continued to be listed as co-editor. Flexner's successor Herbert Gasser served as co-editor from 1935 to 1953, the entire period for which he was director.[41]

In 1918, Jacques Loeb, with John Osterhout of Harvard, launched the *Journal of General Physiology*, which was subsidized by the Rockefeller. With Institute support, Loeb also launched a monograph series designed to advance the development of experimental biology from a quantitative and physiochemical point of view. Through these publications, Loeb helped to unite various fields of field of biology by breaking down barriers among various specialties.[42] The Institute also published numerous other monographs, sometimes at irregular intervals. There was a series entitled *Studies from the Rockefeller Institute for Medical Research*, which by 1930 had seventy volumes of 600 pages each. The *Journal of Biological Chemistry* also was published by the Institute for many years, and Phoebus Levene, Donald Van Slyke, and others at the Institute published a high proportion of their papers there.[43]

During his long directorship (over thirty years), Flexner played a major role in improving the quality of the Institute's publications. These aided the productivity and creativity at the Institute and were important in drawing attention to the Institute's accomplishments. Overall, probably no journal published at the Institute has had greater impact in establishing new trends in biology than the *Journal of Biophysical and Biochemical Cytology*, later renamed the

Journal of Cell Biology. Its founding was inspired by Keith Porter and had the strong support of Herbert Gasser.[44]

Frequent and Intense Interactions

The experience of the Rockefeller Institute demonstrates that diversity and depth of knowledge in a well-integrated research organization have the potential to change the way people view problems and to minimize their tendency to make mistakes and/or to work on trivial problems. Frequent and intense interaction among people with low levels of diversity tends not to lead to major breakthroughs; however, if scientists work in environments where there is moderate to high scientific diversity and depth, and have frequent and intense interaction with those having complementary interests, they increase the probability that the quality of their work will improve. It is the diversity of disciplines and paradigms to which individuals are exposed in frequent and intense interactions that increases the tendency to develop new ways of thinking about fundamental problems. To permit such a process to continue long term requires that the organization provide not only the stimulating, resources, and environment for today, but that it, in a sense, anticipate the future by undertaking whole new lines of research.

Intellectual and social integration were maintained at Rockefeller Institute by a variety of devices. Eating meals together while conversing about serious scientific matters was an important part of the Rockefeller culture and an important means of integrating the scientific diversity and depth of the Institute. There was invariably high-quality food at lunch, served at tables for eight. The idea was that a single conversation could take place at such a table, but not at a larger one.

The degree of intellectual and scientific diversity was much less at the Rockefeller Institute than that at the colleges of Oxford and Cambridge, where eating at "high table" was also an important part of the culture. At the English colleges, diversity ranged all across the board (e.g., from archaeology and as well as ancient and modern languages to chemistry, physics, biology, and mathematics). With so much diversity, it was considered poor etiquette to talk about one's work at the tables, as many of those present would be unable to comprehend the line of discussion. But at Rockefeller, diversity was only within the biomedical and related sciences, and the norm was to carry on lively lunch time discussions about these fields. Indeed, these luncheon experiences not only led to new factual information and changes in philosophical viewpoints, but also to collaborative research projects across fields.[45]

For many, the lunch table at the Institute was the high point of the day. Paul de Kruif, a scientist at the Institute who later was a strong critic, nevertheless thought the dining room was one of its most stimulating characteristics.

> . . . at the lunch break there was balm for my discouragement. Here I could listen to the scintillating talk of my betters . . . I never tired of listening to the philosophy of Alexis Carrel, who had won the Nobel Prize in medicine . . . Carrel, who had been in America a long time, had carefully preserved his French accent, which made him sound to me even more learned than he was. . . . Then at the luncheon table there might be Dr. Peyton Rous, refined, gentle, exquisitely cultured . . . In this refectory there was an air of solemnity to be expected and appropriate to the unveiling of mysteries.[46]

And in the words of Dubos:

> There never was a symposium—in the etymological sense of the word . . . that was more scientifically productive and intellectually pleasurable than those held daily in the lunchroom of the Rockefeller Institute, though coffee and ideas were the only intoxicants.[47]

Apart from lunch, scientific integration was also facilitated by the weekly conference everyone was expected to attend, at which Institute investigators or distinguished scientists from all over the world reported about their work. In the Hospital department, there were afternoon tea times that most scientific staff attended.

One of the most important integrating devices was the journal club, especially the Hospital Journal Club which generally met twice a month. Everyone was expected to attend, and to be prepared to report on a paper outside one's own research field, but of general interest to everyone. No one knew in advance who would be called upon to present materials to the journal club. Why would world-class scientists agree to participate in such activity? Scientists did this because they knew they were members of an extraordinarily distinguished organization, and they believed that one reason it was so outstanding was that they were continuously learning from each other. This kind of regular reading outside one's own specialization and in areas of interest to others in the organization was one way of integrating scientific diversity. In short, the Institute had developed a culture of continuous learning for its scientists.

Its learning environment was compounded by being located in New York City. Before World War II, most distinguished foreign scientists traveling to America arrived in New York and invariably visited the Rockefeller Institute. Certainly, no other biomedical research organization in America was so favored with foreign scientists. If this small institute could not have all the diverse ways of approaching biomedical science represented on its permanent staff, it had the opportunity to have many of the world's leading scientists passing through with reports about their work. Moreover, Rockefeller Foundation grants often brought to New York the cream of the world's crop of young scientists, who typically visited the Institute for days or weeks.

A Temple of Science

Institute scientists took great pride in being associated with what many viewed as a temple of science.[48] As soon as one crossed from York Avenue onto the grounds of the Institute, one was in a sanctuary, separated from the hustle and bustle, the grime and dirt, the shouting and cursing of the city. The original idea of the Institute had been conceived in part by a Protestant minister, Frederick Gates, and throughout the century, some observers have referred to the Institute in religious terms. Not only for Gates but also for the Rockefellers, Flexner, and Welch, biomedical science certainly acquired religious proportions.

How did this happen? Gates spoke for the two John D. Rockefellers when he wrote that "disease is the supreme ill of human life and is the main source of almost all other human ills: poverty, crime, ignorance, vice, inefficiency." He went on to explain that these ills could not be cured by the economic and social restructuring of society, as many socialists believed. Rather, society's problems were technical in nature and required technological solutions, which medical science could provide.[49] For Gates, these views did have a religious quality to them, because scientific medicine was the means for building a new and better world, and for uplifting and civilizing one's fellow men. Thus, the Rockefeller Institute was envisioned to become the functional equivalent of a temple for the new religion, and the medical investigators who would reduce suffering and poverty were to be its priests. Gates referred to the

Institute as a theological seminary, and Flexner as the scientific "Doctor of Divinity." Indeed, de Kruif thought "Flexner looked as if he might be high in the College of Cardinals."[50] And in writing about the Institute, de Kruif reported that for Flexner, the greatest achievement of the Institute was not "the scientific output, its undoubted saving of lives, its contributions to basic knowledge," but rather "it was the harmony, the serenity, [and] the brotherhood with which the staff had always worked together."[51]

Welch had early on advised Flexner to recruit scientists "who agree well together."[52] Both believed that new ways of thinking about scientific problems were most likely to emerge in a scientific environment in which scientists had intense and frequent interaction with one another, so that a fundamental new way of thinking about a problem could occur. For this, an environment of harmony, trust, and dignity is essential because whether one is in a religious or scientific monastery, the priesthood must be passionate in their quest for the truth. Thus, in recruiting staff for this sanctuary of science, it was important to select individuals who were imbued with a spirit of cooperation and to avoid the prima donnas.

To recruit staff who would pursue problems on a large scale, Flexner thought it was important to find scientists concerned with deep philosophical problems. During the first half century of its existence, the Institute had numerous scientists who not only internalized vast scientific diversity, but whose scientific thinking was well integrated with a rich philosophical framework. This kind of scientific staff generated enormous excitement at the Institute lunch tables, which became famous over much of the world. As in most monasteries, there was some conflict. Some members cared little for others. But relative to most research organizations, there was a high degree of communication and cooperation among the scientific staff, and this contributed to its rich learning environment.

Flexner's Achievements

In 1935, Flexner at age seventy-two retired as director of the Institute after more than thirty years of service. Though he had been able to recruit only a "motley" group of scientists at the outset, by the time he stepped down as director, the Institute had emerged as one of the world's leading centers of biomedical science. Whereas in the first decade of the century, most scientists with established reputations would not consider accepting an appointment there, the Institute had long before eclipsed the Pasteur Institute, the Lister Institute of London, and others. During the years that Flexner served as director, ten of the Institute's research scientists were cited for major discoveries in biomedical science. Five—Alexis Carrel, Karl Landsteiner, John Northrop, Peyton Rous, and Wendell Stanley—received Nobel Prizes either during or after Flexner's tenure. Theobald Smith received the Copley Medal for research he conducted at both the Institute and at the Harvard Medical School. Oswald Avery, Simon Flexner, Jacques Loeb, Theobald Smith, and Hideyo Noguchi made breakthroughs that yielded numerous nominations in multiple years for Nobel Prizes in Physiology or Medicine (enough to meet the criteria established in Appendix I as major discoveries). During the Flexner years, no other research organization in the world had more major breakthroughs in biomedical science than the Rockefeller Institute, and for a comparable period (thirty-four years), no research organization in the world since then has had so many major breakthroughs!

During the Flexner years, the Institute had distinctive advantages in identifying both junior and senior talents throughout the world. Although the Rockefeller Foundation was not a major funding agency for the Rockefeller Institute, the Rockefeller Foundation had become a major funding source for biomedical science throughout Europe and North America. To access the quality of scientists and their labs, the Foundation obtained reports about research in every major biomedical research organization in Europe and North America. Because Simon Flexner was a trustee of the Foundation and because his brother Abraham had a long affiliation with the Foundation, Simon had extensive knowledge about who was "up coming" and he was in a strategic position to invite outstanding young scientists to the Institute. Similarly, his prominence in the National Research Council provided him with inside information about many promising young scientists.[53]

During the 1920s, aspiring biomedical scientists in America took the view that they needed to spend at least two to three years at the Institute for postdoctoral training. By 1935, more than 150 Rockefeller-trained scientists had become professors in America's leading universities and were beginning to establish their own training programs, a process which in the long run would narrow the gap in quality between the Rockefeller Institute and other organizations in biomedical science. But until the National Institutes of Health (NIH) became the leading training center for young biomedical scientists during the 1950s and 1960s, the Rockefeller Institute was clearly the major center for postdoctoral training in America, with younger people from Europe increasingly going to the Institute for advanced training. When future Nobel laureate Alan Hodgkin went there in 1938 from the University of Cambridge, he was struck by the high quality of its scientists, its instrumentation, as well as its greater formality and seriousness in contrast to Cambridge.[54]

Among the reasons for the continued excellence of the Rockefeller Institute were its flexibility, derived in large part from its autonomy, and its independence from the institutional environment in which it was embedded. Unlike many research organizations at the time in both Europe and America, it was not dependent on external funding; therefore, it was immune to the kinds of constraints that funding sources place on organizations.[55] Until the mid-1950s, the Rockefeller Institute seldom accepted grants or any funding from sources other than the Rockefeller family. Moreover, it was relatively autonomous from the norms and rules imposed by most scientific disciplines. Most universities, organized around academic disciplines and their academic departments, are constrained in their behavior by the norms and rules of existing academic disciplines. Because the Rockefeller Institute was organized around laboratories rather than scientific disciplines and fields, it had a greater capacity to be flexible and to adapt quickly to new research strategies. And in contrast to the institutional environment in Germany and France, the Rockefeller Institute had high autonomy to appoint anyone to its staff. For example, in Germany, most scientists who became professors first had to qualify for habilitation, which is access to an academic field by preparing an original book-length scholarly work after receiving the PhD. The Rockefeller Institute imposed no such requirement and appointed as members well-trained scientists with credentials from many parts of the world.

Transition to a New Director

The Institute was still performing well when Flexner retired, but it was in need of a new director with different scientific perspectives. Even high-performing research organizations undergo demographic changes and need new leadership from time to time in order to become better adapted to the fast pace of scientific change. In the case of the Rockefeller Institute, many of the original members of the Scientific Board of Directors had died (Biggs [1923], Holt [1924], and Prudden [1924]), as had some of its most distinguished scientific investigators (Meltzer [1920], Loeb [1924], Noguchi [1928], and Smith [1934]).

During the 1930s, the Institute was one of the world's leading centers in enzymology, virology, bacteriology, and pathology. Indeed, there have been suggestions that Herbert Gasser, the next director, was appointed to succeed Flexner in an effort to prevent the Institute from becoming too narrowly concerned with virology and bacteriology.[56] Even though the Institute had attained a high level of excellence in several areas of biomedical science, it had clearly made no effort to cover all fields of biomedical science. Flexner believed that an effort to work in too many fields would lead to uneven quality, and that research programs of low quality would bring down standards of excellence in the entire organization.[57] Hence, during the Flexner years, the Institute had made few or modest efforts to conduct research in several areas in which other research organizations in either Europe or America had already become quite prominent (e.g., research in vitamins and other areas of nutrition, endocrinology, genetics, and neurophysiology). Flexner's strategy had been to have areas of core competence that were complementary and to avoid having too much scientific scope and diversity, lest the organization become less integrated and have less communication among its various component parts.

The decision to bring in an outsider (Gasser) as the new director was a wise one. Many organizations, because they have a distinctive culture, tend to choose their new leaders from within, but such choices may well enhance organizational inertia and hamper the organization's capacity to adopt to the fast changing environment. Among its eight directors or presidents since the founding of the Institute, seven were recruited from the outside, and the sole exception, Torsten Wiesel, spent most of his career elsewhere, moved to Rockefeller University at the age of sixty, and had been at Rockefeller for less than ten years when he was appointed as president. The Rockefeller organization has been much more flexible in adapting to new strategies and different styles of science than would have been the case had they recruited their directors and presidents from among people who had spent most of their careers there.

Gasser, like Flexner, had grown up in America's heartland. He was born in 1888 in the small town of Platteville, Wisconsin; attended the University of Wisconsin–Madison and studied physiology there with Joseph Erlanger, and later was a student at the Johns Hopkins Medical School. He became a colleague of Erlanger at Washington University; and by 1921, he had been appointed professor of pharmacology. Gasser went to London in 1923 to work with A.V. Hill, the neurophysiologist who was awarded the Nobel Prize in Physiology or Medicine in 1922. Gasser also developed a close collegial relationship with Henry Dale and Edgar Adrian, both of whom were awarded Nobel Prizes in the 1930s. In the long run, these relationships were important in establishing a network between English neurophysiologists and the Rockefeller Institute. Gasser later moved to New York to serve as professor of physiology at the Cornell Medical College, which allowed him to become quite familiar with the neighboring Rockefeller Institute.

Like all subsequent directors or presidents, Gasser worked to preserve the culture that Flexner and his colleagues had developed. However, Gasser had his own distinctive style of doing science, and this was enormously beneficial in facilitating the Institute's adaptation to changes in the world of science. Like Flexner, Gasser made continuous efforts to extend the scope and depth of his knowledge. The more he observed increasing specialization in science, especially in American universities, the more he was motivated to contain the centrifugal forces of differentiation within research organizations by promoting the unity of the biomedical sciences. His ideal of an outstanding scientist was someone who internalized considerable intellectual diversity, was a theorist, an experimenter, a mechanic, and an artist. Indeed, he believed that at the Institute there should be serious efforts to blend humanistic and scientific knowledge.[58]

A major difference between Gasser and Flexner was Gasser's greater concern with methods of measurement. By building on his awareness of the new initiatives in measurement, Gasser extended the kinds of problems pursued in existing kinds of research and steadily pushed the organization into new lines of work. This was an example of a major change at the Institute, but folded into ongoing programs. Reaching his scientific maturity during the early days of electronics, Gasser attempted to master areas of physics with implications for biomedical sciences. As director, he demonstrated that he was attuned to the latest methods and ideas in the biological sciences. In his own work, he was at the frontier of using electronic amplifiers and recording for observing the most minute signs of nerve action.

When Gasser became director in 1935, the United States was experiencing the worst economic depression in its history, and this adversely affected the Institute. Even before Gasser arrived, Flexner had written to Rockefeller Jr. assuring him that over the next several years the Institute would be especially frugal and would not ask for additional funds. As a result of the fiscal problems brought about by the Depression, Gasser was severely limited in terms of the new fields of science that he attempted to introduce at the Institute. Salaries were tight and when young scientists left the Institute, most were not replaced. Between 1935 and 1941, the total scientific staff of the Institute declined from 134 to 105. During the Depression, the income from the Institute's endowment declined dramatically, with the result that in 1939 the Institute's expenses exceeded its income by 23 percent. The Institute was able to cover its deficit only because it had accumulated a surplus during the Flexner years.[59]

Partly due to the economic problems of the Depression followed by the disruption of war, Gasser modified the Institute's strategy with regard to younger scientists. During the Flexner years, when a member left the Institute, the lab was closed; but, on numerous occasions, Gasser permitted a remaining associate member to head a lab and to develop a research program. Both Flexner and Gasser were willing to take risks with younger scientists, but Gasser was more inclined to grant some young scientists a high degree of autonomy in developing their own research programs, a strategy which paid off handsomely with several younger scientists who later made major discoveries (e.g., Henry Kunkel, Stanford A. Moore, George Palade, Keith Porter, and William H. Stein). Among these scientists, three were subsequently awarded Nobel Prizes, two Lasker Prizes for Basic Biomedical Science, and two Horwitz Prizes for research conducted at Rockefeller.

A Shift toward Neuroscience

Despite the budget constraints, Gasser provided leadership for altering the research strategies of the Institute. As retirements occurred, the research emphasis on bacteriology and infectious diseases—paramount during the Flexner years—decreased. Gradually, Gasser facilitated the development of different research programs. One of the most significant, with long-term consequences, was neuroscience. Rather quickly, Gasser developed a program in neurophysiology that focused on the fundamental properties of nerve cells, dendrites, and the primary synaptic endings of nerve fibers. He surrounded himself with several competently trained foreign investigators—Harry Grundfest and Rafael Lorente de Nó from Spain, David Lloyd from Oxford, and Jan Friedrich Toennies from the Berlin Technische Hochschule. By the late 1940s, three from the neurophysiology group held the rank of Member: Gasser, Lloyd, and de Nó.[60]

Although the work for which Gasser was to win the Nobel Prize had been done at Washington University before he arrived at the Rockefeller Institute, he did lay the foundation for a rich neuroscience program at the Institute. His successor as director of the Institute, Detlev Bronk, was also a neurophysiologist who expanded on the foundation begun by Gasser's work. This tradition led to H.K. Hartline's work in the neurophysiology of vision that was awarded a Nobel Prize for Physiology or Medicine in 1967. By the mid-1970s, Rockefeller had a major program in three areas of neuroscience: (1) molecular and cellular mechanisms; (2) neurophysiology and behavioral physiology; and (3) information processing, communication behavior, cognition, memory, and brain function. And, the scientists in them composed one of the largest groups in the organization. Eventually, Nobel laureate Gerald Edelman developed one of the most prominent theories in the broad field of neurobiology,[61] and he was instrumental in arranging for the Neurosciences Institute to be at Rockefeller University (where it was located until 1991). Edelman was also instrumental in recruiting Torsten Wiesel, who had received the Nobel Prize for his work in the area of neurophysiology of vision, and who became a professor at the Rockefeller University in 1983. At the same time, Paul Greengard, who was awarded in the year 2000 a Nobel Prize for his neuroscience research, joined the faculty. From the time of Gasser to the present, these and numerous other distinguished scientists have placed Rockefeller in the vanguard of neuroscience.[62]

Proteins to the Fore

Research organizations may stay at the forefront of science by hiring senior scientists who have already been the trail blazers in their field as well as by having their current investigators develop new frontiers. The capacity to do both is a result of past and present strategy choices and good leadership. This is most evident with regard to the role of biological chemistry at Rockefeller. In this case, Emil Fischer's school of organic chemistry was partially transplanted to the Institute in the early part of the twentieth century; this transplantation subsequently branched in numerous directions, one of which was protein chemistry, giving rise to several major discoveries in the process. Indeed, the prophecy of Fisher in his 1902 Nobel lecture was very much realized at Rockefeller: "Since the proteins participate in one way or another in all chemical processes in the living organism, one may expect highly significant information for biological chemistry from the elucidation of their structures and their transformations."[63]

At the Institute, there were several scientists who had studied with Fischer and who in turn inspired many luminaries of protein chemistry (e.g., John Northrop, Moses Kunitz, Wendell Stanley, Stanford Moore, William H. Stein, Lyman Craig, and Alfred Mirsky). Loeb, although not trained as a chemist, also had a major influence in developing the tradition of protein chemistry at Rockefeller.[64] This lineage was responsible for Rockefeller becoming a world-class center for major discoveries within the broad outlines of protein chemistry. In many respects, the critical period for the development of protein chemistry was between 1925 and 1960 when there was increasing evidence in both Europe and America that many important biological activities were due to specific proteins. Although there was vast information that earlier supported this view, it was only during this period that protein chemistry was put on a firm experimental basis, largely as the result of the development of new methods and instruments that substantially increased the knowledge of the function and structure of proteins.

One of the great protein chemists of the twentieth century, Max Bergmann, was appointed to Rockefeller in 1934, leaving Germany after the Nazi ascent to power. A former student of Emil Fischer, Bergmann attracted to the Institute a group of able young scientists who would later develop into some of the leading protein chemists in the postwar world: William Stein, Stanford Moore, Joseph Fruton, Klaus Hoffman, Emil L. Smith, Paul Zamecnik, among others. Work on proteins at the Institute was largely suspended during World War II, and after Bergmann died of cancer at the height of his career in 1944, the lab was without a chief. Gasser, demonstrating that he had an excellent ability not only to discern the direction in which science was moving but also to identify talent, asked Moore and Stein to stay at the Institute and gave them the freedom to do most anything they pleased in the biochemical field. In 1949, they were appointed as associate members and they received permanent appointments at the Institute in 1952. They won the Nobel Prize in Chemistry in 1972 for their collaboration leading to the development of quantitative chromatographic methods for amino acid analysis, especially their automation techniques, which led to the entire sequence for ribonuclease A, the first complete description of the chemical structure of an enzyme.

Gasser also demonstrated imaginative leadership with his support of other young scientists who were engaged in fundamentally new kinds of research. One example was his support of Lyman Craig—long associated with Walter Jacobs—who also worked independently in developing other techniques for purifying some proteins. For this work, Craig was later awarded the Lasker Prize for Basic Biomedical Science.

Rise of Cell Biology

But nowhere did Gasser demonstrate better insight in judging the direction in which science might move than in his support of a group of young cell biologists. Albert Claude had arrived at the Rockefeller Institute in 1929 and worked in the laboratory of James B. Murphy in an effort to purify and characterize the agent (known as the Rous sarcoma virus) that caused a transmissible form of cancer in chickens. Working in the area of virology, Claude used a high-speed centrifuge to spin fractionated cells infected with viruses in an effort to isolate and purify their agents. His investigations led to the determination that cells contained tiny bodies he termed "microsomes." The critical problem was to understand their structure and function. To address this problem, Claude used an electron microscope, a new laboratory tool in the 1940s. Under the pioneering role of Claude's younger colleague, Keith Porter, the Institute then led the way in the development of electron microscopy for the study of cell biology. Aside from Porter, Claude also had the assistance of several other young scientists including George Palade, Rollin Hotchkiss, George Hogeboom, and Walter Schneider.[65]

It was the interdisciplinary environment of the Rockefeller Institute that facilitated Claude's imaginative investigations. He brought to the study of cells deep insights from the fields of oncology, virology, biochemistry, histology, and cytology, and his ability to internalize so much scientific diversity enhanced his ability to see things in fundamentally new ways, and to lay the foundation for the development of cell biology at Rockefeller.

Claude left the Institute in 1949 to return to his native Belgium, and Murphy (the head of the lab) retired in 1950. But Gasser's keen ability to recognize promising research and willingness (as in the case of Stein and Moore) to keep a lab open when its head disappeared from the scene, set the stage for major new advances. Technically, Gasser became the head of the Porter–Palade group so that it might continue to function; nevertheless, for several years Porter actually provided the day-to-day leadership of the newly developed electron microscopy laboratory. It is no exaggeration to suggest that modern cell biology was born at the Rockefeller Institute under the leadership of a diverse group of junior scientists.[66]

Without the nurturing role of Gasser in deviating from the precedent of disbanding laboratories, these developments would not have occurred. Significantly, it was Gasser's support for the development of new technologies needed for new fields of research that facilitated the Institute's becoming one of the world's leading centers for protein chemistry and cell biology.

Avery, MacLeod, and McCarty

Perhaps the single most notable achievement in the entire history of the Rockefeller Institute was the paper published by Oswald Avery and his younger colleagues Colin MacLeod and Maclyn McCarty in 1944, offering evidence that genetic specificity is embedded in the chemical structure of DNA.[67] The story of this work, which had little to do with Gasser's leadership, has been recounted many times, and there is no need to go into great detail here. However, it is worthwhile to note certain aspects of the process of this discovery in order to illustrate how the structure and culture of Rockefeller facilitated scientific creativity.

Today, there is universal recognition that the paper from Avery's group represents one of the most important discoveries in the history of the biomedical science. Nobel laureate Joshua Lederberg has observed that between twenty and twenty-five Nobel Prizes were subsequently awarded for research dependent on it. Similarly, Peter Medawar, the Nobel laureate immunologist, called the discovery "the most interesting and portentous biological experiment of the twentieth century."[68]

Notwithstanding general agreement on the significance of the results, there are several intriguing problems about the Avery paper. Since the Rockefeller Institute was the dominant center of the protein central dogma, how was it that the challenge to this paradigm came from within the Institute and was made by a bacteriologist and physician who lacked formal training in chemistry and genetics? Could this discovery have been made anywhere else at approximately the same time?

As a trained physician, Avery spent much of his career concerned with understanding pneumonia and attempting to devise strategies for either treating or preventing the disease. It is no exaggeration to report that by 1940 he was one of the world's foremost, if not the most prominent, authority on various types of pneumococcus. Over the years, his research shifted from an interest in the development of an effective serum for the treatment of pneumonia to an immunochemical understanding of the chemical basis of the biological specificity of different types of pneumonia. For more than two decades, a dialectic was operating in Avery's mind: the applied scientist's concern with treating and preventing pneumonia, on the one hand, and a basic scientist's concern with the underlying chemical and biological processes on the other hand. It was the tension between these two forms of inquiry and the effort to integrate them that was the key to Avery's scientific creativity. In our own day, as those trained as either basic scientists or physicians tend to drift further and further apart, the story of how Avery integrated the concerns of both the clinician and the basic scientist needs to be carefully considered.

Avery spent his entire Rockefeller career in the pneumonia section of the Hospital Department. Although the leading investigators in the Hospital (e.g., Rufus Cole, Alfred Cohn, A.R. Dochez, Frank Horsfall, Thomas Rivers, and Donald Van Slyke) were clearly distinguished investigators by national standards, there was a tendency after World War I among many in the Laboratory Department to perceive the Hospital investigators as applied investigators and therefore somewhat inferior. Avery was very much aware that although he was highly specialized and knowledgeable about pneumonia, he was an outsider as far as fundamental knowledge of physics, chemistry, and biology was concerned. Like all his colleagues in the Hospital Department, he was obsessed with learning, and he constantly tried to absorb basic knowledge from his Laboratory colleagues in an effort to expand the scope of his specialty, pneumonia.

During the 1930s, Avery had lunch at the Institute's famous tables with such distinguished organic and biological chemists as Phoebus Levene, Karl Landsteiner, Van Slyke, Alfred Mirsky, and Max Bergmann and his brilliant young associates William Stein, Stanford Moore, Joseph Fruton, Emil L. Smith, and Paul Zamecnik. Never has one organization had such a stellar collection of biological chemists all at one place and all clearly working at the frontiers of science. No wonder that on two separate occasions, Linus Pauling, one of the century's greatest chemists and at the other end of the continent, collaborated with members of this group, such as Landsteiner and Mirsky. For Avery, the ability to lunch on a daily basis with such a collection of scientists was exhilarating, but also somewhat intimidating.

Once he set out to identify the substance responsible for transforming one type of pneumococcus to another, Avery was determined to seek information from any available source. He frequently sought the counsel of the Institute's great scientists. Revealing his ignorance about the latest methods in chemical analysis that had been developed at Rockefeller and elsewhere, he was not shy in approaching his scientific colleagues in the privacy of their labs. Had he been a microbiologist in a large university in America, he would never have had the opportunity to learn so much about the recent advances in protein chemistry during the previous twenty years.

Although Avery recognized the need to borrow from other fields in order to address his particular research problems, he generally preferred to work with young scientists who had been trained as physicians rather than as basic scientists. However, on several occasions he did work with young basic scientists, including Michael Heidelberg and René Dubos, with notable success, and those collaborations helped to prepare the way for his 1944 paper. It is doubtful that Avery could have acquired the degree of scientific diversity required to do the experiments underlying his 1944 paper in any other organizational environment.[69]

In his years at the Institute, Gasser had the assistance of many of the country's leading scientists who were on the Institute's Board of Scientific Directors: Detlev Bronk, who during his tenure became president of the Johns Hopkins University, president of the National Academy of Sciences, and chairman of the Board of the National Science Foundation; James B. Conant, president of Harvard University; Vincent du Vigneaud of Cornell University (future Nobel laureate); Warfield Longcope of the Johns Hopkins University and one of the nation's leading professors of medicine; and Nobel laureate George H. Whipple of Rochester University. With their guidance, and the participation of the scientific staff, new pathways were opened not only in such broad areas as protein chemistry and cell biology but also in the mechanisms of heredity and virology.

A Change in Direction

During the Depression and the World War II, the Board of Trustees as well as the Board of Scientific Advisors were troubled by the decline of the Institute's investment income and by rising expenditures. Partly for this reason, the trustees decided in 1947 to close the Institute's research site in Princeton, New Jersey. In addition to financial considerations, the two governance boards were very much concerned by the physical separation of the two facilities. This was a very controversial decision because two members of the Princeton staff, Northrop and Stanley, had recently been awarded the Nobel Prize in Chemistry. With the closure of the Princeton department, some Princeton staff returned to New York City, and others departed from the Rockefeller Institute.

The Institute had never been content to rest on its laurels and had continuously been willing to make serious reassessments of its performance. Accordingly, in anticipation of Gasser's retirement, the trustees appointed a committee in the early 1950s to make recommendations about the Institute's future. Given the fact that by that time no research organization in the world had made so many major discoveries in biomedical science during the twentieth century, it is remarkable that the committee took into account a series of radical options for the future. The committee seriously considered whether the Institute should be closed down and its assets distributed to other research organizations, whether it should move from New York to a less costly environment, or whether the Institute should merge with an existing university.

By the early 1950s, it was clear to the Board of Trustees that the Rockefeller Institute had more than achieved its original purpose of providing a model of a high-quality research organization in biomedical science, one which would set the standard of excellence in biomedical science. Partly because of the existence of the Rockefeller Institute, there were now numerous research organizations making important discoveries and training very good scientists. By 1953, more than 200 former members of the scientific staff held rank of full professor (or the equivalent) in research centers throughout the country. Thus, if the Institute had attained its goal of helping to develop centers of biomedical research excellence in the country, why should it be continued? Perhaps Rockefeller wealth should be used for some other societal purpose not yet being addressed.

The committee consulted with several leading scientists throughout the country. Detlev Bronk, the most influential member of the committee, was adamantly opposed to closing the Institute. Recognizing that the Institute had achieved its initial goals, Bronk took the view that the Institute should revise its goals and purposes. In the future, it should not only be a center of research excellence, but it should also provide graduate education for future scientific leaders of the country. Because it would be a new kind of training center, the Rockefeller organization would continue to do something distinctively different from all other educational centers in America.

A New Vision

Impressed with Bronk's vision, the trustees prevailed upon him to become Gasser's successor. Thus, in 1953, the trustees voted to change the Institute into a graduate university with the authority to grant the degrees of doctor of philosophy and doctor of medical science. As a result, the Board of Scientific Directors was abolished and the Board of Trustees became the sole governing authority of the organization. Rockefeller Institute became a small university, the only solely graduate university in the United States. However, it was not until 1965 that the name was changed to the Rockefeller University.

Bronk, who served as president from 1953 until 1968, was very troubled that the nation's leading centers of training were producing highly specialized people whom he pejoratively characterized as technicians. In contrast, he wanted Rockefeller to produce scientists who had broad knowledge in a variety of fields. He recognized that scientific excellence required a mastery of subject, but thought it was important that scientists understand how their own research was intricately related to other fields of science. A recurring theme in his public speeches was the desire for the unity of knowledge, and for him the ideal university was one in which there would be intense and frequent interaction among scientists from diverse fields. Ideally, each scientist would have a broad competence in many areas of science. Moreover, Bronk was very humanistically oriented, and frequently spoke of the importance of scientists' understanding how they were intricately connected to the past, present, and future of their society. For Bronk, the importance of scientific research was to be measured by its larger humanitarian contributions to society. The transformation that he proposed for the Rockefeller organization was that it would be a training ground for the future leaders of science; these scientists would aspire to break down artificially segregated areas of knowledge and to struggle for the realization of the unity of knowledge for the benefit of society.[70] From time to time, Bronk preached to the Board of Trustees about the kind of university he had in mind, as he did at the Trustees meeting of May 22, 1961:

> It is unwholesome, and indeed dangerous for the future welfare of mankind, for scientists to live and work, to study and teach, in an environment in which they are not in close contact with creative, critical scholars in the humanities and arts. Such associations are a valuable quality of a university. Lack of such contact with those who help determine the future of civilization makes specialized research institutes barren intellectual environments.[71]

But how might a small university attain such goals? Paradoxically, a small university such as Rockefeller had more potential to produce broadly trained scientists than larger research universities that teach most everything. Bronk believed that it was inappropriate to include all fields of science in their research program. In the largest research universities with their increasing fragmentation and specialization, such a goal had become increasingly difficult. When universities attempt to encompass all fields of science, some areas are invariably mediocre, and when mediocrity develops in some fields, it leads to mediocrity elsewhere. Because of the small size of the Rockefeller University, Bronk recognized that it could not offer programs in the humanities. As a result, the university in his presidency offered each student a fund of $1,000 to take advantage of the rich cultural offerings in New York (e.g., concerts, opera, theater, ballet, museums, and galleries). Moreover, he arranged for humanists and social scientists to present frequent public lectures at the University and for concerts to be held in its facilities.

Because it was not feasible to encompass all specialized fields of science, in Bronk's view the University should focus on the "most significant, most fundamental and most broadly relevant areas of mathematics, physics, chemistry, and biology." Moreover, because the University was organized around individuals rather than departments, its structure also should encourage cooperation in teaching and research. Accordingly, in recruiting faculty to the university, emphasis was placed on the choice of people who had broad interests and who by inclination enjoyed collaboration with others in diverse fields of science. However, the emphasis on breadth of scholarly interests and interdisciplinary cooperation did not mean that certain individuals or groups would be recruited simply to provide service for more fundamental areas of science. Indeed, the philosophy at Rockefeller was that every scientist and group was encouraged to be autonomous, with their own identity and dignity.

Growth and Community

The program that Bronk espoused had implications about the growth of the university, however. When Bronk became president in 1953, there were 21 members; in contrast, at the end of his tenure as president, there were 51 professors. In the same period, there was a tripling in the size of the scientific staff from 99 to 303.[72] Although in 1953, there were biological scientists, medical doctors, biophysicists, and physical chemists, the faculty was quickly expanded to include scientists in psychology and animal behavior, physics, mathematics, and philosophy. Moreover, the fields of biology, chemistry, and biophysics were extended. Within three years, Rockefeller appointed as professor several scientists who had either already been awarded or would later be awarded Nobel Prizes: Keffer Hartline from Johns Hopkins, Fritz Lippman from the Harvard Medical School, and Edward Tatum from Stanford University. Other distinguished, senior faculty appointed during the Bronk years were as follows: the philosopher Ludwig Edelstein; the biologist Paul Weiss; the mathematician Marc Kac; physicists George Uhlenbeck and Abraham Pais; behavioral scientists Carl Pfaffmann, Neal Miller, and Floyd Ratliff; the geneticist Theodosius Dobzhansky; the cell biologist Christian de Duve; and the chemist Theodore Shedlovsky. Bronk also arranged for many of the world's leading scientists to spend a week or two with students including Lord Adrian of Cambridge University, Isidor Rabi of Columbia University, David Goddard of the University of Pennsylvania, Ragnar Granit of the Karolinska Institute, John Kirkwood of Yale University, Kaj Ulrik Linderstrom-Lang of the Carlsberg Laboratory, A.M. Monnier of the University of Paris, and Alexander von Muralt of the University of Bern. By the end of Bronk's term as president, Rockefeller University had one of the most distinguished collections of biomedical scientists in the world.

For Bronk, the University was ideally a genuine community of scholars with graduate students, post-docs, and faculty having intense and frequent interactions, all engaged in learning from one another. An important key to such a university was in the selection of students, and he frequently argued that it was important that students be selected with the same care as the faculty. Hence, during his presidency, Bronk personally interviewed most of the students before they were admitted. The only students selected for admission were those whose commitment to advanced study and research was believed to be equal to that of the faculty. All students were considered to be intellectually mature, highly motivated, and capable of self study. As a result, there was to be no core curriculum. Each student was to engage in a program of study based primarily on learning from advanced textbooks, professional journals, tutorials and seminars on special subjects, and work in the labs of some of the world's most distinguished and experienced scientists. In a sense, there was a separate curriculum for each student. Even though Rockefeller technically had been transformed into a university, it remained more of an institute than a research university of the type normally known in American society. Rarely would more than 25 graduate students be admitted a year, and by 1966 there were only 128 students—the level maintained throughout the rest of the century.[73] Because there were so few students relative to the number of faculty, close associations developed among students and faculty.[74]

Normally, admitted students had completed an undergraduate baccalaureate or held a doctor of medicine degree. Students were usually candidates for the degree of doctor of philosophy, but those who were doctors of medicine could pursue a degree of doctors of medical science. Thus, one of the major goals in moving from an institute to a university was to prepare young people to be scientific leaders of the nation, or as David Rockefeller expressed it, "a reaffirmation and an expansion of prior objectives, a reaching out to new opportunities for the pursuit of excellence."[75]

Small and Diverse

During the years of Bronk's presidency and ever since, the Rockefeller organization has been confronted with somewhat conflicting goals. It aspires to have considerable breadth in its scientific interests, but it is determined to remain small and to permit each lab to be autonomous. It has been difficult to maintain strength in chemistry, physics, mathematics, and in different fields of biology, and at the same time to promote interdisciplinary cooperation. The University has attempted to address this paradox by promoting the unity of science through the interpretation of biological phenomena in physical and chemical terms. Perhaps unsurprisingly, several scientists who were recruited to Rockefeller as organic or physical chemists over time became biochemists. Some physicists became biophysicists, and some mathematicians emigrated to other fields as a result of their interests in computer science and various technologies. Thus, at the Rockefeller University, there has long been a strategy of recruiting scientists who have broad interests and who by temperament have been eager to collaborate with and learn from those in other fields. Because of its small size, the University has generally been reluctant to recruit those who by temperament prefer to work in isolation, although over time there have been exceptions.

Another aspect of the continuity between the Bronk years and the culture of excellence institutionalized during the Flexner years was the historical emphasis on providing services for the scientific staff, such as the design and construction of instruments, illustration services, glass blowing, and a spectroscope laboratory. To keep these and other services at a high level of excellence, the organization over the years has recruited an extraordinary staff trained in the techniques of mechanical, electrical, and chemical engineering.[76] Having state-of-the-art support services has been important in keeping the Rockefeller University at the cutting edges of multiple fields of science.

The Limits of Expansion

Accompanying the expansion of faculty during the Bronk years was a building program that reshaped the physical setting of the Rockefeller University. This included a residence for graduate students and a building with two wings: the Abby Aldrich Rockefeller Hall (containing a dining room, lounges, library, and accommodations for visiting scholars) and the Alfred H. Caspary Hall (with administration offices). Connected to Caspary Hall was a new auditorium. A modern nine-story laboratory and several smaller buildings were constructed.[77] Bronk's aesthetic aspirations for the University were revealed by his arranging for one of the world's leading landscape architects, Daniel Urban Kiley, to design the university's grounds in the late 1950s. The result was the development of one of the most beautiful grounds in the city.

Bronk was a dreamer, a person whose ambitions for The University were virtually without limit. Hence, it is not surprising that it soon became obvious that the University could not survive primarily on its endowment, as in the past. Once substantial extramural funding from NIH became available in the 1950s, the Rockefeller organization began to turn to the federal government for research support. This marked a critical turning point in the history of the organization: labs began to grow in size, turned somewhat inward, and became somewhat more independent. No longer did everyone have lunch together. There were too many senior scientists and students for the early twentieth century type of communication and integration to exist. Many labs began to have their own journal clubs, and attendance at the weekly Friday afternoon scientific presentations for the entire organization dropped off dramatically. There was no longer the same degree of horizontal communication across labs as during the first half of the century. Of course, the Rockefeller University was still quite small relative to most American research universities, but as size increased, the degree of integration and communication among the scientific staff diminished.

It is not unusual that an organization undergoing rapid expansion and reorganization under one leader later finds that the rate of change is not sustainable; therefore, the next leader faces a period of major readjustment and stabilization. This is precisely what happened under the University's next president, Fred Seitz (1968–1978), a physicist. Like Bronk, he had been president of the National Academy of Sciences.

With hindsight, it is obvious that the University was extravagant in its expenditures during the Bronk years. Shortly after Seitz became president, the economic environment of the University quickly changed. By 1970 the University, like many others throughout the country, found itself confronting serious financial problems, exacerbated by inflation, including rising salaries as well as construction and energy issues. There were cuts in some federal grant programs, causing the University to draw money from its endowment to support programs to which it was committed. Moreover, the recession that began in 1968 led to a drop in income from the endowment. Because nonacademic pay scales had fallen below city standards during the Bronk years, Seitz and his staff now had to address this problem. For the first time in its history, the organization was not only confronted with a deficit, but a mounting one. This was the shape of things as Seitz completed his first year as president. As during the Depression of the 1930s, the University was forced to undertake a serious assessment of its operations, the result of which was the recognition that the institution could not sustain the rate of growth of the Bronk years.

Overall, the 1970s and 1980s were difficult. For financial reasons, if for no other, Seitz had no alternative but to undo some of the decisions of his predecessor. In contrast to the years of fanfare and ceremony under the presidency of Bronk, the tone during the presidency of Seitz was more restrained, due to the financial difficulties. Recruiting continued, but less aggressively. On-site staff were carefully reviewed, and laboratories were warned that long-term prospects for funding their researcher were very limited.

And yet, the decades of the 1970s and the 1980s also were ones of outstanding achievement and recognition. In 1969, Bruce Merrifield was awarded the Lasker Prize for Basic Biomedical Research for his work in developing a method for the synthesis of polypeptides and proteins. In 1972, Gerald Edelman was awarded the Nobel Prize in Physiology or Medicine (shared with Rodney Porter of Oxford University) while William Stein and Stanford Moore (with Christian Anfinsen of the National Institutes of Health) received the Nobel Prize in Chemistry. Two years later, Albert Claude, George Palade, and Christian de Duve shared the Nobel Prize in Physiology or Medicine for work they had conducted at Rockefeller.

The University trustees became increasingly concerned about their dependence on federal funding for research. Cuts at the federal level could imperil ongoing research, just as, to the contrary, the possible "war on cancer" could cause coffers to open. Fearful that in the distant future, federal funding would prove unstable and would decrease the University's autonomy and flexibility, the trustees instituted campaigns to raise funding from the private sector (individuals, foundations, and business firms). The trustees intended that federal grant money would provide about half of the University's budget, and the other half of the budget would be covered by private fund raising and income from the endowment. Private sector funding was absolutely necessary if the University was to remain at the frontiers of biomedical science, especially to expand its research program in cell biology and molecular biology.

Governance and Administration

By the end of the Bronk years, the trustees approved the creation of a university senate and an academic council, which was the executive committee of the senate. As a result, several senior faculty increasingly insisted on being involved in decision-making in university affairs, very much in contrast to the years when the organization was a relatively small institute. During the Flexner and Gasser years, even senior members rarely knew what major decisions were being made by the director and the two boards. Indeed, during the Gasser years, the Institute offered senior positions to Linus Pauling, Carl Cori, Vincent du Vigneaud, and Francis Schmitt[78] (all of whom declined) but the author of this paper has been unable to find any evidence that any Member of the Institute's staff was informed about these efforts.

During the Bronk years, the scientific staff had continued to be relatively uninvolved in the governance of the Rockefeller University. But difficult choices the University had to make because of the financial deficits of the 1970s and 1980s, drew the faculty into the governance of the University. Although there had been virtually no discussion among the scientific staff in the early 1950s as to whether there should be a graduate program at the University, during the Seitz years the faculty began to discuss what proportion of funds should be devoted to teaching as distinct from research, the degree to which heads of laboratories would have complete autonomy in appointing scientists in their own labs, how many Rockefeller-funded scientists might be in a single lab, and how decisions would be made about the appointment and promotion of laboratory staff. Although the process of institutionalizing new modes of decision making in an era of fiscal constraints created stress within the organization, Seitz was a very able and unflappable administrator. He facilitated the faculty's larger role, long-term financial planning. As research became much more expensive and the structure of research organizations more complex, many more factors entered into the management of the organization. In short, the complex demands of administering the organization between 1970 and 1990 made necessary a marked departure from the more personal style of management that existed before Seitz's presidency.

Nevertheless, Seitz and his successor, Joshua Lederberg (1978–1990) were very attentive as well to the infrastructure of the University, keeping it as a world-class center in instrumentation, design, and construction, and in attempting to add new laboratory space.[79] During the Seitz presidency, Hidesaburo Hanafusa, James Darnell, and several other senior faculty were recruited, but most efforts to add other senior staff were futile. The University continued its efforts to make distinguished appointments during the early years of Lederberg's presidency, and added, most notably, Jan Breslow, Paul Greengard, and Torsten Wiesel to the faculty.

Through the presidency of Lederberg, the financial condition of the University continued to be constrained by the poor performance of the American economy. Believing in the desirability of the continued smallness of the Rockefeller University, Lederberg reduced some layers of administration and attempted to make himself directly available to faculty. Many of his plans—whether very general or more programmatic (e.g., parasitology or toxicology)—were hard to realize without more discretionary funds. Meanwhile, a great deal of administrative, trustee, and faculty energy was invested in addressing fundamental issues such as fund-raising and problems attendant upon life in the city (e.g., lack of affordable housing for both junior and senior faculty).

Throughout the twentieth century, the two John D. Rockefellers and David Rockefeller were always available to lend support to the Rockefeller organization during times of stress. In fact, David Rockefeller joined the Rockefeller Institute Board of Trustees in 1940 and served for more than fifty-five years. In 1950, he succeeded his father as president of the board. It is difficult to imagine how Rockefeller could have remained a center of scientific excellence without his counsel, his financial assistance, and his ability to be a bridge between the University and other sectors of American society.

Years of Turmoil

Several perspectives about the behavior of organizations need to be kept in mind in order to understand some of the internal turmoil that occurred at the Rockefeller University between 1989 and 1991. By the late 1980s, there was an increased perception both within and outside of Rockefeller University that it was not performing as well as it had some decades earlier. Changes in the environment, apart from the availability of NIH funding, had a major effect on the University. The center of gravity of basic science research had shifted westward, as increasing numbers of scientists were willing to have careers in Berkeley, Seattle, Los Angeles, San Diego, and elsewhere on the West Coast. Furthermore, as the cost of living in the New York area escalated, it had become increasingly difficult for the University to recruit scientists of their first choice, a constraint that had been quite rare in earlier years.

In the early part of the twentieth century, ambitious young biomedical scientists were eager to spend a few years at the Rockefeller Institute. By the latter part of the century, there were many centers of biomedical excellence in the United States, and the best of the nation's young scientists were increasingly unwilling to go to the University, largely because most young scientists were not able to be heads of their own labs until they attained the rank of full professor. By the late 1980s, it was well known that for many years it had been common for the nation's best biomedical scientists to head their own labs when they were quite young (including Joshua Lederberg and Howard Temin at Wisconsin, Paul Berg and Dale Kaiser at Stanford, Jim Watson and Walter Gilbert at Harvard, Mike Bishop and Harold Varmus at the University of California, San Francisco). With numerous research centers throughout the country, good young scientists increasingly expected to have more autonomy and their own laboratories before becoming senior professors. This was a widely discussed problem within the Rockefeller University; but by the late 1980s, more often than not, young scientists were not heads of labs. As senior scientists retired, it became increasingly difficult to recruit distinguished replacements. At the same time that these problems arose, the Rockefeller University, like most of the nation's leading research universities, was required to institute salary and wage freezes in response to the poor performance of the American economy.

Apart from the fiscal problems and the junior staff problems, the University faced the persisting tasks of developing new labs and renovating old ones—a constant at all serious research organizations. With changes occurring at an ever-increasing rate in the larger world of science, there were unrelenting pressures to recruit new faculty in molecular biology, neurobiology, and cancer research, as well as in other areas. However, by 1990, the University had recruited only one senior scientist in the previous five years. The average age of the tenured faculty was fifty-eight in 1990, meaning that within another decade, many distinguished faculty would retire.

In the midst of these changes in the larger environment, David Baltimore, a Nobel laureate, became president of the Rockefeller University in July of 1990. A former graduate student at the University, Baltimore was one of the nation's most productive scientists and was widely perceived to have been a very successful administrator of the Whitehead Institute for Biomedical Research, an affiliate of the Massachusetts Institute of Technology (MIT). His appointment was strongly opposed by a sizable minority of the University's faculty, primarily because of the complex and unresolved investigations of a scientific paper that he and several of his MIT collaborators had published in *Cell* in 1986.[80] There were allegations that some of the experiments in the paper were misreported by the senior author, Thereza Imanishi-Kari. Although there were no suggestions that Baltimore personally misrepresented the data in the paper, he was widely criticized for failure to conduct a proper investigation into the allegations about the paper and for defending the "flaws" in the paper too long and vigorously. Because of this cloud over Baltimore, his tenure as president of Rockefeller became very controversial.[81] His most vocal critics, both inside and outside the University, charged that he had been extraordinarily arrogant in his handling of many of the issues related to the disputed paper.

By the time Baltimore arrived in the summer of 1990, the Rockefeller University had undertaken efforts to address some of its outstanding problems. A new laboratory building was under construction, and in 1989 several junior faculty had been appointed as heads of laboratories. Still, numerous procedures for dealing with the retention, dismissal, and promotion of junior faculty had not been resolved and the University's budget was seriously unbalanced, with a deficit of $12.3 million during Baltimore's first year.

Authority and Legitimacy

Baltimore immediately initiated a $250 million fund-raising drive and instituted a wage freeze. At the same time, he established several search committees to recruit junior and senior faculty, and proposed major changes with regard to the status of junior faculty. In short, although Baltimore addressed problems already on the University's agenda, he was clearly a catalyst, dramatizing the University's problems and acting decisively with regard to some of them.

This was not an auspicious time. With so many major issues crowding his agenda, it was especially difficult for Baltimore, as a new president, to establish his authority and legitimacy. He was attempting not only to manage the University; but simultaneously to operate his laboratory. Relocating and setting up his own lab was quite time consuming. The tensions created over the 1986 *Cell* paper continued, casting a pall over his presidency. Within Rockefeller, turmoil over the paper was compounded by the fact that a few of the senior faculty had known Baltimore since his graduate student days at the University, and several disliked him intensely. Moreover, some senior faculty resented Baltimore's demeanor as president: they felt that he viewed himself as the man on horseback who was coming to save the University from a group of entrenched oligarchs. Some faculty were embittered by rumors heard around the country that he had long bad-mouthed the University. The sentiment of one senior faculty member captured the views of many others: "To portray this faculty as a bunch of old dying swans who have lost touch with modern biology is complete and utter nonsense."[82]

Almost everything Baltimore proposed quickly became controversial in one way or another. Although the senior faculty was essentially in agreement about the desirability of changing the role of the junior faculty with regard to heading labs (as indicated by the virtually unanimous approval of the Academic Senate in the fall of 1990 of Baltimore's proposals for junior faculty), controversy continued about even this issue. Despite the agreement on the principle that some scientists who were not professors might head labs, issues about which junior faculty would head labs were unresolved. In May 1991, five assistant and associate professors were selected as heads of labs, bringing the number of nontenured heads of laboratories to sixteen.[83] As Baltimore rewarded some junior faculty with their own labs, cleavages emerged within the junior ranks. It appeared as though a two-tiered system of junior faculty was emerging. Some junior faculty received internal promotions, whereas others realized that their long-term chances of heading labs were no better than before Baltimore's arrival.

The issue of the *Cell* paper would simply not disappear. In early 1991, there were leaks in the press to the effect that the U.S. Secret Service had uncovered evidence of fraud by Imanishi-Kari. In the spring, Baltimore's public comments about the *Cell* paper led to an intensification of criticism of him and the University both in the press and among some of the nation's most respected scientists about the paper. As these criticisms reverberated within the University, Baltimore turned to junior faculty for support, leading to criticism that he "was using the junior faculty at some risk to their own careers."[84]

Finally, in the fall of 1991, in the midst of all of this turmoil, the overwhelming sentiment of the senior faculty was conveyed to the trustees that Baltimore was incapable of being an effective president, and shortly thereafter he resigned.[85] With hindsight it is obvious that the Baltimore presidency was unfortunate for the University as well as for Baltimore. In July 1996, a three-person board appointed by the Department of Health and Human Services concluded that the "preponderance of evidence" indicated that the allegations about misconduct in producing the data in the *Cell* paper could not be proven.[86]

There was a great deal of ill-chosen rhetoric on the part of both supporters and critics of Baltimore during the affair. Some of the rhetoric of Baltimore and his supporters early on suggested that the University's faculty was depleted and that the quality of science was no longer distinguished. The validity of these claims requires some perspective. It is true that there was a time when it was believed at Rockefeller that anyone receiving a permanent appointment at the organization should do work of a caliber to make the person a serious contender for a Nobel Prize. But with increases in size and the emergence of several dozen major centers of biomedical scientific research throughout the nation, it was clear that such goals were unrealistic and that Rockefeller no longer exercised the hegemonic influence over biomedical science as it had in the past. However, by 1990, the organization was still a distinguished and major center for biomedical research: within a decade, many of its most innovative scientists were singled out for major recognition with Nobel Prizes, the Lasker Prize for Basic Biomedical Science, and the Louisa Gross Horwitz Prize. Just a few years earlier, Hidesaburo Hanafusa received the Lasker Prize for Basic Biomedical Science. Also, Gerald Edelman was one of the world's most creative theoreticians in neuroscience, though his work, like most other theoretical work, was controversial. Although Bruce Merrifield had done the research for which he was awarded a Nobel Prize some years earlier, his lab was still very active in work involving ever more difficult synthetic challenges and much higher molecular numbers. Moreover, there were numerous other scientists doing excellent science at the University.

Wiesel Appointed

Upon Baltimore's resignation, the trustees appointed as president Torsten Wiesel, a world-renowned neurobiologist who had shared a Nobel Prize in Physiology or Medicine with David Hubel in 1981, and who had moved to the University from Harvard Medical School in 1983. The trustees could not have found a more suitable person for the task. Wiesel, who served until 1998, was an excellent president, one of the very best in the history of the organization.

Wiesel, born and educated in Sweden, had moved to the United States in 1955. When he became president of the Rockefeller University, he was sixty-seven years old, and he immediately became completely focused on serving the University. Wiesel had many of the traits of an outstanding president: a good sense of the direction in which science was moving, a keen ability to identify talent and to raise money to support good science, and a capacity to create a nurturing environment for both senior and junior scientists. After the intense cleavages of the Baltimore presidency, the University's faculty was eager to have stability and harmony and to rebuild their damaged reputation. Wiesel, an eminent scientist with considerable modesty and humility, was highly successful in bringing people together. Almost intuitively, he was able to integrate the traditions of the Rockefeller University with the directions in which science was changing as it moved toward the twenty-first century. Early in his presidency, he encouraged open faculty participation in discussions of both the weaknesses and strengths of the University. He then coordinated the development of an Academic Plan, an effort involving unprecedented collaboration of faculty, administration, and trustees. His strategy of bringing all parties to the table was typical of a rather low key management style, very different from the bombastic style of Bronk. Very quickly, a consensus emerged that the University would build on its current 70 laboratories, and slowly expand to between 80 and 100 labs as resources became available and appropriate talent was identified.[87]

Because the University was structured around laboratories rather than departments, a critical problem was how to keep the centrifugal forces created by so many different labs from becoming unmanageable. Wiesel seemed to have an innate ability to solve the problem, especially by emphasizing the tradition and culture of excellence that had been institutionalized at Rockefeller. Through the use of a broad array of rituals, the organization throughout the 1990s highlighted its strong, widely shared culture, a process that helped to promote harmony and communication among the different laboratories. Without a strongly shared culture, it would have been much more difficult to generate the trust and predictability necessary for a well-functioning organization.

New Centers, New Funding

In addition to the emphasis on the common culture, the Rockefeller University also promoted the coordination of labs by grouping them around seven research centers, in recognition of the natural affinities among the interests of scientists. The seven centers financed in part by successful University fund-raising in the private sector during the 1990s were (1) the Center for Biochemistry and Structural Biology; (2) the Center for Sensory Neuroscience; (3) the Center for Human Genetics; (4) the Center for Research on Alzheimer's Disease; (5) the Center for Studies in Physics and Biology; (6) the Center for Immunology and Immune Diseases; and (7) the Center for Mind, Brain, and Behavior.[88] These centers were intended to enhance communication and strengthen collaboration across labs, and to provide coherence for fund-raising from both federal and private sector sources. Depending on the interests of scientists, they could be affiliated with more than one center. In the process of developing the centers, some faculty gained a much better understanding of the complementary interests of different labs. Although the centers have varied in their performance, as well as in size and resources, they have provided a meaningful strategy for promoting communication across laboratories. The functioning of the centers has been complemented by the fact that in recent years, labs at the University have become somewhat smaller, reducing the tendency for labs to be so internally focused.

Although governance of the University is shared by the labs, the research centers, the academic council, and the university senate, the office of the president played an extremely important role in governing by making financial and personnel decisions, and in determining the allocation of laboratory space and laboratory budgets (if non–grant funds are being used). During Wiesel's first four and a half years as president, the Rockefeller University raised approximately $135 million in private gifts and pledges, much of which was used to support the recruitment of new faculty and to create state-of-the art laboratories. The University increased the number of laboratories and recruited many junior and senior scientists. During these same years, 20 new laboratories were headed by nontenured scientists.

When Wiesel left the presidency in 1998, there was a widespread perception both within and beyond the University that Rockefeller was once more in very sound condition, both scientifically and financially. The University had restored stability to its budgets and operations, and had increased its endowment by over 50 percent in a five-year period. Part of this increase resulted from the performance of the American economy, but much of the improvement was also due to the management team Wiesel and the trustees had put in place.[89]

Into a Second Century

Very mindful of the turmoil and embarrassments of the early 1990s, the University by the turn of the new century was anything but complacent. There was a tone of rebuilding, but with modesty as the University attempted to learn from its competitors. In retrospect, perhaps the turmoil of the early nineties had been healthy for the University, as one of its effects had been to create more of a community among its faculty than had existed for decades.

To lead the Rockefeller University into its second century, the trustees in 1998 appointed Arnold Levine as president, a renowned cancer researcher and former chair of the Department of Molecular Biology at Princeton University. Levine epitomized the Rockefeller scientist, as he internalized a great deal of scientific diversity (with broad knowledge of molecular biology, cell biology, and genetics) and had a good sense of the history of various fields of science. As was the case with the first director Simon Flexner, Levine thought strategically. He had a good sense of where science was moving, was conscious from the beginning of where he wanted to direct the University, and was keen to promote the training of young scientists.

Levine took leadership of an organization that had undergone profound changes over the past century. Even in its recent past, there had been exponential growth in its infrastructure, with hundreds of new research associates, post-docs, technicians, and other support staff. However, it was still very small relative to other American universities, with approximately fifty full professors, twenty-seven associate professors, and fifty-three assistant professors.[90] Because of its small faculty, there was far more frequent and intense communication among a larger proportion of its scientific staff across diverse fields of science than at any other American research university. True, Rockefeller was more fragmented than it was forty years ago because it had so many labs, but it was much less differentiated internally than every other American university. The fact that there still were no departments and that a lab was likely to close down when the head of the lab departed meant that the organization had an extraordinary flexibility to adapt to the fast pace of change in the global environment of science.

This flexibility and adaptiveness explain why in its centennial year of 2001 Rockefeller University, despite its small size, still towered over most research organizations in America. It had a higher proportion of its faculty who were either members of the National Academy of Sciences or Howard Hughes investigators than any other research organization in the United States; and, its scientists received more funding for biomedical research per scientist from the NIH than in any other research organization in the United States. In 1999 and 2000, the Rockefeller University demonstrated that its extraordinary excellence as a center for major discoveries is still very much alive when members of its faculty received four of the most coveted prizes in biomedical science: Robert Roeder received the Louisa Gross Horwitz Prize in basic biomedical science, Roderick MacKinnon received the Lasker Prize for Basic Biomedical Science, and Günter Blobel in 1999 and Paul Greengard in 2000 received Nobel Prizes in Physiology or Medicine. These four prizes in a two-year period represent more recognition for major discoveries than four-fifths of the leading American research organizations received in the whole of the twentieth century.[91] In short, at the turn of the millennium there was excellent evidence that the Rockefeller University was still one of the world's premier biomedical research organizations.

Appendix I: Defining Major Breakthroughs in Biomedical Research

For purposes of this essay, and my related research, a major breakthrough in biomedical science is defined as a finding or process, often preceded by numerous "small advances," which leads to a new way of thinking about a problem.[92] This new way of thinking is highly useful for numerous scientists in diverse fields of science in addressing problems. This is very different from the rare paradigm shifts Thomas Kuhn analyzed in his classic *The Structure of Scientific Revolutions* (1962).[93] Major breakthroughs about particular problems in biomedical science occur within the paradigms about which Kuhn was writing. Historically, a major breakthrough in biomedical science was a radical or new idea, the development of a new methodology, or a new instrument or invention. It has usually not occurred all at once, but has involved a process of investigation taking place over a substantial period of time and a great deal of tacit and/or local knowledge.

The indicators of major discoveries are as follows: (1) discoveries resulting in Copley Medals (awarded since 1901 by the Royal Society of London), insofar as the award was for basic biomedical research; (2) discoveries resulting in a Nobel Prize in Physiology or Medicine since the first award in 1901; (3) discoveries resulting in a Nobel Prize in Chemistry, also since the first award in 1901, if the research had high relevance to biomedical science (this includes discoveries in biochemistry as well as an occasional breakthrough in several other areas of chemistry); (4) discoveries resulting in ten nominations in any three years before 1940 for a Nobel Prize in Physiology or Medicine, or in Chemistry if the research had high relevance to biomedical science. (The rationale is that this number of nominations suggests that broad support existed in the scientific community to the effect that the research represented a major scientific breakthrough even if it did not result in a Nobel Prize. Because the number of people who could make nominations for Nobel Prizes in the first half of the twentieth century was quite restricted by present day standards, this criterion of "10 and 3" represents broad recognition among nominators during those years.) (5) Every year, the Royal Swedish Academy of Sciences and the Karolinska Institute each appointed a committee to study major discoveries and to propose Nobel Prize winners (in Chemistry, and in Physiology or Medicine, respectively). These two committees have made short lists of discoveries considered to be "prize worthy," and some of the discoveries were recognized for Nobel Prizes. I include in my population the discoveries on the short lists through 1940 that were not recognized for Nobel prizes. I have access to the Nobel Archives for the Physiology or Medicine Prize at the Karolinska Institute and to the Archives at the Royal Swedish Academy of Sciences in Stockholm for this period, but for reasons of confidentiality, access to these archives is not permitted for the past fifty years.

To capture the variety of major scientific discoveries during this period, I also use several other criteria. I included (6) discoveries resulting in the Arthur and Mary Lasker Prize for basic biomedical science; (7) discoveries resulting in the Louisa Gross Horwitz Prize in basic biomedical science; and (8) discoveries in biomedical science resulting in the Crafoord Prize (awarded by the Royal Swedish Academy of Sciences). For purposes of this essay, I have included the aforementioned forms of recognition through the fall of 2000.

The emphasis on diverse fields of science is critical for my definition of a major breakthrough. Most biomedical research is highly specialized and is therefore reported to highly specialized audiences. And while I do not suggest that this kind of research is trivial or unimportant, its impact is more confined to specialized researchers, whereas the research that is perceived as a major breakthrough is accorded the kind of recognition described above because it is knowledge absorbed by scientists in many different specialties.

Appendix II

Scientists Whose Major Discoveries, All or Part, Were Made at Rockefeller Institute/University and the Forms of Recognition for Them

Name of scientist	Forms of recognition
Oswald Avery[a,b]	Nominated ten times in three different years for Nobel Prize in Physiology or Medicine 1931. For the discovery that the immunological specificity of type II pneumococcus is due to a polysaccharide. Copley Medal 1945. For recognizing the transforming principle of DNA.
Günter Blobel	Horwitz Prize 1987; Lasker Prize 1993; Nobel Prize in Physiology or Medicine 1999. For his discovery that proteins have intrinsic signals that govern their transport and localization in the cell.
Alexis Carrel	Nobel Prize in Physiology or Medicine 1912. For his work in suturing blood vessels and in the transplantation of organs.
Albert Claude	Horwitz Prize 1970; Nobel Prize in Physiology or Medicine 1974. For applying the techniques of centrifugation and electron microscopy to the isolation and identification of subcellular structures.
Lyman Craig	Lasker Prize 1963. For his countercurrent distribution technique as a method for the separation of biologically significant compounds, and for the isolation and structure studies of important antibiotics.
Christian de Duve	Nobel Prize in Physiology or Medicine 1974. For combining subcellular fractionation with biochemical analysis in order to discover the cell organelles of lysosome and peroxisome and for identifying their functions.
Gerald Edelman	Nobel Prize in Physiology or Medicine 1972. For determining for the first time the complete chemical structure of immunoglobulins (antibodies), the key molecules of immunity.
Simon Flexner[a]	Nominated ten times in three different years for Nobel Prize in Physiology or Medicine 1911. For developing serum treatment of cerebrospinal meningitis.
Paul Greengard	Nobel Prize in Physiology or Medicine 2000. For his discoveries concerning signal transduction in the nervous system.
Hidesaburo Hanafusa	Lasker Prize 1982. For demonstrating how RNA tumor viruses cause cancer, and elucidating their role in combining, rescuing and maintaining oncogenes in the viral genome.
H.K. Hartline	Nobel Prize in Physiology or Medicine 1967. For work on the physiology and chemistry of vision.
Bertil Hille[c]	Horwitz Prize 1976; Lasker Prize 1999. For elucidating the functional and structural architecture of ion channel proteins, which govern the electrical potential of membranes throughout nature, thereby generating nerve impulses and controlling muscle contraction, cardiac rhythm, and hormone secretion.
Henry Kunkel	Lasker Prize 1975; Horwitz Prize 1977. For his discoveries in immuno-pathology.
Karl Landsteiner	Nobel Prize in Physiology or Medicine 1930. For his classification of blood groups and for his further discoveries over the years of subgroups within the original groups which he identified.
Jacques Loeb[a]	Nominated ten times in three different years for Nobel Prize in Physiology or Medicine 1911. For his research on the colloidal behavior of proteins.
Roderick MacKinnon	Lasker Prize 1999. For elucidating the functional and structural architecture of ion channel proteins, which govern the electrical potential of membranes throughout nature, thereby generating nerve impulses and controlling muscle contraction, cardiac rhythm, and hormone secretion.
Bruce Merrifield	Lasker Prize 1969; Nobel Prize in Chemistry 1984. For his development of a simple and ingenious method for synthesizing peptides and proteins.
Stanford Moore	Nobel Prize in Chemistry 1972. For research on enzymes, body proteins central to life; particularly for working out for the first time the chemical structure of pancreatic ribonuclease, an enzyme that breaks down ribonucleic acid (RNA).
Hideyo Noguchi[a]	Nominated ten times in three different years for Nobel Prize in Physiology or Medicine 1921. For his research in demonstrating the relationship between Oroya Fever and verruca peruviana and cultivation of the causative agent.
John Northrop	Nobel Prize in Chemistry 1946. For the preparation of enzyme and virus proteins in pure form.

Scientists Whose Major Discoveries, All or Part, Were Made at Rockefeller Institute/University and the Forms of Recognition for Them(continued)

Name of scientist	Forms of recognition
George Palade	Lasker Prize 1966; Horwitz Prize 1970; Nobel Prize in Physiology or Medicine 1974. For contributing important techniques of centrifugation and electron microscopy and using them to define how cells synthesize proteins and how they package proteins for secretion.
Keith Porter	Horwitz Prize 1970. For his fundamental contributions to the electron microscopy of biological materials.
Robert Roeder	Horwitz Prize 1999. For his research on the processes of gene activation.
Peyton Rous	Nobel Prize in Physiology or Medicine 1966. For establishing a virus as the cause of chicken sarcoma.
Theobald Smith[a]	Nominated ten times in three different years for Nobel Prize in Physiology or Medicine 1921; Copley Medal 1933. For his research on host-parasite interrelationships.
Wendell Stanley	Nobel Prize in Chemistry 1946. For the preparation of enzyme and virus proteins in pure form.
William Stein	Nobel Prize in Chemistry 1972. For research on enzymes, body proteins central to life; particularly for working out for the first time the chemical structure of pancreatic ribonuclease, an enzyme that breaks down ribonucleic acid (RNA).

[a]Scientists who are included in this study as a result of having 10 nominations in three different years are identified as "10 in 3" and the date listed for them is the first odd-numbered year in the decade in which they received the largest number of nominations. Thus, a scientist receiving two nominations in 1911, three in 1913, and five in 1921 would be listed with the year 1921.

[b]Oswald Avery received recognition for two major discoveries. One was his work on polysaccharides in the 1920s, and the other was his work on DNA in the 1940s (Dale, 1946; Dubos, 1976; McCarty 1985; Amsterdamska, 1993; Bearn, 1996).

[c]The body of work for which Hille was recognized began while he was a student at the Rockefeller University.

This essay is part of a larger study of major discoveries in biomedical science in research organizations in Britain, France, Germany, and the United States in the twentieth century. I wish to express my appreciation to the following organizations for financial assistance: the National Science Foundation (SES 96 18526), the Alfred P. Sloan Foundation, the Andrew W. Mellon Foundation, the Humboldt Foundation, the Rockefeller Archive Center, and the Graduate School of the University of Wisconsin. Numerous individuals have been enormously helpful, but I would like especially to acknowledge the assistance of Jerald Hage, Darwin Stapleton, and Harriet Zuckerman. My wife, Ellen Jane Hollingsworth, has participated in every aspect of the larger project, as well as in the research for and writing of this essay. I regret that she has not permitted me to include her in the authorship. Ragnar Björk of Uppsala, Sweden, conducted the archival work at the Karolinska Institute and the Royal Swedish Academy of Sciences in Stockholm. Finally, I wish to acknowledge the indispensable help of David Gear in many aspects of the research for this essay.

Endnotes

1. The theoretical literature for confronting this problem consists of the following: J. Rogers Hollingsworth, Ellen Jane Hollingsworth, and Jerald Hage, eds., *The Search for Excellence: Organizations, Institutions, and Major Discoveries in Biomedical Science* (New York, forthcoming); Michael L. Tushman and Elaine Romanelli, "Organizational Evolution: A Metamorphosis Model of Convergence and Reorientation," *Research in Organizational Behavior* 7 (1985): 171–222; Michael L. Tushman and Charles A. O'Reilly III, "Ambidextrous Organizations: Managing Evolutionary and Revolutionary Change," in *California Management Review* 38 (1996): 8–30; Elaine Romanelli and Michael L. Tushman, "Organizational Transformation as Punctuated Equilibrium: An Empirical Test," *Academy of Management Journal* 37 (1994): 1141–66; Michael E. Porter, "Toward a Dynamic Theory of Strategy," *Strategic Management Journal* 12 (1991): 95–117; Jerald Hage and J. Rogers Hollingsworth, "Idea Innovation Networks: A Strategy for Integrating Organizational and Institutional Analysis," *Organization Studies* 21 (2000): 971–1004; J. Rogers Hollingsworth, "Doing Institutional Analysis: Implications for the Study of Innovation," *Review of International Political Economy* 7 (2000): 1–50.
2. J. R. Hollingsworth, E. J. Hollingsworth, and J. Hage, eds., *The Search for Excellence.*
3. Abraham Flexner, *Medical Education in the United States and Canada* (Boston, 1910).
4. Simon Flexner and James Thomas Flexner, *William Henry Welch and the Heroic Age of American Medicine* (New York, 1941); Charles Eliot, *Harvard Memories* (Cambridge, 1923), 28, 35; Kenneth M. Ludmerer, *Learning to Heal: The Development of American Medical Education* (New York, 1986); J. Rogers Hollingsworth, *The Political Economy of Medicine: Great Britain and the United States* (Baltimore, 1986), 82–125.
5. Peter Collier and David Horowitz, *The Rockefellers: An American Dynasty* (New York, 1976), 48.
6. Frederick T. Gates, *Chapters in My Life* (New York, 1977), 165; Richard E. Brown, *Rockefeller Medical Men* (Berkeley, CA, 1979), 179–88.
7. Peyton Rous, "Simon Flexner," *Obituary Notices of Fellows of the Royal Society* 6 (1949): 417; George W. Corner, *A History of the Rockefeller Institute, 1901–1953: Origins and Growth* (New York, 1965), 35; Paul F. Clark, "Theobald Smith: Student of Disease," *Journal of the History of Medicine* 14 (1959): 490–514; Hans Zinsser, "Theobald Smith," *Biographical Memoirs of the National Academy of Sciences* 17 (1937): 261–303.
8. Donald Fleming, *William H. Welch and the Rise of Modern Medicine* (Baltimore, 1954), 131–7; S. Flexner and J. T. Flexner, *William Henry Welch.*
9. Simon Flexner, "The Rockefeller Institute for Medical Research, New York," in *Forschungsinstitute: Ihre Geschichte, Organisation und Ziele*, eds. Ludolph Brauer, Albrecht Mendelsohn Bartholdy, and Adolf Meyer. 2 vols (Hamburg, 1930), 2: 458; S. Flexner and J. T. Flexner, *William Henry Welch*, 462–464; Gates, *Chapters in My Life*, 1979–88.
10. Adrea K. Blumenthal, "Leadership in a Medical Philanthropy: Simon Flexner and the Rockefeller Institute for Medical Research," (PhD diss., Drew University, 1991). 326 pp.
11. Rous, "Simon Flexner" (n. 7 above), 417.

12. Philip J. Pauly, *Controlling Life: Jacques Loeb and the Engineering Ideal in Biology* (New York, 1987), 134–136; Rous, "Simon Flexner" (n. 7 above), 418.
13. Rous, "Simon Flexner" (n. 7 above), 418.
14. Flexner, "Rockefeller Institute" (n. 9 above), 2:461–2.
15. Simon Flexner served as director until 1935 and Herbert Gasser from 1935 to 1953. After 1935, the title director was dropped in favor of president. Detlev Bronk served as president from 1953 to 1968; Fred Seitz, 1968–1978; Joshua Lederberg, 1978–1990; David Baltimore, 1990–1991; Torsten Wiesel, 1991–1998; and Arnold Levine 1998–2001.
16. Tom Rivers, *Reflections on a Life in Medicine and Science* (Cambridge, 1967), 198; unpublished and untitled lecture by Simon Flexner, folder Simon Flexner, box 6, RG 303.1 Bronk Papers, Rockefeller University Archives, Rockefeller Archive Center, Sleepy Hollow, New York (hereafter RAC).
17. Paul F. Clark, *Pioneer Microbiologists of America* (Madison, WI, 1961), 172; see also Simon Flexner to Abraham Flexner, July 4, 1924, Flexner Letters, Flexner Papers, American Philosophical Society, Philadelphia, Pennsylvania.
18. Flexner, "Rockefeller Institute" (n. 9 above), 461.
19. Rous, "Simon Flexner" (n. 7 above), 427.
20. Ibid, 425.
21. Elvin A. Kabat, "Michael Heidelberger," *Journal of Immunology* 148 (1992): 301–307.
22. Rous, "Simon Flexner" (n. 7 above), 421.
23. Peyton Rous, "Simon Flexner and Medical Discovery," *Science* 107 (11 June 1948): 613.
24. Clark, *Pioneer Microbiologists* (n. 17 above), 172.
25. Rous, "Simon Flexner" (n. 7 above), 427; Alfred E. Cohn, "On Simon Flexner," *No Retreat From Reason* (New York, 1948), 228; Rivers, *Reflections on a Life* (n. 16 above), 123–27.
26. Rivers, *Reflections on a Life* (n. 16 above), 124–125; Rous, "Simon Flexner" (n. 7 above), 425.
27. The process of funding science at the Rockefeller was very different from the process of funding science by the National Science Foundation (NSF) and the National Institutes of Health (NIH) in contemporary America. With numerous proposals arriving before study groups and program officers, these two organizations are less well positioned to assess the degree of risk involving a researcher and a research project. The NSF and NIH grant proposal submission process and the decision-making process about research funding have become more standardized and bureaucratized, with the consequence that high risk research tends to be discouraged.
28. Rous, "Simon Flexner and Medical Discovery," 612; Bayne Jones, "Simon Flexner," *American Philosophical Society Yearbook* (Philadelphia, 1946), 295; Rous, "Simon Flexner" (n. 7 above), 424.
29. Rous, "Simon Flexner" (n. 7 above), 424.
30. Rivers, *Reflections on a Life* (n. 16 above), 121.
31. Simon Flexner to Phoebus A. Levine, November 30, 1931, Simon Flexner Papers, APS.
32. Gates, *Chapters in My Life* (n. 6 above), 182–183; Fleming, *William H. Welch* (n. 9 above), 157.
33. Lily E. Kay, "W.M. Stanley's Crystallization of the Tobacco Mosaic Virus, 1930–1940," *Isis* 77 (1986): 454; Corner, *History of Rockefeller* (n. 7 above), 134.
34. Paul de Kruif, *The Sweeping Wind: A Memoir* (London, 1962), 3–35.
35. Robert Olby, *The Path to the Double Helix*, 2d ed. (New York, 1974); Roger M. Herriot, "A Biographical Sketch of John Howard Northrop," *Journal of General Physiology, Supplement* 45 (1962): 4–5.
36. S. Flexner and J.T. Flexner, *William Henry Welch*, 295–96; Corner, *History of Rockefeller* (n. 7 above), 313.
37. Norman W. Pirie, "The Viruses," in *Scientific Thought, 1900–1960*, ed. R. Harré. (Oxford, 1969), 232–33; John T. Edsall, "Wendell M. Stanley," *American Philosophical Yearbook* (Philadelphia, 1971), 184–90; Wendell M. Stanley, "The Isolation and Properties of Crystalline Tobacco Mosaic Virus: Nobel Lecture, December 12, 1946," *Nobel Lectures: Chemistry, 1942–1962* (Amsterdam, 1964), 137–59.
38. Wendell M. Stanley, "Isolation of Crystalline Protein Possessing the Properties of Tobacco Mosaic Virus," *Science* 81 (1935): 644–5.
39. Corner, *History of Rockefeller* (n. 7 above), 320.
40. Kay, "W.M. Stanley's Crystallization" (n. 33 above), 450–472; Pirie, "The Viruses," 232–3; Norman W. Pirie, "Recurrent Luck in Research," in *Selected Topics in the History of Biochemistry: Personal Recollections*, ed. G. Semenza. (Amsterdam, 1986), 502–3.

41. Corner, *History of Rockefeller*, 62–63; S. Flexner and J.T. Flexner, *William Henry Welch*, 243–50; Renato Dulbecco, "Francis Peyton Rous," *Biographical Memoirs of the National Academy of Sciences* 48 (1976): 275; C.H. Andrews, "Francis Peyton Rous," *Biographical Memoirs of Fellows of the Royal Society* 17 (1971): 653; O.H. Robertson, "Presentation of Kober Medal to Peyton Rous," *Transactions of American College of Physicians* 66 (1953): 25.
42. Pauly, *Controlling Life* (n. 12 above), 150; L.R. Blinks, "Winthrop John Van Leuven Osterhout," *Biographical Memoirs of the National Academy of Sciences* 44 (1974): 213.
43. R.S. Tipson, "Phoebus Aaron Theodore Levene," *Advances in Carbohydrate Chemistry* 12 (1957): 1–12; Melville L. Wolfram, "Phoebus Aaron Theodore Levene," in *Great Chemists*, ed. Eduard Farber. (New York, 1961), 1319; "Herter, Christian A. Obituary," *Journal of Biological Chemistry* 8 (1910): 437–9.
44. George E. Palade, "The American Cradle," unpublished paper (1998).
45. Réne J. Dubos, *The Professor, the Institute, and DNA* (New York, 1976), 31.
46. de Kruif, *Sweeping Wind* (n. 34 above), 16–7.
47. Dubos, *Professor and DNA* (n. 45 above), 31.
48. de Kruif, *Sweeping Wind*, 13.
49. Howard S. Berliner, "Philanthropic Foundations and Scientific Medicine" (PhD diss., The Johns Hopkins University, 1977), 7.
50. de Kruif, *Sweeping Wind*, 12; Brown, *Rockefeller Medical Men* (n. 7 above), 125; Pauly, *Controlling Life* (n. 12 above), 136.
51. de Kruif, *Sweeping Wind*, 56.
52. Rous, "Simon Flexner" (n. 7 above), 425.
53. Robert E. Kohler, *Partners in Science: Foundations and Natural Scientists, 1900–1945* (Chicago, 1994).
54. Alan Hodgkin, "Chance and Design in Electrophysiology: An Informal Account of Certain Experiments on Nerves Carried Out Between 1934 and 1952," in *The Pursuit of Nature: Informal Essays on the History of Physiology*, eds. Alan Hodgkin and A.F. Huxley (Cambridge, 1977), 1–21; Alan Hodgkin, *Change and Design: Reminiscences of Science in Peace and War* (Cambridge, 1992).
55. J. Rogers Hollingsworth and Ellen Jane Hollingsworth, *Controversy about American Hospitals* (Washington, DC, 1988).
56. Rivers, *Reflections on a Life* (n. 16 above), 195–6; Olby, *Path to Double Helix* (n. 35 above), 183.
57. Simon Flexner, *The Evolution and Organization of the University Clinic* (Oxford, 1939).
58. E. D. Adrian, "Herbert Spencer Gasser,"*Lancet* 25 (May 1963): 1168; E. D. Adrian, "Herbert Spencer Gasser," *Biographical Memoirs of Fellows of the Royal Society* 10 (1964): 75–82; Detlev W. Bronk, "Herbert Spencer Gasser," *Rockefeller University Quarterly Review*, June 1963, 12–4.
59. Rivers, *Reflections on a Life* (n. 16 above), 580–81; Corner, *History of Rockefeller* (n. 7 above), 329–32.
60. Hodgkin, "Chance and Design" (n. 54 above), 7–8; Corner, *History of Rockefeller* (n. 7 above), 332–40.
61. Gerald M. Edelman, *Neural Darwinism: The Theory of Neuronal Group Selection* (New York, 1987); Gerald M. Edelman, *The Remembered Present: A Biological Theory of Consciousness* (New York, 1989); Gerald M. Edelman, *Bright Air, Brilliant Fire: On the Matter of the Mind* (New York, 1992); Gerald M. Edelman and Giulio Tononi, *A Universe of Consciousness: How Matter Becomes Imagination* (New York, 2000).
62. Gerald Edelman, research director, Neuroscience Institute, La Jolla, CA, and former professor and dean, The Rockefeller University, interview by author, Klosters, Switzerland, 17 January 1995; Gerald Edelman, interview by author, La Jolla, CA, 13 January, 16 January, 19 January, 30 January, 14 February, 20 February, 22 February, 5 March, 16 March, 17 March 1996, 12 February 1998, 4 April, 11 April, and 18 November 2000; Gerald Edelman, telephone interview by author, La Jolla, CA, 3 April 2001; Paul Greengard, professor, The Rockefeller University, interview by author, New York, 16 May 2001; Torsten Wiesel, president, The Rockefeller University, interview by author, New York, New York, 14 April 1995, 14 July 1997, 7 February, 4 May, 25 May 2001; Victor Wilson, professor emeritus, The Rockefeller University, interview by author, New York, 2 February and 10 May 2001.
63. Emil L. Smith, "Amino Acid Sequences of Proteins: The Beginnings," *Annals of the New York Academy of Sciences* 325 (1979): 116.
64. Pauly, *Controlling Life* (n. 12 above), 152–3, 170–1.
65. George E. Palade, "Albert Claude and the Beginnings of Biological Electron Microscopy," *The Journal of*

Cell Biology 50 (1971): 5D–19D.

66. Ibid; George E. Palade, "Keith Roberts Porter and the Development of Contemporary Cell Biology," *The Journal of Cell Biology* 75 (1977): 3D–19D; Palade, "American Cradle" (n. 44 above).
67. Maclyn McCarty, *The Transforming Principle: Discovering that Genes Are Made of DNA* (New York, 1985); Joshua Lederberg, "Review of McCarty *The Transforming Principle,*" *Journal of Genetics* 64 (1985): 173–5.
68. Joshua Lederberg, "Oswald Avery Discussion, Part 2: The Research Theme in Dr. Avery's Laboratory," in *Interview with Maclyn McCarty,* (August 1998), Lasker Foundation Website, (http://www.laskerfoundation.com/awards/library/1947b_int_oajl.shtml), accessed 16 April 2003; Alexander G. Bearn, "Oswald T. Avery and the Copley Medal of the Royal Society," *Perspectives in Biology and Medicine* 39 (1996): 550–4; The Rockefeller University, *Announcement of Celebration of 50 Years of DNA* (New York, 1993), 2.
69. Olga Amsterdamska, "From Pneumonia to DNA: The Research Career of Oswald T. Avery," *Historical Studies in the Physical and Biological Sciences* 24 (1993): 25–7; Dubos, *Professor, Institute, and DNA* (n. 45); Olby (n. 35 above), 183–5.
70. Britton Chance, "Detlev W. Bronk," *Yearbook of the American Philosophical Society, 1978* (Philadelphia, 1979), 54–66; E. D. Adrian, "Detlev Wulf Bronk," *Biographical Memoirs of Fellows from the Royal Society* 22 (1976): 1–9; Frank Brink Jr., "Detlev Bronk and the Development of the Graduate Education Program," in *Institute to University* (New York, 1977), 69–78; Frank Brink Jr., "Detlev Wulf Bronk," *Biographical Memoirs of the National Academy of Sciences* 50 (1979): 3–87.
71. Minutes of the Rockefeller University Trustees, 22 May 1961, Rockefeller University Archives, RAC.
72. Academic Affairs, folder 9, box 7, RG 303 Bronk Papers, Rockefeller University Archives, RAC; Report of Six Faculty Committees, September 9, 1968, folder 4, box 17, RG 303 Bronk Papers, Rockefeller University Archives, RAC.
73. Brink, "Detlev Bronk and Development," 69–78; Peter Lyon, "The Rockefeller Institute," *Holiday,* September 1965, 54ff.
74. Brink, "Detlev Wulf Bronk," 67.
75. The Rockefeller University, *Annual Report* (New York, 1976), 88.
76. Memo, September 18, 1968, folder 4, box 17, RG 303 Bronk Papers, Rockefeller University Archives, RAC.
77. Rockefeller University, "From Institute to University: A Historical Sketch of the Rockefeller University," 1983, p. 13, box 2, RG 455 Duplicate Publications, Rockefeller University Archives, RAC.
78. Summary of W.F. Loomis interview with Herbert Gasser, page 26, n.d., folder 534, box 51, RG 3 Rockefeller Family and Associates, Rockefeller Family Archives, RAC.
79. Rockefeller University, "From Institute to University: A Historical Sketch of the Rockefeller University," 1983, p. 18, box 2, RG 455 Duplicate Publications, Rockefeller University Archives, RAC.
80. Richard Saltus, "Nobel Winner Baltimore Ponders Offer," *Boston Globe,* 5 October 1989, 43.
81. Daniel J. Kevles, *The Baltimore Case: A Trial of Politics, Science, and Character* (New York, 1998).
82. *Science,* 13 December 1991, 1577.
83. *News and Notes,* 17 May 1991.
84. *New York Times,* 4 December 1991.
85. *Science,* 13 December 1991, 1578.
86. Kevles, *The Baltimore Case.*
87. The Rockefeller University, *Report of the Academic Plan to the Board of Trustees* (New York, 1994).
88. Ibid; Rockefeller University, *New Research Programs at the Rockefeller University* (New York, 1997); Mark B. Brennan, "An Oasis for Medical Research," *Chemical and Engineering News* 77 (1999): 47–62.
89. The Rockefeller University, *Annual Report* (New York, 1997); The Rockefeller University, *Annual Report* (New York, 1998).

Brennan, "Oasis for Medical Research," 47.

90. J. R. Hollingsworth, E. J. Hollingsworth, and J. Hage, eds., *The Search for Excellence.* (n. 2 above).
91. Ibid.
92. Thomas S. Kuhn, *The Structure of Scientific Revolutions* (Chicago, 1962).

Selected Bibliography

This essay is based on archival materials, interviews, and extensive published sources. Because of limitations of space, only published sources are cited. However, the following archival materials were consulted, and interviews were conducted with the individuals listed below.

Archives Consulted in Connection with Rockefeller Institute/University

Max Bergmann Papers. American Philosophical Society, Philadelphia, Pennsylvania (hereafter APS).
Detlev Bronk Papers. Rockefeller University Archives, Rockefeller Archive Center, Sleepy Hollow, New York (hereafter RAC). The Rockefeller Archive Center is a division of the Rockefeller University.
Albert Claude Papers. RAC.
Lyman Craig Papers. RAC.
René Dubos Papers. RAC.
Herbert M. Evans Papers. RAC.
Simon Flexner Papers. APS.
Herbert S. Gasser Papers. RAC.
General Education Board Archives. RAC.
Frank B. Hanson Diaries. RAC.
Frank L. Horsfall Jr. Papers. RAC.
Rollin D. Hotchkiss Papers. RAC.
International Education Board Archives. RAC.
Mark Kac Papers. RAC.
Moses Kunitz Papers. RAC.
Henry G. Kunkel Papers. RAC.
Louis O. Kunkel Papers. RAC.
Fritz Lipmann Papers. RAC.
Jacques Loeb Papers. RAC.
Philip D. McMaster Papers. RAC.
Alfred E. Mirsky Papers. RAC.
James B. Murphy Papers. APS.
Nobel Archives, Karolinska Institute, Stockholm, Sweden.
Nobel Archives, Royal Swedish Academy of Science, Stockholm, Sweden.
Peter Olitsky Papers. APS.
Winthrop John Van Leuven Osterhout Papers. APS.
Richard Pearce Diaries. RAC
Gertrude Perlmann Papers. RAC.
Tom M. Rivers Papers. APS.
Rockefeller Family Archives. RAC.
Rockefeller Foundation Archives. RAC.
Rockefeller Institute/University Minutes of the Board of Trustees. RAC.
Rockefeller Institute/University Minutes of the Board of Scientific Directors, 1901–1953. RAC.
Rockefeller University Administrative Services Files. RAC.
Rockefeller University Annual Reports. RAC.
Rockefeller University Business Manager Files. RAC.
Rockefeller University Report of the President. RAC.
Peyton Rous Papers. APS.
Frederick Seitz Papers. RAC.
Richard E. Shope Papers. RAC.
Wendell M. Stanley Papers. RAC.
Wendell M. Stanley Papers. Bancroft Library, University of California Berkeley.
William H. Stein Papers. RAC.
Edward L. Tatum Papers. RAC.

Augustus Trowbridge Diaries. RAC.
Donald Dexter Van Slyke Papers. RAC.
Warren Weaver Diaries. Rockefeller Foundation Archives, RAC.
Warren Weaver Papers. RAC.
Peter Weiss Papers. RAC.
D. W. Woolley Papers. RAC.

Interviews about the Rockefeller University conducted by J. Rogers Hollingsworth[a]

Vince Allfrey, professor emeritus, The Rockefeller University. Interview in his office, 22 February 2000.

Reginald M. Archibald, professor emeritus, The Rockefeller University. Interview at The Rockefeller University, 2 February 2001.

William Baker, chairman of the Board of Trustees Emeritus, The Rockefeller University, and former head of Bell Labs. Interview at The Rockefeller University, 30 January 2001; telephone interview 2 February 2001.

Evan Balaban, fellow at Neurosciences Institute. Former student, The Rockefeller University. Interviews at Neurosciences Institute, San Diego, CA, 6 February 1996, 7 January 1998, and 12 April 2000.

David Baltimore, professor of biology, Massachusetts Institute of Technology. Interview in his office, 28 April 1995.

Alexander Bearn, executive director, American Philosophical Society. Interviews in his office, 15 February and 23 August 2000. Former trustee and professor, The Rockefeller University.

William Beers, vice president for facilities and research support, The Rockefeller University. Interview in his office, 18 May 2001.

Günter Blobel, professor, The Rockefeller University and Howard Hughes Medical Institute (hereafter HHMI) Investigator. Interview in his office, 12 April 1995. Subsequent interviews in his office, 16 March 2001 and 18 March 2001.

Fred Bowen, former executive vice president, The Rockefeller University. Interview at the Rockefeller University, 14 March 2001.

Jan Breslow, professor, The Rockefeller University. Interview in his laboratory, 14 April 2001. Second interview 18 April 2001.

Stephen K. Burley, professor and deputy to the president of Academic Affairs and HHMI investigator, The Rockefeller University. Interview in his office, 10 April 2001.

Anthony Cerami, director, Kenneth S. Warren Laboratories. Former professor and dean of Graduate Studies, The Rockefeller University. Interviews at Rockefeller Archive Center, 12 March 2001, 10 May 2001.

Purnell Choppin, president emeritus HHMI and adjunct professor, The Rockefeller University. Interview at the Rockefeller University, 14 November 2000.

Philippa Claude, senior scientist, Department of Zoology, University of Wisconsin, Madison. Interview in her office, 13 March 2000.

Joel Cohen, professor, The Rockefeller University. Interview in his office, 8 February 2001.

Kathryn Crossin, section head, Neurobiology Laboratory, Scripps Research Institute. Former postdoc at the Rockefeller University. Interview at Neurosciences Institute, San Diego, CA, 19 January 1996.

Bruce Cunningham, professor, Scripps Research Institute, and former professor, The Rockefeller University. Interviews at Neurosciences Institute, 7 February 1996 and 11 March 1998.

James E. Darnell Jr., professor, The Rockefeller University. Interview in his office, 10 April 1995. Other interviews 8 March 2001, 18 April 2001, and 29 May 2001.

Robert Darnell, professor, The Rockefeller University. Interview in his office, 25 January 2001.

Eric Davidson, professor of biology, California Institute of Technology and former associate professor, The Rockefeller University. Interview in his office, 5 May 2000.

Titia De Lange, professor, The Rockefeller University. Interviews in her office, 6 April 2001, 10 April 2001.

[a]Titles are listed as of the time of the interview.

Gerald Edelmann, research director, Neuroscience Institute. Former professor and dean, The Rockefeller University. Interviews in Klosters, Switzerland, 17 January 1995, and at Neurosciences Institute, La Jolla, CA, 13 January, 16 January, 19 January, 30 January, 14 February, 20 February, 22 February, 5 March, 16 March, and 17 March 1996; 12 February 1998; 4 April, 11 April, and 18 November 2000. Interview by phone 3 April 2001.

Marilyn G. Farquhar, professor of cellular and molecular medicine, University of California, San Diego. Former professor, The Rockefeller University. Interview in her office, 25 May 2000.

Jeffrey Friedman, professor, The Rockefeller University and HHMI Investigator. Interviews in his office, 16 March 2001, 18 April 2001.

Richard Furlaud, former chair of the Board of Trustees, The Rockefeller University (1990–1998), member of the Board of Trustees (1976–1998), and president of Rockefeller Council (2001). Interview at the Rockefeller University, 17 May 2001.

Einar Gall, director, Neurosciences Institute, San Diego, California. Interviews at the Institute, 15 March, 1996, 7 January 1998, and 6 and 17 February 1998.

Neva Goodwin, co-founder and co-director, Global Development and Environment Institute at Tufts University and trustee of the Rockefeller University. Interview in her home, in Cambridge, MA, 16 February 2001.

Paul Greengard, professor, The Rockefeller University. Interview in his office, 16 May 2001.

Nathaniel Heintz, professor, The Rockefeller University and HHMI investigator. Interview in his office, 28 March 2001.

Jules Hirsch, professor, The Rockefeller University. Interview at the Rockefeller University, 14 March 2001.

Rollin C. Hotchkiss, professor emeritus, The Rockefeller University. Interview in Chicago, 14 October 1993. Interview by telephone, 18 March 2000. Interview in his residence in Lenox, MA, 17 February 2001.

James Hudspeth, professor, The Rockefeller University and HHMI investigator. Interview in his laboratory, 17 April 2001.

Neen Hunt, executive vice president, Albert and Mary Lasker Foundation. Interview in her office in New York City, 26 March 2001.

Fred Jones, associate professor, Scripps Research Institute, San Diego and former student at the Rockefeller University. Interview at Scripps Institute, 16 January 1996.

Eric R. Kandel, director of Center for Neurophysiology and HHMI investigator, Columbia University School of Physicians and Surgeons, member of the Board of Trustees, The Rockefeller University. Interview at Columbia University, 19 April 2001.

John Kuryian, professor, The Rockefeller University and HHMI Investigator, Interview in his laboratory, 20 April 2001.

Joshua Lederberg, president emeritus, The Rockefeller University. Interviews at the Rockefeller University, 16 September 1993, 13 April 1995; interview by telephone 27 August 1999, interviews in his office, 25 February 2001, 4 April 2001.

Arnold Levine, former president, The Rockefeller University. Interview in his office, 14 May 2001.

Albert Libchaber, professor, The Rockefeller University. Interview in his office, 11 May 2001.

Alice Lustig, former senior vice president, The Rockefeller University. Interview in her office 29 May 2001.

Roderick MacKinnon, professor, The Rockefeller University and HHMI Investigator. Interview in his office, 1 March 2001.

Maclyn McCarty, professor emeritus and vice president emeritus, The Rockefeller University. Interview in his office, 6 February 2001.

Bruce Merrifield, John D. Rockefeller Jr. emeritus professor, The Rockefeller University. Interview in his office 11 February 2000.

Carol Moberg, senior scientist, The Rockefeller University. Interview in her office, 11 February 2000, by telephone, 15 March 2000.

Peter Model, professor, The Rockefeller University. Interviews at the Rockefeller University, 26 March 2001, 8 May 2001.

Geoffrey Montgomery, special assistant to the president, The Rockefeller University. Interviews at the Rockefeller University, 13 April 1995 and 14 July 1997.

Tom Muir, head, Laboratory of Synthetic Protein Chemistry, The Rockefeller University. Interview in his office, 28 February 2001.

Rodney Nichols, executive director, New York Academy of Science, and former executive vice president, The Rockefeller University. Interview in his office. 26 February 2001.

George Palade, dean, Medical School University of California San Diego. Also former professor, Yale University and The Rockefeller University. Interviews in his office in San Diego, CA, 7 March 1996 and 13 March 1998.

Marnie Pillsbury, trustee, The Rockefeller University. Interview in her office at Rockefeller Center, 30 May 2001.

George Rieke, associate professor, The Rockefeller University. Interview 25 April 2001.

Hans Ris, professor of zoology, University of Wisconsin, Madison and former postdoc at the Rockefeller University. Interview in his office, 15 March 2000.

David Rockefeller. Interview in his office, New York, 24 July 1997.

Robert Roeder, professor, The Rockefeller University. Interviews at The Rockefeller University 24 April 2001 and 8 May 2001.

Marjorie Russell, associate professor, The Rockefeller University. Interview at The Rockefeller University, 8 May 2001.

David Sabatini, professor and chair of the Department of Cell Biology, New York University Medical School. Interview at The Rockefeller University, 28 March 2001.

Frederick Seitz, president emeritus, The Rockefeller University. Former president, National Academy of Sciences, and former professor of physics, University of Illinois (Champaign-Urbana). Interviews in his office in New York, 15 April 1995, 24 February 2000, 4 May 2001.

Philip Siekevitz, professor emeritus, The Rockefeller University. Interview in his office, 11 February 2000.

Charles Stevens, scientist, Salk Institute, Interview in his office, 13 December 2000.

Sidney Strickland, professor and dean of Graduate Studies, The Rockefeller University. Interview in his office, 2 April 2001.

Alexander Tomasz, professor, The Rockefeller University, Interview at The Rockefeller University, 8 February 2001.

Torsten Wiesel, former president, The Rockefeller University. Interviews in his office, 14 April 1995, 14 July 1997, 7 February 2001, 4 May 2001, and 25 May 2001.

Victor Wilson, professor emeritus, The Rockefeller University. Interviews in his office, 2 February 2001 and 10 May 2001.

Norton Zinder, John D. Rockefeller professor, The Rockefeller University. Interview in his office, 18 April 1995; Second interview at Cold Spring Harbor Laboratory, Cold Spring Harbor, New York, 24 August 1995. Other interviews at The Rockefeller University, 11 February 2000, 25 January 2001, 28 February 2001, and 30 April 2001.

Part II: Case Studies

New Images of a New Medicine: Visual Evidence for the Widespread Popularity of Therapeutic Discoveries in America after 1885

Bert Hansen

Associate Professor of History, Baruch College, City University of New York, New York, NY

Editor's Note During the last fifteen years of the nineteenth century, there was intense publicity regarding accomplishments in the new field of scientific medicine that helped to set the stage for the founding of the Rockefeller Institute for Medical Research in 1901. Professor Bert Hansen's insightful recounting of how New Yorkers learned about the work of Pasteur, Koch, and others, and began to understand the promise of biomedical research, is republished here with the permission of Johns Hopkins University Press.

It was only during the closing decades of the last century that America's daily newspapers and weekly magazines began to give high visibility to medical discoveries. But these first episodes of widespread news coverage quickly prompted significant public interest and enthusiasm for major therapeutic achievements, and they initiated a pattern of proclaiming medical breakthroughs in the media that continues to the present. While only some of these new therapies maintained their status as true medical advances in the long run, each—in its moment of celebrity—garnered headlines and achieved popular notoriety. This wide acclaim stands in contrast to the minimal, muted, and mixed receptions granted in earlier decades of the nineteenth century to advances that scholars have usually regarded as significant: the stethoscope, anesthesia, antisepsis, and the identification of microbial agents of disease.

In certain cases, advances of limited value, such as rabies vaccine (1885) and organotherapy (1889), captured people's imagination and enthusiasm; in others, such as the introduction of diphtheria antitoxin (1894) and the X ray (1896), an initial renown was sustained in both popular consciousness and the annals of medical history. The prominence of these four, along with tuberculin therapy in 1890, helped to establish in mass culture two new intertwined notions: "medicine is scientific" and "medicine makes progress." Regarding the general public's notion of therapeutic progress, it may be noted that while no single event or single date can mark the "transition from a largely ineffective to a largely beneficial era of clinical medicine," participants in a recent symposium on the famous question "When did a random patient benefit from a random physician"? generally favored a traditional dating of this watershed to around 1910, or even later.[1] It seems, then, that an imagery of effective, science-based therapies entered the circulation of mass culture some years ahead of the objective transformations that historians usually emphasize.

Breakthroughs as a Source of New Images and Attitudes

Popular attitudes about medicine changed significantly because of the publicized series of discoveries that started in 1885. This study makes the pictures and portrayals of those breakthroughs its subject while acknowledging that images are only part of the story, if an essential one. Several factors justify examining this graphic imagery. First, the pictures demonstrate the widespread attention garnered rapidly by some medical novelties far beyond the confines of the profession. Second, the appearance of these discoveries in political caricatures and joke cartoons of the era shows that they had become so familiar as to be used without explanation in nonmedical contexts. Third, this largely unexamined genre of nontechnical portrayals of medical advance suggests some possible feedback loops from ordinary citizens' concerns and enthusiasms to the social status of the profession and to the willingness of elected officials and philanthropists to support expensive new institutions like the medical laboratory and the rapid growth of health departments and hospitals across the United States. Because I am focusing here primarily on pictorial coverage of breakthroughs, I will limit description of the science, the personalities, and other parts of the story to what is essential for understanding and appreciating the visual records.

The recent popularity of the word breakthrough (it seems to appear every few days in reports of medical news) highlights the public engagement with medical discoveries. These innovations (real or apparent) are seen as major advances by the public at large. The breakthroughs examined here were more than just laboratory discoveries, more than just reporting or coverage: they engendered wide familiarity and popular enthusiasm. A convergence of factors made Louis Pasteur's rabies cure the first medical breakthrough acclaimed in the United States. It remained front-page news for months all across the country, and the constant attention to the apparent miracle cure created in the laboratory helped to established new iconography and new institutions. In the process, popular consciousness gained an entirely new idea that medical research could provide widespread benefits.

This new expectation about progress offered a challenge to the centuries-old understanding (shared by physicians and patients alike) that little ever changed in medicine. Even by the early 1880s—with important new studies under way in anatomy, physiology, cell biology, and bacteriology—medicine had seen very few successful therapeutic advances, and none that made a sensation in the press. Evidence of popular cynicism about the value of doctors and doctoring in this era of transition is widely available, but two brief jokes that appeared in *Judge*, a national magazine of political and social satire, neatly illustrate how long-standing pessimistic feelings were repackaged in the 1880s. In late 1885, readers were informed that "a doctor in Chicago became crazy by dosing himself with cocaine. The case is a rare one. It is to the credit of the intelligence of the medical profession that they do not often make the mistake of taking their own medicines."[2] Early in 1886, *Judge* targeted the profession again, blending the criticism this time with anti-feminist sentiments: "Five times as many ambitious women take to medicine as to law. This contradicts that generally-received idea of the sex that they delight in scandals and quarrels, but abhor cruelty and killing."[3] But we must keep in mind that attitudes and actions need not be mutually consistent: this popular pessimism seems not to have inhibited people's seeking out professional medical help when they were ill. Nor did it keep them and their physicians from having confidence that the treatments worked, as Charles Rosenberg has shown in his now-classic study of doctor–patient interaction and the meaning it held for participants.[4]

Suddenly, in late 1885, the public was offered pictures in newspapers and magazines quite different from the routine scenes of bandaging, dosing, clystering, accidents, and epidemics—an entirely unprecedented depiction of spectacular medical advance. Almost overnight, the physician seemed to have become a miracle worker. This imagery of breakthroughs both tapped and stimulated the public's new fascination with medical novelties.[5]

I am not claiming here that medicine entered popular culture only by means of the major episodes of frenzied, sensationalist coverage that centered on certain breakthroughs. Nor am I saying that science was absent from American medicine before 1885. For example, Robert Koch's identification of the cholera germ in 1884 was not ignored by the press, but it failed to provoke sustained headlines or a ripple effect in other media.[6] For several decades, scientific medicine had been a prominent goal and a partial achievement of some American practitioners and medical educators, as recent scholarship has made clear.[7] Further, while I endorse a colleague's cautions about historical work that tends "to see the emergence of laboratory medicine as the emergence of scientific medicine,"[8] my analysis below shows that popular attitudes in the decade surrounding 1890 exhibited exactly that conflation of ideas. Though that era's sense of the novelty of science in medicine may have been faulty history, it is possible to explore their picture of things without either making this picture our own or ignoring it as something naive and inaccurate. But by attending to the different pictures of medicine in the minds of three distinct groups (elite physicians, ordinary practitioners, and lay people), we will notice two important variations. First, rank-and-file physicians and the general public had far less engagement with the developments of science in medicine before the 1880s than did members of the European-trained medical elite. Second, when the science-based breakthroughs started appearing in the 1880s, the public usually raced ahead of the profession in embracing the novelties.[9] It is this initial wave of public enthusiasm that the present study illustrates and examines.

If the medical breakthroughs of the 1880s and 1890s were planted by workers within medicine, they grew in the soil of new mass media and were aggressively promoted by those in journalism and publishing. The popular press has its own history, as does its changing use of illustrations. The images studied in this article did not arise by spontaneous generation, but were produced by the efforts and decisions of editors, artists, and publishers at a definite moment in the development of American print media: a stage often recognized simply as "the new journalism." For convenience and brevity the change may be dated from 1883, when Joseph Pulitzer purchased the *New York World.* His innovations were copied by William Gordon Bennett, Jr., in the *New York Herald*, and by other papers, and then by Pulitzer's great rival William Randolph Hearst in the *San Francisco Examiner.* The readership and power of the daily press were greatly expanded by three important clusters of changes whose features are so familiar today that we can easily forget that newspapers lacked them before the closing decades of the nineteenth century. All three helped in creating popular enthusiasm for the medical breakthroughs studied here. That era saw, first, a transformation of the recently invented human-interest story into blaring sensationalism; second, the inception of various editorial novelties (including advocacy crusades, public fund-raising subscriptions, stunts, and interviews); and third, the introduction of new typesetting and printing technologies that offered unprecedented graphic capabilities. Pictures entered the American press on a daily basis in the *New York Daily Graphic*, founded in 1873 (but closed down in 1889 after other papers successfully adopted its visual strengths).

Popular graphic materials from the nineteenth century offer a great deal to historians, although they have not been used extensively by medical historians, who are often more at home with the professional journals of the era. Two particular utilities of this kind of evidence have been succinctly differentiated by John Kouwenhoven in his "graphic history" of New York: on the one hand, "pictures...are often the source of factual information about topography, manners, and customs which is available nowhere else. On the other, they are a clue to attitudes and interests, to blind spots and perceptions, of which there may be no other surviving evidence."[10] Both uses are found below, with emphasis on the second.

In presenting these pictures, my intention is to take readers on a verbal walking tour of historic landmarks and their environs, while providing the background information and interpretation needed to observe the crucial features and to discern the meaning of these images in their original contexts. Readers may enjoy the remarkable freshness and humor of many of the graphics reproduced here, finding them worthy of interest in themselves, in addition to their service as documentation of mass culture a century ago.[11] In examining the images of breakthrough discoveries, my analysis emphasizes their audiences over their origins, their effects over their causes—pursuing what they can tell us about the thoughts and feelings of those who saw them in daily and weekly papers. I do not utilize them as "representations" (whether accurate or inaccurate) of the medical events, or as "illustrations" of a medical history narrative—though both are quite legitimate uses. They are more interesting, I believe, for what they can tell us about how ordinary people envisioned physicians, medical tools, and health-care institutions in an era of rapid change.

Looking for What Pictures Reveal

Five initial images will provide orientation for the tour that follows. First is an 1890 political caricature of Benjamin Harrison, who had been elected president two years earlier (Fig. 1). This cartoon is one in a long series of satirical attacks in which Benjamin's supposed deficiencies are indicated by his increasingly diminutive stature, as measured by the large top hat of his successful grandfather, William Henry Harrison, elected president in 1840. Our interest here is not in the Harrisons, but in the prominent microscope—which was apparently familiar in form and function to a mass audience, even in an era when relatively few physicians had acquired the necessary skill or an interest in using this instrument. While only other kinds of historical sources can document the extent of microscope training within the profession, or the development of the instrument itself, this cartoon shows how nonmedical sources can demonstrate that a wide public had ready familiarity with this instrument in 1890—for without such familiarity the cartoon's point would be utterly lost.[12] It is also significant that the slides visible on the table are not ones prepared for the mid-century medical sciences of histology or cellular pathology, but rather are examples of the latest popular fascination: Bacteria and Microbes.

A pair of images will carry this argument further and provide a methodological clarification. An 1884 newsmagazine engraving of Louis Pasteur among his caged rabbits (Fig. 2) seems immediately accessible and intelligible, and it has thus been a popular choice for reproduction in historical books and articles. It appears to take us directly into his laboratory—and as historians, we are delighted to be offered such access. Yet, for all its seeming transparency as a document, we would be hard put to know just what the readers of that time knew or thought about Pasteur's work. For historians, the picture may embody what we have already learned about his work from other sources, and it can thus be used by us to "illustrate" that information. But compare this image with another political cartoon of the same era, "The Democratic Doctors Attempting to Vaccinate Political Tramps in Congress" (Fig. 3): while this might seem at first less revealing than Pasteur-at-work, since we are not shown much detail of the medical instruments or technique, my point is that its goal of conveying a political message (not a medico-historical one) requires that the medical activity be immediately recognizable and familiar—perhaps even routine. From Pasteur and his rabbits we cannot tell whether readers knew what his experiments were about; but from the vaccination picture, we can

Fig. 1. "The Smallest Specimen Yet," by Frederick Opper. *Puck*, 19 February 1890, cover. (The original page is in color, 10″ × 13″.)

Fig. 2. "M. Pasteur in His Laboratory." Detail (9" × 5") from a full-page illustration, "Hydrophobia—M. Pasteur's Experiments," *Harper's Weekly*, 21 June 1884, p. 392.

Fig. 3. "The Democratic Doctors Attempting to Vaccinate Political Tramps in Congress," by Frederick Opper. *Frank Leslie's Illustrated Newspaper*, 19 April 1879, p. 112 (the image is 10″ × 6″).

infer with some confidence that the artist and his editor assumed most readers to have already in their visual memories public vaccination campaigns, or depictions of them.[13] This political cartoon thus provides better evidence of a shared awareness than we could glean simply from a news engraving of a vaccination scene that presumes no prior familiarity with the subject.

A second pair of contrasting images will complete our orientation and furnish a bridge to the first of the breakthroughs. Pasteur watching the youthful Jean Baptiste Jupille receive an injection of rabies vaccine is a lovely and widely reproduced image (Fig. 4). Jupille was the second known rabies victim under Pasteur's care, and the treatment took place in October 1885.[14] This picture was published in the United States several times in November and December 1885.[15] As with Pasteur among the rabbits, historians have gravitated to this naturalistic representation, for it seems so real—even though, unless we find independent documentation, we cannot be sure how accurate it was. As a contrast, consider a political cartoon of December 1885 showing *New York Tribune* publisher Whitelaw Reid being rushed to Paris for Pasteur's new treatment in "Another Patient for Pasteur" (Fig. 5). Reid was, of course, not in danger of succumbing to hydrophobia, and he never went to Paris for any treatment. The cartoon's point is a (complicated) political one, not of interest here; but for medical history, this cartoon provides more information on its own than does the figure of Jupille's treatment. Even without ancillary documentation, it establishes firmly that the notion of a new rabies cure available in Paris was assumed to be widely current among the readership of *Puck*. And, as we shall see from other images below, ordinary Americans had more than an awareness, they shared an enormous enthusiasm. Rabies shots were "The Topic of the Day!"

Hydrophobia Cured: The First Medical Breakthrough

A treatment for dog-bite victims at risk for rabies was announced by Louis Pasteur in Paris in late 1885. Although his name was at that time not entirely unknown in America, he was hardly famous, and his contributions were appreciated at this time by only a small segment of elite physicians and scientists. (The process we call "pasteurization" was already being used in a limited fashion, but that word came to prominence only much later.) His method required that the victim of bites from a recognizably rabid animal be injected with a series of increasingly virulent extracts of partially attenuated infectious material over about twelve days, thereby gradually building up—according to Pasteur's thinking—an artificial resistance to the disease in advance of the natural infection from the bite. In late October he proclaimed the success of the treatments administered to Joseph Meister in July, and announced favorable progress in a more recent series of injections for Jean Baptiste Jupille.[16] Modern readers may be surprised that we know the identities of individual patients, but it was a characteristic of coverage then that personal stories were employed to increase the public's engagement with the news. Pasteur's announcement was reported in American newspapers, but these initial accounts were very brief, with little emphasis, and none were front-page stories. Pasteur, being a chemist, used physician collaborators and did not administer the injections himself; while the press accounts usually maintained an awareness of the distinction, he nevertheless came in time to be seen as the provider of this cure, not simply its discoverer.[17]

Then, in early December, the Pasteur treatment suddenly became front-page news across the United States when four working-class children from Newark, New Jersey, were bitten by

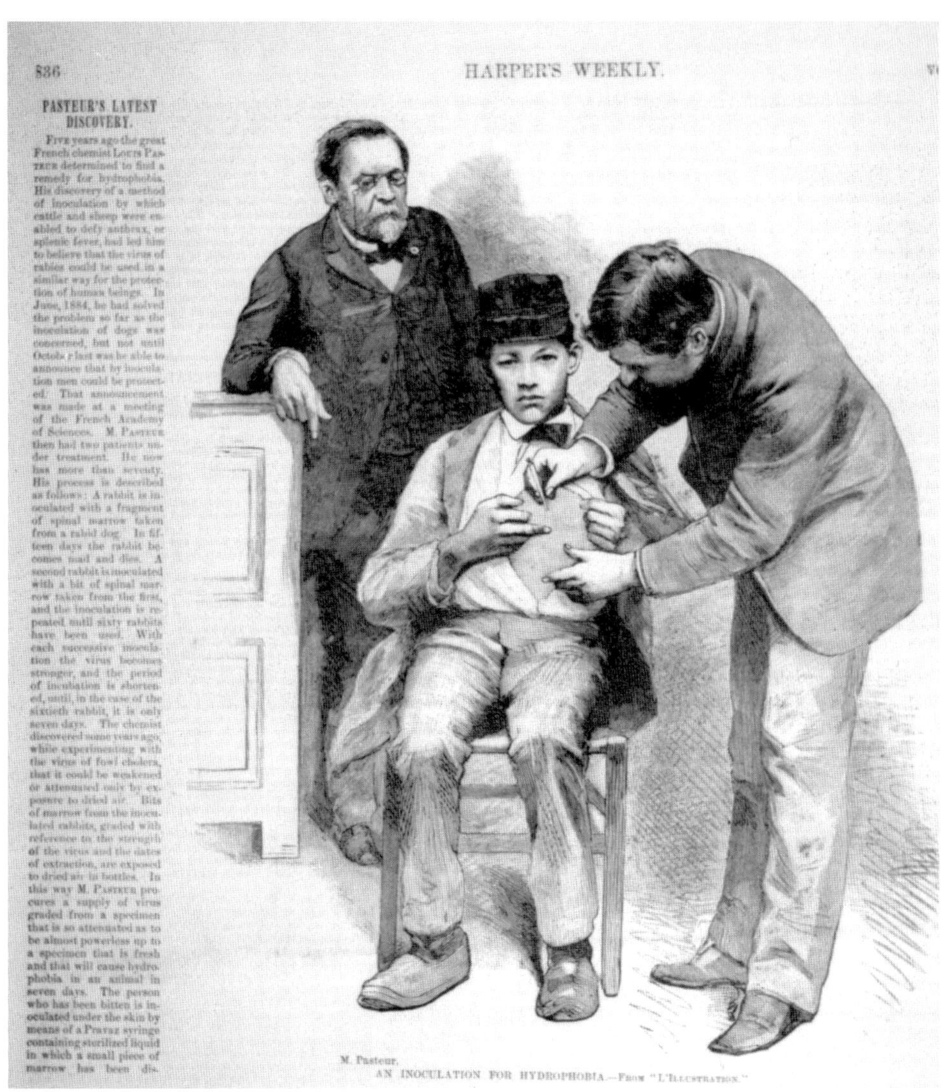

836 HARPER'S WEEKLY.

PASTEUR'S LATEST DISCOVERY.

Five years ago the great French chemist Louis Pasteur determined to find a remedy for hydrophobia. His discovery of a method of inoculation by which cattle and sheep were enabled to defy anthrax, or splenic fever, had led him to believe that the virus of rabies could be used in a similar way for the protection of human beings. In June, 1884, he had solved the problem so far as the inoculation of dogs was concerned, but not until October last was he able to announce that by inoculation men could be protected. That announcement was made at a meeting of the French Academy of Sciences. M. Pasteur then had two patients under treatment. He now has more than seventy. His process is described as follows: A rabbit is inoculated with a fragment of spinal marrow taken from a rabid dog. In fifteen days the rabbit becomes mad and dies. A second rabbit is inoculated with a bit of spinal marrow taken from the first, and the inoculation is repeated until sixty rabbits have been used. With each successive inoculation the virus becomes stronger, and the period of incubation is shortened, until, in the case of the sixtieth rabbit, it is only seven days. The chemist discovered some years ago, while experimenting with the virus of fowl cholera, that it could be weakened or attenuated only by exposure to dried air. Bits of marrow from the inoculated rabbits, graded with reference to the strength of the virus and the dates of extraction, are exposed to dried air in bottles. In this way M. Pasteur procures a supply of virus graded from a specimen that is so attenuated as to be almost powerless up to a specimen that is fresh and that will cause hydrophobia in an animal in seven days. The person who has been bitten is inoculated under the skin by means of a Pravaz syringe containing sterilized liquid in which a small piece of marrow has been dis-

M. Pasteur.

AN INOCULATION FOR HYDROPHOBIA.—From "L'Illustration."

Fig. 4. "An Inoculation for Hydrophobia—From *L'Illustration*." *Harper's Weekly*, 19 December 1885, p. 836; the related article, "Pasteur's Latest Discovery," runs on pp. 886–837 (the image is 7″ × 9″).

Fig. 5. "Another Patient for Pasteur. Let Him be Taken to Paris and Treated for Blainiac Rabies without Delay," by Frederick Opper. *Puck*, 16 December 1885, cover. (The original page is in color, 10" × 13".)

a stray dog. On 3 December, the day after they were bitten, a local physician urged that they be sent to Paris for the only treatment that could save their lives, and he called for donations from the public to cover their expenses. Tickets were secured for passage on a steamer sailing to Europe within a few days. Newspapers quickly promoted the fund-raising so successfully that when a millionaire industrialist offered to send them, his offer could be declined. As contributions arrived, the donors' names appeared in the daily papers. The press churned public interest with large and small stories about the boys' families, gifts of winter clothes for the ocean voyage, Pasteur's prior achievements, hydrophobia remedies of all sorts, municipalities' attempts at dog control, various physicians' opinions on hydrophobia, the theory of inoculation, the boys' "hospital" room on the ship, and the germ theory in general. Over the next four months, newspapers would also report at length on such topics as other countries' rabies patients being treated in Paris, American attempts to produce the vaccine, the death of a young girl in Paris after she had received the new treatment, and an international campaign for funds to create a treatment center in Paris, which would ultimately open in November 1888 as the Pasteur Institute.

The coverage was not only varied, it was extensive. For the first two months, a news article appeared almost every day in each of the New York papers, with as many as four (and occasionally more) in the same paper on certain days—in addition to editorials, readers' letters, and comic items. At least twice, the *New York Herald* used more than 10 percent of its space for rabies and its cure. In December alone, the *Herald* (admittedly the leader in rabies news) published 17 editorials, 31 letters to the editor, 17 cable dispatches from Paris or London, and 73 news articles. In January, the *Herald* printed 98 different items. Slightly less numerous were *New York Times* articles, with 70 items on some aspect of the rabies story before the end of February. Nor were reports on the rabies discovery and the related American adventures limited to the New York and Newark papers: the Newark boys' adventures were reported in big-city and small-town papers all over the country.

Thanks to the recently reconnected Atlantic cable, Americans could read daily dispatches from Paris. Even before the boys reached Europe, an American newspaperman had interviewed Pasteur. When they arrived, the correspondent accompanied them to the first treatment and cabled back a full report, pumping up the historic event with solemn details and inserting the comic relief of a child's more limited perspective on this great moment:

> At exactly twelve minutes before seven the Doctor inserted the point of a silver needle beneath the skin...and injected the virus. Lane has thus the honor of being the first American ever inoculated for rabies. As the needle was withdrawn he gave a slight squirm and burst into a boisterous laugh, explaining, "Why, it's like the bite of a big mosquito. It doesn't hurt a bit."[18]

Newspaper readers across the United States were treated to hundreds of further reports from abroad of the daily injections, more interviews with Pasteur and his colleagues, the boys' antics in their hotel, the Christmas gifts they received, and their departure for home.

While the boys were still on their return voyage, their miracle cure was immortalized in a new exhibit at New York's Eden Musée a very popular wax museum: "The Topic of the Day, Monsieur Pasteur Operating on One of the Newark Children."[19] But the boys themselves became celebrities too—whether because they were drawn back from the jaws of death, or just because they had been in the news and had been touched by the great chemist, is not clear—

and thousands paid to see them onstage in the working-class entertainment venues known then as dime museums. For weeks they told their story to overflow crowds in New York, Philadelphia, and possibly other cities.

American enthusiasm for the new rabies cure was not, however, limited to a trivial fascination with passing celebrity: some Americans also recognized the necessity of being able to produce the new biological reagent on this side of the Atlantic if patients were to be treated in time, and in several cities physicians and entrepreneurs gathered to imitate Pasteur's work.[20] Dogs bitten by the Newark stray were quarantined for observation by a group of local physicians, and rabbits were inoculated with matter from the dog that had bitten them and the children. Before the end of December, groups in New York and in St. Louis were pursuing corporate status under the (unauthorized) name of Pasteur Institute. These efforts preceded Pasteur's own call for such an endeavor by more than two months. His institute in Paris was to open only in 1888, but it would flourish; the initial American efforts had far less success. Nonetheless, they started a movement toward the creation of new institutions to undertake laboratory research and offer the public up-to-date treatments. Over the next twenty years, the name "Pasteur Institute" was used by several American institutions in Ann Arbor, Baltimore, Chicago, New York, Pittsburgh, and perhaps Philadelphia.[21]

Illustrations were a crucial element in the flood of newspaper and magazine articles creating the rabies cure sensation, and they made certain aspects much more memorable. Often humorous, they deepened people's engagement with the story; sometimes, as in the case of political cartoons (like Fig. 5, earlier), they took advantage of its familiarity to make other arguments. Examples of high-quality news drawings reprinted from European magazines are seen in Figs. 2 and 4 above; they are elegant and dignified images, in contrast to the hurried sketches assembled by American artists when the unanticipated and entirely unprecedented story broke in early December. Typical of the impromptu efforts are the postage-stamp-sized images that accompanied "The Children's Farewell" (Fig. 6), a two-column article in Joseph Pulitzer's *New York World* on 10 December 1885. Small images like these were the norm in the newspapers of that era, which had not yet adequately solved the technical problem of holding together a page of type in which something crossed the rigid boundaries of the column rules. Despite their minute size and generalized character, these pictures nicely convey what was offered to satisfy the public's curiosity: the children boarding the ship, the stateroom converted into a dormitory (labeled "The Steamer's Hospital" despite the fact that all four were in good health), portraits of the four boys, a head-shot of Dr. Pasteur, and a full-length figure of Dr. Frank Seaver Billings (who accompanied the boys to Paris) in top hat with cane. The boys' pictures in the *World* were probably copied from the *Sun's* four portraits printed two days earlier, and the image of Pasteur is not a good likeness (the *New York Evening Post* caustically suggested that this was simply the face of a local politician relabeled to fill a sudden need). Our interest is not in judging the accuracy of the illustrations or settling the priority disputes, but in noticing how images and comments about them added momentum to the tidal wave of this sensation.[22]

In less than two weeks there had been so much attention to this novelty that satirists could make it a target. Their whimsy did not puncture the balloon of excitement, but inflated it further. A large cartoon, "The Pasteur Boom: High Times for Hydrophobists," with its central image captioned, "Now Is the Time to Get Bitten by a Rabid Dog and Take a Trip to Paris" (see Fig. 7), makes light of the masses' enthusiasm for the trip, without challenging its impor-

THE WORLD: THUR

THE CHILDREN'S FAREWELL.

DR. PASTEUR'S LITTLE PATIENTS SAIL ON THE STEAMER CANADA.

THE CITADEL OF POLYGAMY.

SAINTS AND GENTILES CARRYING ON A POWERFUL WAR OF WORDS.

Fig. 6. "The Children's Farewell. Dr. Pasteur's Little Patients Sail on the Steamer Canada." *New York World*, 10 December 1885, p. 5, cols. 1–2 (columns are 2" wide). *Source*: General Research Division, The New York Public Library, Astor, Lenox, and Tilden Foundations.

Fig. 7. "The Pasteur Boom—High Times for Hydrophobists," by Frederick Opper, *Puck*, 23 December 1885, back cover. Captions for the inset boxes read: "Householder: 'Is that dog mad?' Policeman: 'I dunno, but he snores so I can't sleep'"; "The Latest 'Been bit yet?'"; "An Epidemic of Politeness." (The original is in color, 13″ × 10″.)

tance to the four little boys and without taking a stand on the value of Pasteur's new therapy. Indicative of how the press was feeding upon itself in the creation of news is the fact that when this cartoon arrived in Europe by steamer a few weeks later, it was shown to Pasteur by the *New York Herald's* correspondent, who then cabled a report of Pasteur's comments across the Atlantic in time to make the next morning's papers in New York. This cartoon also mocks the fashion of ladies' lap dogs and the traditional policeman's role as urban dog killer.

Taking a different tack, a cartoonist at the *New York Daily Graphic* adapted the traditional scene of a daughter buying her father's beer to the new passion for getting some of Pasteur's life-saving virus, as one of ten jokes covering its entire front page (Fig. 8). That the ribbing is gentle and aimed at popular enthusiasms rather than at the medical innovation is indicated by a long story in the same newspaper two weeks later on "Pasteur's Methods in America," which includes drawings of "The Newark Scientists" and "The Recent Experiments for the Cure of Hydrophobia."[23]

It seems that in a matter of just a few weeks, the general public had assimilated the announcement of a new life-saving discovery, had learned that the curative extract was produced in the bodies of rabbits that were then killed, had faced the puzzling idea that the same virus that killed so brutally could be modified to have fabulous healing power, and had become excited at the prospect that these new ideas and techniques would be transforming the routines of medicine and medical education. This heady moment of rapid change was captured by *Puck* in a cartoon of six frames under the double entendre, "The Profession Gone Mad": scenes show the traditional anatomist's skeleton cast aside in the medical lecture room, replaced by a box labeled "VIRUS"; medical students engaged in "cat-snatching instead of body-snatching"; medical-school demonstrators performing trephination on a live rabbit; physicians swarming to get a look at a case of rabies, the newly fashionable disease; and a physician apologizing at a patient's bedside, "Excuse me, but I have an experiment to make."[24]

But Pasteur's protective inoculation for rabies reached the pinnacle of visibility in American graphic imagery in mid-February, when one of America's leading artists, T. Bernhard Gillam, turned President Grover Cleveland into Louis Pasteur within a satirical setting that placed him in the very center of the cartoon. Gillam drew "Pasteur Cleveland" just below the *New York World's* Joseph Pulitzer (portrayed as Lady Liberty) and just above Jake Sharp (an entrepreneur who had gained approval to build a street railway on Broadway by bribing the aldermen, but was then arrested, convicted, and later released on appeal) trimming the claws of the Tammany Tiger (Fig. 9). In this densely populated cartoon, Gillam employed the device of fashioning about twenty-five of his political targets into wax museum figures.[25] Interestingly, he used the name of New York's Eden Musée, where, indeed, a new display featured "Pasteur Operating on One of the Newark Children." This wax-figure group was described in the Eden Musée's printed catalog in terms that illustrate how profoundly Pasteur's work was changing ordinary people's expectations about medical progress:

> Of late M. Pasteur's name has become a household word in every country on account of his experiments in trying to prevent the dreadful effects of the bite of mad dogs, by inoculating the victims with the virus of the rabid animal....Patients from all parts of the world have flocked to his laboratory to undergo the new process.[26]

Expectations about the nature and meaning of a medical breakthrough were firmly planted in mass culture during the winter of 1885–86, when Pasteur's name became "a household word"

Fig. 8. "What Are We Coming To: 'Fifteen Cents Worth of Hydrophobia Virus for Pa.'" Detail (3" × 5") from a full-page spread of ten cartoons. "Hydrophobia!" by H. C. Coultaus, *New York Daily Graphic*, 19 December 1885, p. 1. *Source*: General Research Division, The New York Public Library. Astor, Lenox, and Tilden Foundations.

Fig. 9. "Pasteur Cleveland Inoculating the Democracy against Spoils-Rabies." Detail of central section of "Judge's Wax Works—The Political Eden Musée," by T. Bernhard Gillam, *Judge*, 20 February 1886, pp. 8–9. (The original cartoon is in color, 19" × 13" in full). In the usage of that era, "the Democracy" means "the Democratic Party."

and changed the thinking of newsmen, medical leaders, and the general public alike. Many features of the pattern continued for a few decades, evolving gradually as new discoveries took center stage in turn, and as the frequency of discoveries increased. Portrayals of subsequent episodes show how the springing up of medical novelties was becoming a routine phenomenon, and they reveal how quickly the political cartoonists could tap into popular awareness of a discovery. Like the rabies cure, the next two major breakthroughs, organotherapy and tuberculin, were European discoveries, with American physicians involved only secondarily. The diphtheria antitoxin and the X ray, following shortly thereafter, were innovations in which American physicians, scientists, and health administrators played more active roles.

Organotherapy Makes the Headlines

When the multinational physician and physiologist Charles-Edouard Brown-Séquard announced in early June 1889 that he had succeeded in effecting rejuvenation by injections of testicular extracts from animals, many aspects of the story captured widespread interest—not the least of which was that this elderly physician had tested the extracts on himself.[27] The research also tapped popular curiosity about sex, masculinity, aging, and the use of animal extracts in humans. Brown-Séquard was then seventy-two years old, a member of the French Academy of Sciences, and successor to Claude Bernard as professor of medicine at the Collège de France—at the peak of a rather peripatetic career in which he had practiced medicine, taught in medical schools, and performed research in Boston, London, New York, Nice, Paris, Philadelphia, and Richmond, Virginia. Press coverage of his new technique in the United States was sporadic until the complete text of his paper appeared in English translation in the *Scientific American Supplement* for 10 August 1889.[28] The news coverage then swelled, and it would unfortunately come to include two reports of fatal outcomes at the hands of American physicians trying to replicate the experimental treatment.[29] The weekly *Frank Leslie's Illustrated Newspaper* headlined its report "An Astonishing Medical Discovery"; citing American experiments by former U.S. Army Surgeon-General William A. Hammond, this article claimed that "the result of the application to several old gentlemen has been to renew their vital energies to a noticeable extent, and to give them an invigoration that was sensibly felt."[30] Hammond published medical articles about his own research with testicular extracts, and also disseminated his findings to a much broader public in the *North American Review*.[31]

But beyond these magazine stories, the most striking evidence of the therapy's hold on the popular imagination comes from songs, comic poems, satires, and its use in political caricature. Even before the end of August, the two leading magazines of political and social commentary had both employed the apparently well-known words Brown-Séquard's "Elixir of Life" in full-color, double-page centerfold cartoons about national politics (Figs. 10 and 11). "Elixir of Life" was not a new phrase: it had an established use among patent-medicine makers, and it had even appeared in political cartoons before—but a therapy that used piston syringes and hollow needles to inject tired men with juice from sexual organs gave the old alchemical term a comic new lease on life. Risqué jokes were irresistible. Louis Dalrymple at *Puck* (a magazine of Democratic leanings) fashioned organotherapy into a lively attack on the Republican administration's new pension policy by which Commissioner of Pensions James Tanner had proposed using a government surplus to expand pension benefits for Civil War veterans and their relatives (see fig. 10). Like the other political cartoons that used medical-breakthrough

Fig. 10. "It Beats Brown-Sequard.—Tanner's Infallible Elixir of Life, for Pension-Grabbers Only," by Louis Dalrymple. *Puck*, 28 August 1889, pp. 8–9. (The original cartoon is in color, 19" × 13".)

imagery, "It Beats Brown-Séquard" is less interesting today for its role in partisan wrangling than for the evidence it provides of the public's fascination with the latest headline innovation.

Brown-Séquard's American notoriety is further confirmed by Grant Hamilton's "Hopeless Cases" in the Republican-inclined weekly, *Judge* (Fig. 11). Here the Brown-Séquard figure is Samuel Jackson Randall, a Democratic congressman from Pennsylvania, who had lost President Cleveland's favor two years earlier; he had been a protectionist since the 1860s, despite that position's being unpopular in his party. Here he is well supplied with two large tanks of "Protectionism" as an "Elixir of Life"—but it is too late, he says, for this rejuvenation juice to revive the Democratic Party and its debilitated Free Trade policy. This up-to-date physician declares: "Take them away! They're too near dead for treatment."[32]

These two political cartoons are interesting as well for their crude, but recognizable, depictions of the hypodermic needle and syringe, which was not yet a commonly-pictured device, either realistically or exaggerated for comic effect. As will be seen below, when the hypodermic reappears the following year in connection with Koch's tuberculin, it is portrayed more accurately (if still humorously enlarged). With respect to changes in medical iconography more generally, it may also be noted that the seated figure was recognizable as a physician in 1889 by his medication bottle and syringe—not yet by a white lab coat, thermometer, or stethoscope, for these were still in the future for popular imagery.

Whether or not partisan cartoonists and their readers deemed the new organotherapy effective, such images signal widespread familiarity with the latest medical breakthrough. In fact, by mid-October, there had been so much excitement among the lay public that *Scientific American* felt it necessary to defend Brown-Séquard's character and his work against distortions and exaggerations in the popular press.[33] Another indication of just how quickly and widely the excitement spread is offered by a historian's claim that by the end of 1890 "more than twelve thousand physicians were administering the extract to their patients."[34] The kind of sudden, radical advance that had long been unimaginable in medicine was now coming to be seen as expected, and almost routine.

Koch's Consumption Cure: Tuberculin Therapy

Just about a year after the testicular-extract sensation, another European scientist captured American headlines, this time with a cure for tuberculosis. It would be hard to imagine a more significant or gratifying breakthrough, and for a while the frenzy of the press's and the public's shared enthusiasm knew no bounds. Not only was this a disease whose morbidity and mortality dwarfed that of rabies by many orders of magnitude, its cure was at the hands of the great physician Robert Koch, whose discoveries about the etiologic agents of anthrax, cholera, and tuberculosis had already carried him to the pinnacle of professional recognition internationally. If his name had not yet become the "household word" that Pasteur's was, it was to acquire that status in a flash. The excitement blossomed so quickly that it put the attention accorded Pasteur five years earlier into a shadow. If Pasteur was an experimentalist hero and a kindly gentleman who fussed over the children arriving for treatment, Koch was a St. George slaying the dragon of monstrous disease.[35] Unfortunately for Koch and for the world, his tuberculin therapy was shown within several weeks to lack effectiveness and even to be harmful in some cases. Because the rise and fall of tuberculin as a therapy have been recounted by others, only its visual presence in the mass media is examined here.[36]

Fig. 11. "Hopeless Cases," by Grant Hamilton. *Judge*, 31 August 1889, pp. 336–37. (The original is in color, 19″ × 13″.) Reprinted by permission of the William H. Helfand Collection, New York, NY.

For a few months the media, the public, and the profession in America were captivated by what seemed to be laboratory medicine's crowning achievement. On 15 November 1890, the front page of the *New York Times* carried a translation of Koch's complete text from the *Deutsche medizinische Wochenschrift* of 14 November (received by cable). But this was not a big-city story only: we can look, for example, to the coverage in Connecticut's *Danbury Evening News* (a paper appearing five times a week in a small city with fewer than three thousand listed taxpayers in 1885) to illustrate the nature of the public's interest, and to reveal as well the intense competition among cities and medical institutions to be pioneers, receiving national publicity for their participation in this breakthrough.[37] The following summary highlights important themes and key events in the Danbury articles, without attempting to capture all the coverage or the depth of the stories:

> 15 November: The University of Pennsylvania is sending a physician to Berlin.
> 18 November: Boston will have a Koch Institute.
> 22 November: "Will It Cure Cancer, Too? Professor Koch Looking for More Diseases to Conquer." (The article includes a small portrait of Koch.)
> 22 November: Pasteur sends Koch congratulations and is sent a vial of the lymph.
> 4 December: New Haven receives a small portion of the lymph. "It is believed that the lymph is the first received and injected in America."
> 5 December: Lymph is used in New Haven and its effects described.
> 9 December: More tuberculin is received in New Haven.
> 11 December: Danbury expects some next week, and the lymph is used in New York by Dr. Jacobi at Mount Sinai Hospital.
> 12 December: A Paris physician prevents its use at the Bichat Hospital.
> 15 December: "Koch's Lymph at the Capital" (its use in Washington) and "Secrecy at Johns Hopkins" (physicians not revealing initial reactions of fourteen treated patients).
> 18 December: The first Philadelphia injections.
> 19 December: Lymph is expected in Danbury.
> 30 December: The patients at Johns Hopkins are doing well.
> 12 January: The return of a New York physician from Berlin with two bottles of lymph that he will use, but not on advanced patients.
> 15 January: "The Lymph Curing Lupus" at City Hospital in Worcester, Massachusetts.
> 16 January: "Koch's Cure Described: The Discoverer Tells the World All About It. Several Criticisms Answered....While It Is Young, Yet Many Cures Have Resulted."
> 22 January: "Lymph for the President" (President Harrison receives from the U.S. minister at Berlin five vials that are being distributed to hospitals in Washington, D.C., Chicago, Indianapolis, and New Orleans).

Reflecting on the previous winter's media coverage, the pioneering Chicago surgeon Nicholas Senn observed that "for days and weeks the public press devoted a liberal space to telegraphic messages, to editorials and messages from medical men, relative to the new treatment"; he then claimed (with some embarrassment) that "no other event in the world's history ever attracted so much attention and no discovery in medicine and surgery ever found such ready introduction and universal acceptation."[38] Popular graphic images drew the public once again—and even more deeply this time—into an enthusiasm for laboratory research and science based therapies.

American papers and magazines frequently printed a rather engaging portrait of a handsome and younger-than-he-actually-was Robert Koch.[39] In some papers this was paired with a rather lifeless sketch of the physician in his laboratory. *Frank Leslie's Illustrated Newspaper* printed a full-page suite of pictures that combined these two images with four technical drawings labeled "Fresh Bacilli from the Lungs of a Consumptive Patient, as Seen under the Microscope," "Bacilli after Two Weeks' Growth, under the Microscope," "Tube Containing a 'Culture' of Tuberculous Bacilli," and "Tube Containing 'Culture' of Comma (Cholera) Bacilli." The page carried a firmly optimistic caption: "The Prevention and Cure of Consumption—Dr. Koch's Great Discovery" (see Fig. 12).[40] Even though microscopes, specimens, and "cultures" had at this date not yet become routine aspects of medical training and practice, they were familiar to a broad segment of the public from parlor science activities, microscopical societies, and such cartoons as seen in Fig. 1 above, which earlier that same year had portrayed the U.S. president under Uncle Sam's microscope.

The tuberculin cure—like Pasteur's rabies treatment—quickly came to be represented as much by the lucky patients in their moment of celebrity as by the physicians involved. When an American patient was sent to Berlin for treatment with funds raised by *Frank Leslie's Illustrated Newspaper*, an artist accompanied him to record the life-saving interventions, starting with the patient's pretreatment examination in New York by Dr. George F. Shrady, a leading New York physician and editor of the *Medical Record* from 1866 to 1904 (see Fig. 13). Note the inset portrait of the patient, William Degan, on the lower right, given the same individuality and prominence as the physician's portrait on the upper left. *Frank Leslie's* would, of course, shortly provide the American public with a full-page illustration of this patient's treatment in Berlin.[41] In another issue, this paper also printed a quarter-page engraving of "Sir Morell Mackenzie Injecting Dr. Koch's Lymph at the Throat Hospital, London."[42]

Without delay, political cartoonists grabbed new images from this "latest sensation," sometimes even jumping ahead of the news engravings, as they tapped the public's excitement about tuberculin as the greatest breakthrough of the era—and perhaps of all human history! *Puck*'s leading artist, Joseph Keppler—possibly encouraged by the similarity of Robert Koch's oval face with full beard to that of Keppler's favorite target, James G. Blaine (of the "Blainiac rabies" cartoon in Fig. 5, as well as many other caricatures)—made the lymph cure for consumption the centerpiece of its major cartoon for the 10 December issue (probably printed a week earlier). In "A Bad Case of Consumption—Dr. Blaine Tries an Injection of His Reciprocity Lymph," the sick Republican Party elephant is surrounded by top-hatted physicians consulting on the case; one of them is timing the elephant's pulse with a watch in one hand and the animal's tail in the other.[43] The elephant and the doctor were stock images of medical caricature, but here they are pushed to the side by two important novelties: the hypodermic syringe (made popular via the Brown-Séquard elixir shortly before) and its injectable medication ("Reciprocity Lymph"). While the political issues of reciprocity, free trade, and protectionism were commonplaces of the era, the latest therapy's bring-them-back-from-death's-door potential was quite new, echoing the miraculous rabies cure of just five years before. To exaggerate the mysterious power of the lymph as well as Blaine's mercurial character (he is shown standing on "Blaine's reversible platform"), the cartoonist has dressed Blaine as a wizard, unlike the recognizably contemporary physicians to his left and right.[44]

Widespread familiarity with the new lymph and with Koch as its inventor was implied as well by *Judge* magazine's cartoon attack on problems in the Democratic party just a week later (Fig. 14): dressed in the traditional top hats and armed with carefully depicted (if enlarged) syringes, Dr. Koch-Cleveland and Dr. Koch-Hill proffer competing therapies to revive the ailing Democratic Party tiger.[45] As with *Puck*'s cartoon, the political issues were old hat

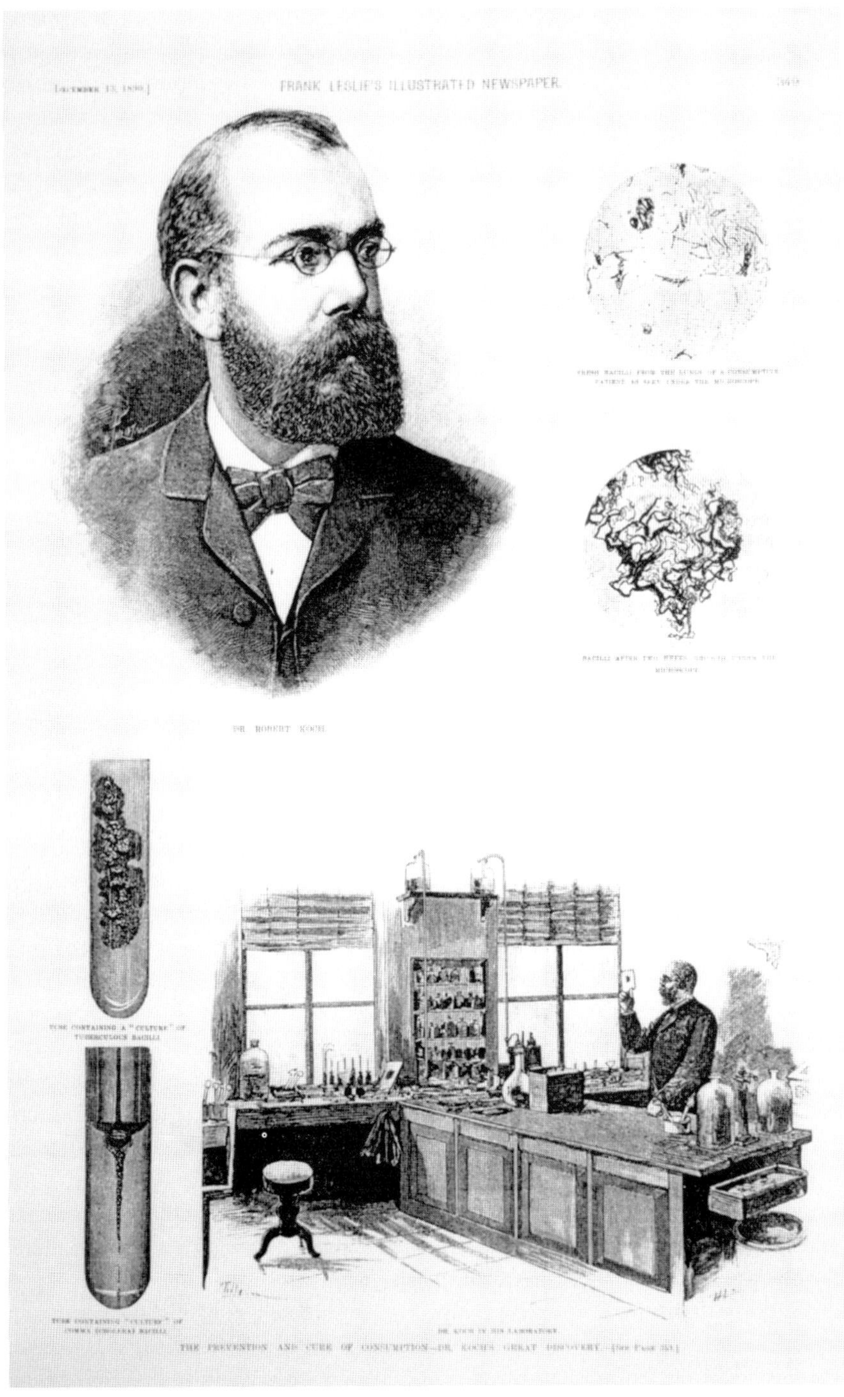
FRANK LESLIE'S ILLUSTRATED NEWSPAPER

DR. ROBERT KOCH

Fig. 12. "The Prevention and Cure of Consumption—Dr. Koch's Great Discovery." *Frank Leslie's Illustrated Newspaper*, 13 December 1890, p. 349 (the page is 11″ × 16″).

Fig. 13. "Dr. Koch's Treatment of Consumption.—Examination by Dr. George F. Shrady, at St. Francis's Hospital, of the Patient Sent to Berlin by 'Frank Leslie's Illustrated Newspaper.'—From a Sketch by C. Bunnell." *Frank Leslie's Illustrated Newspaper,* 3 January 1891, p. 408 (the image is 10″ × 8″).

("humbug reform lymph" vs. "spoils system lymph"), but the medical metaphors used to mock them were then brand new.

When disappointing results of the tuberculin treatment started appearing in January 1891, humorists, journalists, physicians, and patients turned against Koch. *The Danbury Evening News* was typical, reporting on 23 January 1891 (the day after it heralded the delivery of five vials from Berlin to President Harrison) that people were finding Koch's lymph "a failure"; William Degan, the first American patient to be treated in Berlin, was said to believe he had derived no benefit and was in poorer health than when he went abroad.[46] On 3 February, this paper reported the death in New Haven of George M. Bradley, "the first person treated in America with Dr. Koch's lymph," and the near-death condition of "the son of Professor Blake" of Yale.[47] But another Yale professor (probably Russell Chittenden, the eminent teacher of physiological chemistry) defended the lymph as not to be judged by one extreme case. Two days later, this paper reported that a package containing lymph from Berlin had arrived in Danbury, that it would be discussed at a medical society meeting that evening, and that the lymph would be "on exhibition today at Reed & Co.'s drug store."[48]

While everything seemed so promising, most were willing to overlook Koch's reticence about the formulation of his tuberculin lymph, and his rush to treat hordes of patients without preliminary studies on a limited number. When the lymph failed to cure, and sometimes aggravated, a patient's consumption, the media and the medical profession challenged him for being mercenary as well as for having failed, and they accused him of inappropriately pursuing publicity and fame. Without admitting their own complicity in creating a sensation, papers started to offer comic put-downs like the following quip: "A Voice from the Medical Limbo.—'Hello there, Koch's lymph! I'm expecting you.'—'Who are you?'—'I'm Brown-Sequard's elixir of life."[49] And the following January, in a back-page cartoon of seven vignettes entitled "A Chapter on Cranks," the artist Emil Flohri included Dr. Koch's Lymph for Consumptives along with the Brown-Séquard Elixir of Life, Dr. Pasteur's Treatment for Rabies, and Dr. Keeley's Bichloride of Gold treatment for drunks under the rubric "Cranks who made it pay while it lasted."[50] From today's perspective, the innovations of Pasteur, Brown-Séquard, Koch, and Keeley are quite dissimilar in origin, medical value, and intellectual achievement; yet this cartoon, despite its broad brush, offers confirmation that breakthroughs were already coming to be seen by the public as a continuous series.[51]

Serum to Save Sick Children

By the summer of 1894, European results were accumulating to show that diphtheria "anti-toxine" injections sharply reduced the mortality from this frightening childhood malady.[52] Like rabies vaccine, testicular extract, and tuberculin therapy, this was an injectable biological product derived from laboratory experiments with small animals—but unlike those breakthroughs, this one earned permanent recognition by historians and the public alike as a major triumph over disease.[53] Stimulating rapid recovery in mortally ill patients, especially children, was far more dramatic than explaining illnesses or even preventing them; and this was a sudden and striking therapeutic achievement, often lowering case mortality from 50 to 15 percent.

The creation of this anti-toxine had been founded on the identification of pathogens, but it took that knowledge in a new direction by manipulating animals' immune response to create a potent biological product: blood serum (most effectively produced by horses) containing

Fig. 14. "The Rival Doctor Kochs. The Debilitated Party—'Begob, I have me own private opinion that yez are both quacks!'" by Grant Hamilton. *Judge*, 13 December 1890, back cover. (The original page is in color, 13" × 10".) Dr. Koch-Cleveland's bottle is marked "Humbug Reform Lymph—A Hypocritical Preparation," and Dr. Koch-Hill's reads "Hill's Spoils System Lymph—with Peanut Essence."

high concentrations of a diphtheria antagonist that, when injected in people, would help their bodies combat the disease. It was the result of collaboration and competition between French and German laboratories. Americans did not create the cure, but they quickly found ways to manufacture it effectively on this side of the Atlantic, and they made it their own once they had managed to secure the new levels of public funding required for its production. The pioneering effort in America was that of laboratory-based public health physicians in New York City, with other cities and commercial firms quickly following their lead.[54]

America's daily newspapers began in the summer of 1894 to print encouraging reports of European trials of the new serum treatment. In mid-September, *Harper's Weekly* editorialized on "The New Remedy for Diphtheria." This rather long and unillustrated piece established in firm and measured tones several key features that shaped the events to follow:

> A representative of the New York Board of Health has just returned from a trip abroad, made for the purpose of investigating a new German remedy that is said to be almost a certain cure for diphtheria. His report is so enthusiastic that our authorities are to be asked to establish a laboratory or the development of the remedy here. The outcome will be awaited with anxious interest by every one who truly understands how much is at stake.[55]

The second paragraph argued the special urgency of this cause with revealing numbers and a picture of definite historical progress:

> Two years ago there was much ado because typhus fever seemed to have gained a foothold in the city. That much-heralded disease caused 40 deaths; diphtheria, unheralded, caused 1436. Last year there was no little apprehension in some quarters because small-pox was mildly epidemic in the city, claiming a few victims who by their folly or ignorance had invited it. Yet small-pox during the decade 1883–'92 caused only 335 deaths in the city; diphtheria caused 15,066. Thanks to sanitary science, typhus may be held at bay. Thanks to Jenner, the terrors of small-pox are only traditional. But the terrors of diphtheria are still real and ever-present.[56]

The editorial then noted the discovery, ten years before, of the cause of diphtheria. It explained that the bacilli produce toxins, which may be developed in media other than the human body; and that toxins, when attenuated, may be injected into animals whose bodies then produce something that had now been shown to cure cases of diphtheria in humans. "If the reports are to be credited, diphtheria will soon take its place beside small-pox and hydrophobia behind the victorious chariot of preventive medicine."[57] In closing, the editor reminded readers not to let optimism go beyond actual achievement, as had sadly been the case with Koch's tuberculin. (Note the use of what was becoming a customary list of triumphs: smallpox, rabies, and diphtheria, with tuberculin as the single failure that highlighted the successes in the series.)

News reports in the dailies continued sporadically through the fall. In November, *Scientific American* published a more substantial report whose three illustrations established the leading visual elements for all the successive depictions: medical personnel injecting the remedy into the belly of a sick child (Fig. 15a), white-coated laboratory workers surrounded by flasks and tanks, and docile and dignified horses patiently receiving injections or allowing their blood to be drawn (Fig. 15b).[58] None of the participants in these scenes was identified, nor was a specific hospital, laboratory, or city named. Though generic (perhaps created by American artists merely from verbal accounts), these pictures were to become iconic.[59]

THE NEW CURE FOR DIPHTHERIA, CROUP, ETC.

THE NEW CURE FOR DIPHTHERIA, CROUP, ETC.—INJECTING THE SERUM.

Fig. 15a. "The New Cure for Diphtheria, Croup, etc.—Injecting the Serum." *Scientific American*, 17 November 1894, p. 308 (the image is 6" × 5"). This image also appeared in the *New York Herald*, 11 December 1894, p. 3, cols. 2–5; in *Review of Reviews*, January 1895, p. 4; and in *Leslie's Illustrated Weekly*, 17 January 1895, p. 46.

NOVEMBER 17, 1894.] Scientific American. 309

Dr. Roux's wonder cure. The 24 per cent represents the saving of the lives of 120 children in six months in one institution. The gain would have been more considerable but for the deplorable hygienic conditions of the Hopital des Enfants Malades. Many of the deaths, too, were a result of further complications, such as heart disease and broncho-pneumonia, which made the work of the physician very difficult. Generally speaking a single injection is sufficient, and Dr. Roux has never given more than two. The dose consists of two-fifths of amount of serum injected into the side by one puncture. The temperature then decreases, which is an excellent beginning. The leather-like membrane which is suffocating the little sufferer ceases, within twenty-fours, to increase, and after thirty-six hours it comes away altogether, and the diphtheritic bacilli disappear. The serum also has a marvelous effect on the appearance of the patient. The dull and leaden complexion, with its accompa-

the shell of the boiler, as shown in Fig. 6, the outer end of the bushing being engaged by a general steam distributing box, from which the steam is distributed by pipes to the various parts of the locomotive. In case of an accident carrying off this box from its support on the shell of the boiler, or any sudden shock to the box, the valve will be automatically seated, the steam being in every case shut off. For the whistle, for the safety valve in the top of the dome, and for the injector check valve, similar automatically working check valves are provided. The inventor has lately received a prize as a successful competitor for a design for a consolidation engine to which this system was applied.

THE NEW CURE FOR DIPHTHERIA—DRAWING THE SERUM FROM THE HORSE.

Regulation of Mineral Water Traffic.

The Academie de Medecine, of Paris, as the result of a close investigation of the trade in the so-called "natural" mineral waters of France, has arrived at the

water companies annually exporting to America, alone, millions of bottles of water in excess of the output of their springs. By a strange ruling of our customs officials, these manufactured mineral waters have been allowed for years past to come into this country as "natural waters," and thus not merely to enter into competition with our domestic products, natural and manufactured, but to "hold the age" on the latter as "the product of nature's laboratory," a fetich of great power among the unthinking multitude.

The steps suggested by the Academie, by showing the French people what poor stuff their natural waters really are, may have the effect of waking other governments up, and thus lead to legislation in this direction. If so, nothing but good can come of it.—National Druggist.

Annual Convention of the American Institute of Architects.

The twenty-eighth annual convention was held in this city, October 15, 1894, in the Fine Arts building; 105 members being present—a larger number than usual. President D. H. Burnham of Chicago delivered an interesting address, in which he deprecated the practice of showing designs to customers without payment. Other interesting papers were read and discussed. Secretary Stone read the annual report of the Board of Directors, from which it appears there is a membership of 475 fellows. There are also 26 chapters, chartered by the Institute, having an aggregate of 600 members, of which about 500 are practicing architects, and from these members the fellows are chiefly selected. The New York Chapter has the largest membership, namely 86, of which 69 are practicing members, the remainder honorary and junior. Illinois has 82 members, of which 80 are practicing. Philadelphia 55, of which 31 are practicing. The other chapters range from 8 to 20 members. The next convention meets at St. Louis. Daniel H. Burnham, of Chicago, was re-elected president; William S. Eames, St. Louis, secretary.

A CARRIAGE WRENCH.

The illustration shows a wrench more specially designed for conveniently removing the nuts on the axles of vehicles. The improvement has been patented by Mr. Julius L. Stambaugh, of Standart, Texas. Fig. 1 shows the wrench applied to the nut in the wheel hub

Fig. 15b. "The New Cure for Diphtheria—Drawing the Serum from the Horse." *Scientific American*, 17 November 1894, p. 309 (the image is 6″ × 4″). This image also appeared in the *New York Herald*, 12 December 1894, p. 3, cols. 2–5; and in *Leslie's Illustrated Weekly*, 17 January 1895, p. 46.

The stream of brief newspaper accounts widened in early December, when the *New York Herald* began an aggressive campaign in support of funding to set up the laboratory and stables needed for the production of anti-toxine. This was the newspaper that had led the pack in coverage of the Newark boys' trip to Pasteur's laboratory in Paris back in 1885. By 1894, changes in printing technology allowed daily newspapers to run pictures that were more than one column wide.[60] This had two effects: it provided a new hook for quick emotional engagement, and it made possible much larger graphics to compete with those in the heavily illustrated weeklies. On Monday, 10 December, the *Herald* published five pictures in an article that covered five columns of a six-column page. Opening this piece, a tall stack of headlines announced the issues and pumped up the excitement:

> ANTI-TOXINE FOR THE POOR.
> Popular Subscription Started by the *Herald*
> to Provide Dr. Roux's Great Remedy for Diphtheria for the Public.
>
> HEADS THE LIST WITH $1,000.
> Public Invited to Join in the Work of
> Supplying the Health Restoring Fluid.
>
> PHYSICIANS APPROVE THE PLAN.
> Drs. Curtis, Edson, Shrady, Gibier, Jacobi, and
> Loomis Indorse [sic] the *Herald*'s Enterprise.
>
> NEED OF SERUM URGENT.
> Many Lives Will Be Saved If It Can
> Be Brought Within the Reach of All.[61]

A two-column-wide portrait of Dr. Émile Roux dominated the page, supplemented by four single-column images: Professor Emil Behring, M.D.; "In the Laboratory" (a man standing at a bench covered with glassware); Dr. Cyrus Edson; and Dr. Paul Gibier.

The following day, 11 December, the *Herald*'s mass audience was presented with the sketch that had earlier been seen only by the more restricted readership of *Scientific American*: "Inoculation with Anti-toxine" (the same image as Fig. 15a here). This print was four columns wide (about 7 inches by 10) and was placed at the top of the page, next to another batch of self-promoting headlines:

> ALL EAGER FOR ANTI-TOXINE.
> Enthusiastic Support of the *Herald*'s
> Project for Manufacturing the Great Diphtheria Remedy in This Country.
>
> UNIVERSAL COMMENDATION.
> Physicians and Other Scientists Approve
> the Enterprise in Flattering Terms.
>
> IT MEANS A SAVING OF LIFE.
> Leaders in Medicine Pronounce the
> Undertaking One of Commanding Importance.
>
> OTHER CITIES APPLAUD IT.
> Prompt Assistance Means Early Success, and
> Money Is Imperatively Required.[62]

On the next day the *Herald* reprinted the horse picture from *Scientific American* (same as Fig. 15b here) over the caption "Taking the Serum from a Horse," again in four-column width at the top of the page, with headlines proclaiming "Anti-Toxine Is Greatly Needed. A Chorus of Approvals Everywhere....Physicians Greatly Hampered by Their Inability to Obtain the New Cure."[63]

We cannot here follow more fully the *Herald's* fascinating and unprecedented campaign to make this miraculous breakthrough cure available to thousands of threatened children, as we must restrict our attention to the ways in which widely published pictures—in the *Herald* and elsewhere—of the medical heroes, their laboratory-based efforts, and their compliant horses made key features of the new medicine familiar and favored in a wide segment of the public. While the media's graphics were not the only shaper of the new consciousness of medical advance that took hold in America after 1885, these resonant snapshots could remain in memory long after the particular verbal details of any day's news had faded.

The frequent reiteration of horse pictures suggests that these were especially engaging.[64] But even if horses heightened the emotionalism of the pictures, didacticism was present as well. The public was served with numerous images of serious men handling the precious serum and manipulating elaborate glassware in settings that nicely mingled hectic activity and scientific order. In some, there were impressively neat rows of flasks; in others, the important work took place on benches crowded with apparatus in less discernible order. "Separating the Serum from the Red Corpuscles of the Blood" was the caption for the *Herald's* picture on 13 December, encouraging the public's curiosity about the underlying components of an apparently homogeneous fluid.[65] Then, after three days without illustrations, the horses returned on 17 December in three new images about the preparation of the serum and care of the horses.[66] Three days later, on the 20th, a two-column picture showed five men "Inoculating a Horse at the Veterinary College."[67] Another three days, and the *Herald* printed an interior view of a generic stable with three of these noble animals and no attendants, "Horses under Treatment," in an article headlined "Life Saved by Anti-Toxine—The Remedy Reduces the Death Rate from Fifty to Fourteen Per Cent....Doctors Actively at Work—Bacteriologists Who Supervise the *Herald* Fund Busily Engaged in Producing Curative Serum."[68]

January 1895 saw the American edition of the British monthly *Review of Reviews* opening its first issue of the new year with "The Progress of the World," whose very first entry was "A New Medical Discovery"—including a portrait sketch of "Professor Roux, Discoverer of Anti-toxine," and "Inoculating a Diphtheria Patient," an (uncredited) reprint of the child's inoculation that had appeared in Scientific American (Fig. 15a above) in mid-November and in the *Herald* in mid-December.[69] The latter picture was to be published again shortly in *Leslie's Illustrated Weekly* on 17 January, where it was joined by the horse providing serum (Fig. 15b above), likewise printed earlier in both *Scientific American* and the *Herald*.[70] *Harper's Weekly* opened the new year with a full-page article and four pictures on 5 January 1895 (Fig. 16).[71] These are the last major graphics for this episode, and they point, perhaps unknowingly, toward the dominant iconography of the future: the long-familiar engravings from artists' sketches that had dominated popular pictorial media for decades—Winslow Homer, Frederick Remington, and Thomas Nast virtually defined the Victorian newsmagazine's visual style—were here replaced by unsigned photographs. While photography was not entirely new in these magazines in 1895, it was beginning to achieve a clarity and power that would eventually dominate reportorial images and magazine covers. (For several decades, artist-illustrators did manage to hold their own in advertising and cover art—think of J.C. Leyendecker with his

HOW ANTITOXINES ARE DEVELOPED.

The new treatment of diphtheria is a practical application of the latest advances of experimental bacteriology. The general facts upon which it is based are briefly these: Certain bacteria, when developing in the organism of an animal or man, produce an albuminoid poison called a toxine, which, circulating in the blood, causes disease. For example, the Klebs-Lœffler bacillus growing in the throat of a child, generates a toxine that produces the systemic condition called diphtheria.

If some of these bacteria be removed from the organism and placed in artificial media, such as broth, under proper conditions they will grow and multiply and produce the same toxine as before. This toxine may now be separated from the bacteria by filtration, and if introduced into an organism by inoculation it will produce the disease as readily as if it had been formed in the organism. But the virulence of the disease thus produced will vary with the quantity of the toxine injected. Moreover, if the first dose given is so small as to produce only slight illness, a larger quantity may be introduced a few days later without producing a corresponding effect; and progressively larger doses may be administered from time to time, until at last the animal receives with impunity doses many times larger than could possibly be borne at first.

In the case of the diphtheria toxine, for example (obtained, as has been said, by growing the diphtheria bacillus in meat broth), if fifteen drops of the filtrate containing the toxine be injected into a vein of a horse, the animal will be severely poisoned. But by repeating the injection from time to time in progressing doses, at the end of three or four months the animal will bear a dose of two hundred times the original quantity. In other words, the animal has become immune to the disease.

If now a vein of the immune animal be opened and some blood withdrawn, the serum of that blood (the other constituents being removed) may be injected into the system of another animal or a human being without ill effect, and the animal or human being thus inoculated becomes immune to the disease in virtue of the inoculation. More than that, if the organism inoculated had already acquired the disease, the inoculation, within reasonable limits, is curative. For example, if a child has been exposed to diphtheria, inoculation with the serum of a horse rendered immune to diphtheria as above described will prevent development of the disease. At a later stage inoculation tends to cure the disease.

These are the facts as applied to the new serum treatment of diphtheria.

Exactly what happens in the system of the animal during the process of its becoming immune no one at present knows. The toxine as it is injected is in some way rendered harmless, but whether by transformation of the toxine itself, or by the secretion of an antidotal substance, is still in doubt. The latter hypothesis seems to most investigators more probable.

But in either case it is convenient to speak of the antidotal substance which the serum of the immune animal contains as an antitoxine. This word, like its antithesis toxine, is a generic term. There are as many toxines and antitoxines of this series as there are forms of germ disease, though most of them have been but little investigated.

[illegible]

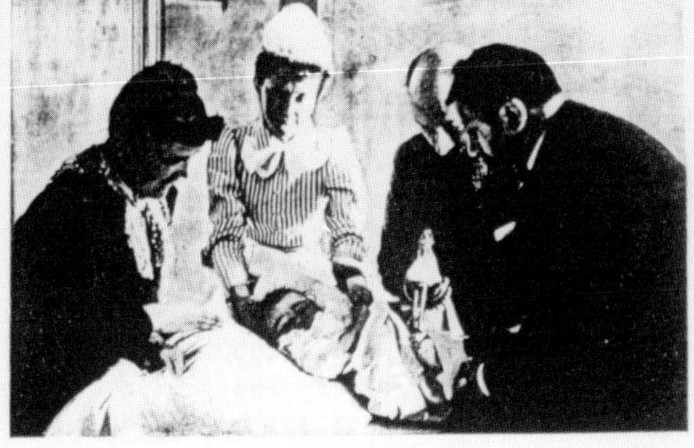

INOCULATING A CHILD WITH ANTITOXINE

INCUBATOR CONTAINING [illegible] ERLENMEYER FLASKS
[illegible]

PASTEUR INSTITUTE, WHERE ANTITOXINE IS MADE, IN NEW YORK.

[illegible]

Fig. 16. Henry Smith Williams, M.D., "How Antitoxines Are Developed." *Harper's Weekly*, 5 January 1895, p. 8 (the page is 10″ × 15″).

Arrow-shirt-collar men or Norman Rockwell with his all-American folks.) Three of the *Harper's* photographs used the new medium to capture very familiar scenes: male physicians inoculating a child, with a female nurse's assistance; ordered ranks of Erlenmeyer flasks (given their formal name); and a laboratory worker among flasks, tanks, and sterilizing equipment. The fourth image also was very traditional in appearance, just a six-story building of undistinguished architecture, but its caption revealed how innovative it was: "Pasteur Institute Where Antitoxine Is Made in New York." This five-year-old organization, headed by Dr. Paul Gibier, had taken not only its name from the creator of the rabies breakthrough, but also its purpose: the ongoing production of fresh biological material used in the rabies treatment. When the need arose to manufacture diphtheria anti-toxine by a similar biological method, Gibier's institute had the infrastructure already in place to supply some of the first anti-toxine in America.[72]

As we have seen, the popular pictorial materials connected with the introduction of diphtheria anti-toxine largely continued the features established in the preceding breakthrough episodes. But there was one difference: humor seems to have been completely absent. While news drawings and magazine photographs had become even more numerous than before, the usual cartoons, caricatures, and jokes about the latest sensation disappeared for a while.[73] This change was not permanent, however, for in less than two years the discovery of ways to produce X-ray pictures of the body's interior would draw delighted humorists back into the business of toying with the latest medical breakthrough. The American media's fascination with X rays in early 1896 also illustrates how the pictorial dimensions of the medical breakthrough would persist even as the instances proliferated. The X-ray story is not included here because it has received more scholarly attention than these first four episodes, and a number of its images have been reproduced in other studies.[74]

Publicity, Public Attitudes, and the Image of a New Kind of Medicine

By early 1895, a family magazine of middle-class leisure time was calmly discoursing about toxins, anti-toxines, incubators, Erlenmeyer flasks, autoclaves to sterilize chicken broth for colonies of diphtheria microbes to feed upon, and serum extracted from horses. It was also inviting readers to admire (and perhaps to consider supporting) a substantial building devoted exclusively to this new kind of life-saving work. The daily papers, reaching farther down the range of social class than the weeklies, showed many of the same images and used the same vocabulary, although they worked more horses into the visual mix. This was historically a new vocabulary, drawn more from the laboratory than from the clinic, based on the mid-century achievements of cell theory and bacteriology and their powerful offspring, germ theory and immunology. Much of it was more than ten years old, but it had achieved its new visibility and social power from the intense enthusiasm connected with breakthroughs in just the few years since the rabies announcement of 1885. It seems likely that this enthusiasm for innovative therapeutic interventions may have had a wider and deeper effect on American culture than just making people familiar with new kinds of injections for hydrophobia, consumption, and diphtheria. Research itself had become visible; medical innovation was now a public thrill.

Published materials like the graphics examined above can take us only part of the way toward an understanding of what the public thought. Even if these publications shaped public attitudes, they cannot, by themselves, reveal people's thoughts and feelings; yet the limitation inherent in such evidence may be overcome when it is complemented by more private sources, such as letters and diaries—or by people's actions. For this reason it is useful to glance back for a moment and observe that within the cases examined above, at least a few such actions are documented. Since thousands of people paid admission fees to enter a museum or a theater to see Pasteur in wax or Pasteur's patients in the flesh, we can discern with confidence a mass involvement in the rabies vaccine excitement. When hundreds, perhaps thousands, of individuals mailed in their contributions to the newspaper campaigns, first to send the Newark boys to Paris, and then to establish diphtheria-serum production facilities, they made concrete the effects of the articles and pictures. When twelve thousand physicians were injecting patients with an animal-testicle extract of questionable safety and value within eighteen months of its introduction, they were responding to an irresistible popular enthusiasm for the newest production of the medical laboratory (and this in an era when some people hesitated to accept vaccination for smallpox because it employed lymph taken from a calf!).

These episodes of popular excitement about medical advances (or apparent advances) have not received much attention in the standard accounts of nineteenth- and early-twentieth-century American medicine, perhaps because the discoveries that garnered the headlines often lacked the intellectual significance that most historians have used as the criterion for medical landmarks. But in neglecting these episodes, scholars may have overlooked a significant mechanism by which the general public came to replace an attitude of cynical disdain about medicine's pretensions with an unalloyed enthusiasm and a passion for more and bigger discoveries. While historians have recognized for some time that around the turn of this century the medical profession rose to cultural and social authority, a change best described in the brilliant synthesis of Paul Starr's *The Social Transformation of American Medicine*, Starr and others have provided only a rather general sense of the role played by science in bringing this about.[75] The specific breakthroughs whose imagery has been documented here seem likely to have been crucial stimuli of public acclaim for medicine. Additionally, they help us picture what kind of science played this role, what the general public got excited about, when the shift occurred, and which particular features of medical research were prominent in the transition. While the general public's new enthusiasm in the 1880s and 1890s for sudden, headline-grabbing therapeutic advances was not the only factor in establishing the broad cultural authority that medicine held for most of the twentieth century, it deserves a place of recognition alongside such factors as the rise in medical philanthropy (which it helped to promote), the expansion of knowledge in physiology and other basic medical sciences, and the general expansion of the profession's surgical and therapeutic powers.

In any analysis of the penetration of the news about useful discoveries into mass culture, the particular role of widely disseminated graphic images must be paramount. Photographs and cartoons ensured that the headlines were more memorable and gave the ideas and attitudes a purchase that was not available to the more mundane expositions of teachers, schoolbook writers, or popularizers of science. While the portrayal of these matters in the popular press did not mean that they were comprehended or valued by all members of the public, or even by all members of the medical profession, it did mean that public awareness of laboratory science in medicine, of medical advance, and of therapeutic success had been planted and was taking root. With each new success came new pictures of medicine and new expectations—and the American public never saw medicine in the same old way again.

An early version of this study was presented at the seventieth annual meeting of the American Association for the History of Medicine, Williamsburg, Virginia, 5 April 1997. I wish to acknowledge the assistance and suggestions of many colleagues, especially Kenneth L. Caneva, Ronald J. Fasano, Evelynn M. Hammonds, William H. Helfand, Jean Howson, Adele A. Lerner, Howard Markel, Ronald L. Numbers, and Charles E. Rosenberg.

It is a pleasure also to acknowledge several forms of support for my research: a Eugene M. Lang Junior-Faculty Research Fellowship; funding from the PSC-CUNY Awards Program; released time from the George and Mildred Weissman School of Arts and Sciences of Baruch College; and residence at the Institute for Advanced Study, Princeton, N.J. All illustrations except for figures 6, 8, and 11 are the property of the author.

Endnotes

1. William G. Rothstein, "When Did a Random Patient Benefit from a Random Physician: Introduction and Historical Background," *Caduceus* 12, 3 (1996): 2–8, quotation on page 3. The special section of the journal, "When Did a Random Patient Benefit from a Random Physician," was edited by Rothstein and contains six brief but perceptive essays on the question, its significance, and possible answers to it. In addition to Rothstein (introduction), the contributors are Rosemary Stevens (technology and institutions), Dale C. Smith (surgery), Steven J. Peitzman (internal medicine), John Parascandola (drug therapy), and Gerald N. Grob (psychiatry). Most place the shift solidly after 1900, with Parascandola locating it after World War II. While this question, along with an answer of 1910 or 1912, has long been attributed to Lawrence J. Henderson, it has not been documented in his writings.
2. *Judge*, 12 December 1885, 2.
3. *Judge*, 2 January 1886, 10.
4. Charles E. Rosenberg, "The Therapeutic Revolution: Medicine, Meaning, and Social Change in Nineteenth-Century America," in *The Therapeutic Revolution: Essays in the Social History of American Medicine*, ed. Morris J. Vogel and Charles E. Rosenberg (Philadelphia, 1979), 3–25.
5. For an extended account, see Bert Hansen, "America's First Medical Breakthrough: How Popular Excitement about a French Rabies Cure in 1885 Raised New Expectations for Medical Progress," *Am. Hist. Rev.* 103 (1998): 373–418. The Pasteur section below recapitulates only those features of the story essential for understanding its pictorial documents and the momentum it generated for the breakthroughs that followed.
6. On the cholera germ, see William Coleman, "Koch's Comma Bacillus: The First Year," *Bull. Hist. Med.* 61 (1987): 315–42. Similarly, Pasteur's anthrax triumph garnered little press, even though twentieth-century accounts often imply that it received substantial coverage and much popular interest. Even in France, it received relatively little attention in newspapers, contrary to what is implied by the title of a recent study by Massimiano Bucchi, "The Public Science of Louis Pasteur: The Experiment on Anthrax Vaccine in the Popular Press of the Time," *History and Philosophy of the Life Sciences* 19 (1997): 181–209. Mass culture's invasion by certain medical ideas has been elegantly chronicled in Nancy Tomes, *The Gospel of Germs: Men, Women, and the Microbe in American Life* (Cambridge, 1998). Important insights about certain aspects of public reactions to laboratory medicine are found in Susan E. Lederer, *Subjected to Science: Human Experimentation in America Before the Second World War* (Baltimore, 1995).
7. A number of scholars have explored the place of science in American medicine; see especially essays in Vogel and Rosenberg (n. 4 above), and John Harley Warner, "The History of Science and the Sciences of Medicine," *Osiris* 10 (1995): 164–93, especially pages 178–83. Also important are several other works by Warner: "The Fall and Rise of Professional Mystery: Epistemology, Authority, and the Emergence of Laboratory Medicine in Nineteenth-Century America," in *The Laboratory Revolution in Medicine*, eds. Andrew Cunningham and Perry Williams (Cambridge, 1992), 110–41; "Ideals of Science and Their Discontents in Late Nineteenth-Century American Medicine," *Isis* 82 (1991): 454–78; *The Therapeutic Perspective: Medical Practice, Knowledge, and Identity in America, 1820–1885* (Cambridge, 1986; reprinted, Princeton, 1997); *Against the Spirit of System: The French Impulse in Nineteenth-Century American Medicine* (Princeton, 1998). While W. F. Bynum's *Science and the Practice of Medicine in the*

Nineteenth Century (Cambridge, 1994) intentionally directs its focus more to Europe than America, it nonetheless provides an effective overview of relevant material and offers perceptive attention to the popular press and the public face of medicine.

8. John Harley Warner, preface to the 1997 edition, *The Therapeutic Perspective* (n. 7 above), ix.
9. That the profession at times exhibited more skepticism about highly touted unfamiliar therapies than did the public (which was normally skeptical about the profession's therapies in general) has been noted by others. For example, Susan E. Lederer observed of the medical profession that "like antiseptic surgery, rabies vaccine and virtually all bacteriological claims in this period, the introduction of [diphtheria] anti-toxin was muddied by initial scepticism and disillusionment. In the case of diphtheria, the complex aetiology of the disease process and the disappointment just three years earlier of Koch's tuberculin cure hindered the acceptance of the anti-toxin by the medical profession" ("The Controversy over Animal Experimentation in America, 1880–1914," in *Vivisection in Historical Perspective*, ed. Nicolaas A. Rupke (London, 1987), 236–58, specifically page 242). In France, a similar picture emerges; for example, in a rich examination of how the bacteriological revolution was played out both in the profession and in the general population, Evelyn Bernette Ackerman observed that "popular eagerness about diphtheria antitoxin was much more immediate and much less nuanced than medical response" (*Health Care in the Parisian Countryside, 1800–1914* (New Brunswick, NJ, 1990), 99).
10. John A. Kouwenhoven, *The Columbia Historical Portrait of New York: An Essay in Graphic History in Honor of the Tricentennial of New York City and the Bicentennial of Columbia University* (Garden City, NY, 1953), 11. On the use of comic art, see also Thomas Milton Kemnitz, "The Cartoon as a Historical Source," *J. Interdiscip. Hist.* 4,1 (1973): 81–93. An important recent study of late-nineteenth-century news illustrations and readership is Joshua Brown, "Reconstructing Representation: Social Types, Readers, and the Pictorial Press, 1865–1877," *Rad. Hist. Rev.* 66 (Fall 1996): 5–38. See also Marianne Doezema, "The Clean Machine: Technology in American Magazine Illustration," *J. Am. Cult.* 11, 4 (1988): 73–92.
11. For images of this sort from the period before 1870, see the 125 figures in William H. Helfand, *Medicine and Pharmacy in American Political Prints (1765–1870)* (Madison, WI, 1978). For the decades following 1860, a brief introduction to pictorial satire and propaganda related to public health is offered in Bert Hansen, "The Image and Advocacy of Public Health in American Caricature and Cartoons from 1860 to 1900," *Am. J. Pub. Health* 87 (1997): 1798–1807. In the public health cartoons, however, physicians are not usually portrayed as heroic, but rather as neglectful, negligent, or evil. For an especially perceptive essay, see the opening chapter, "How and Why Do Historians of Medicine Use or Ignore Images in Writing Their Histories?," of Sander L. Gilman, *Picturing Health and Illness: Images of Identity and Difference* (Baltimore, 1995), chap. 1, 9–32.
12. The microscope's increasing employment by the profession has been observed by historians, but its chronology has not been traced with more quantitative precision than assigning it generally to the 1880s or 1890s. Joel D. Howell observed that "only a small minority" of physicians used it in 1879 (*Technology and American Medical Practice, 1880–1930: An Anthology of Sources* (New York, 1988), 63). Prior to the 1880s, the microscope was much more popular among laymen than among physicians, as John Harley Warner has shown in "'Exploring the Inner Labyrinths of Creation': Popular Microscopy in Nineteenth-Century America," *J. Hist. Med. Allied Sci.* 37 (1982): 7–33; see especially pages 19 and 30 for change after the late 1880s. For the situation at mid-century, see also James H. Cassedy, "The Microscope in American Medical Science, 1840–1860," *Isis* 67 (1976): 76–97; and Deborah Jean Warner, "The Campaign for Medical Microscopy in Antebellum America," *Bull. Hist. Med.* 69 (1995): 367–86. On its relatively limited use by physicians even later in the century, see a variety of comments in *The Education of American Physicians: Historical Essays*, ed. Ronald L. Numbers (Berkeley, 1980). In 1881, it was not useful in practice (p. 35); prior to 1870, there was some use in medical schools (p. 59); and in 1840s and 1850s, it made its entrance into various branches of medicine (pp. 131–32). The famous advice book by D. W. Cathell refers to a practitioner's microscope as an aid to precision recognizable by patients and describes it as one of the instruments that improve a patient's confidence in the physician: *The Physician Himself and What He Should Add to His Scientific Acquirements*, 3d ed. (Baltimore, 1883), 11, 18. But as late as 1884, when William Osler first held the chair of clinical medicine at the University of Pennsylvania, his personal microscope was the only one in use at the University Hospital; see George T.

Harrell, "Osler's Practice," *Bull. Hist. Med.* 47 (1973): 545–68, especially page 550.

13. Examples of contemporary news pictures of group vaccinations in public are found in *Harper's Weekly* (6 May 1871, 16 March 1872, and 28 October 1893) and in *Frank Leslie's Illustrated Newspaper* (19 April 1879, 14 May 1881, and 19 November 1881). *Puck* offered a full-color centerfold cartoon on 24 June 1885 (pp. 264–65), by Joseph Keppler: "Scientists know that all diseases can be prevented by inoculation. Now, my friends, step right up and be vaccinated for all forms of disease to which bank officials are liable."
14. Joseph Meister, who received injections in July 1885, was the first; Meister's "cure" and the recent vaccination of Jupille were announced by Pasteur in the same late-October report. Meister and Jupille have long been regarded in all accounts as the first and second patients to receive this novel and untried remedy. Only recently did an examination of Pasteur's private notebooks by Gerald L. Geison reveal that Pasteur and his physician collaborators tried some form of rabies therapy on two earlier patients in May and June 1885: *The Private Science of Louis Pasteur* (Princeton, 1995), 195–205. The existence of these earlier cases raises important questions about how accurately Pasteur discussed his work at the time, but it does not change the significance of the two public patients who received the full series of injections that became standard procedure. Additionally, my examination of American newspapers turned up a lengthy account of what would be—if true—a third pre-Meister patient: see "Pasteur's Sure Success; His Hydrophobia Discoveries Put to the Test; Report of the Commission Sustaining Him; Some of His Methods; Work on a Human Subject," *New York Times*, 26 August 1884. 3. (with a related editorial on page 4). Given the early date for such a treatment, I assume that this unsigned article with a dateline of Paris, 13 August, is either fortuitously prescient fiction or a hoax—or perhaps a faithful transmission of some European fiction or hoax.
15. All nineteenth-century magazines and weekly papers are cited herein by the "cover date" of the issue. But with respect to priority issues and for establishing a day-by-day narrative, it must be kept in mind that weeklies were printed earlier and were sometimes available to readers as much as seven or eight days before the cover date; this means that a magazine image might appear to follow a daily's story while in fact preceding it. This image of Jupille was also published in *Scientific American*, 19 December 1885, 391—the same day that it appeared in *Harper's Weekly*. In the United States, it had previously appeared in the *New York Daily Graphic*, 19 November 1885, 4. The cover date for *L'Illustration*, the French source of these reprints, was 7 November 1885.
16. I am giving here the simple picture presented in Pasteur's public statements and the early authorized accounts. The recent scholarship of Gerald Geison gives us a far more complex picture of Pasteur's thinking, research, and practice; see Geison (n. 14 above), chaps. 7–9. Since the more accurate version of events that Geison has uncovered was not known in the 1880s, however, only the traditional picture is relevant to my examination of the public's response in the nineteenth century.
17. For more on the varied American engagements with Pasteur's hydrophobia discovery, see Hansen, (n. 5 above).
18. *New York Herald*, 22 December 1885, 2.
19. *New York Tribune*, 9 January 1886, 7.
20. Modern historians and epidemiologists, knowing how infrequent an ailment hydrophobia was, may hesitate to accord the Pasteurian preventive treatment the landmark character that the public gave it in the 1880s: in a large city of that era, the annual mortality from rabies was usually ten or fewer, while deaths from tuberculosis and the other major killers were measured in the tens of thousands. But in the late nineteenth century, medical professionals and ordinary citizens alike knew that the cities were filled with stray dogs, that dog bites were all too common (especially among children), and that—in the absence of any quick and accurate diagnostic test—every single dog bite prompted fear and panic about possibly facing a horrible death in a month or so, even if the wounds healed quickly.
21. The Pasteur Institutes in the United States were independent of each other and of the institute in Paris, unlike those in the network of roughly thirty French-founded institutes around the world. Few historians seem even to have noticed the American organizations, and fewer still have examined any aspect of their activity in print. There is no full account. For references to published and unpublished studies, see Hansen (n. 5 above), 407–8.
22. See "The Boys Who Were Bitten. More Than $1,000 Subscribed to Send Them to Paris. The Views of

Dr. Billings on Cauterization for Mad Dog Bites. The Boys Go Aboard the Steamship Canada This Afternoon," *New York Sun*, 8 December 1885, 1; "The Children's Farewell. Dr. Pasteur's Little Patients Sail on the Steamer Canada. They Bid Good-By to America with Tears in Their Eyes—Dr. Billings Accompanies Them, and Promises to Take Every Care of Them—One of the Dogs Shows Symptoms of Hydrophobia," *New York World*, 10 December 1885, 5; and an unsigned editorial, *New York Evening Post*, 10 December 1885, 2 ("We do not always agree with the Sun, as our readers know, on public questions, but justice compels us to call attention to the fact that it had what is called in journalism a 'clean beat,' as against its rival, the World").

23. *New York Daily Graphic*, 19 December 1885, 1; and 3 January 1886, 4. The full cover and the sketch of the Newark scientists inoculating a rabbit are reproduced in Hansen (n. 5 above), 392, 394.
24. G.E. Ciani, "The Profession Gone Mad," *Puck*, 13 January 1886, 314. This cartoon is reprinted in Hansen (n. 5 above), 402.
25. Fig. 9 shows just the middle section of a large centerfold image measuring 13 x 19 inches. A highly reduced black-and-white photograph of the entire caricature is reproduced in Hansen (n. 5 above), 400.
26. *Monthly Catalogue of the Eden Musee* (New York, August 1886), 29 (emphasis added). The Pasteur group was placed in the Museum's Central Hall. I am very grateful to Fred and Margaret Whitaker of Pine Bush, NY, for kindly sending me a photocopy of pages from this rare catalog.
27. Brown-Séquard was born a British subject of an American father and French mother; he later became a French citizen. On this episode, see Newell Dunbar, "The Elixir of Life." *Dr. Brown-Sequard's Own Account of His Famous Alleged Remedy for Debility and Old Age, Dr. Variot's Experiments...To Which Is Prefixed a Sketch of Dr. Brown-Sequard's Life, with Portrait* (Boston, 1889); J.M.D. Olmsted, *Charles-Edouard Brown-Sequard: A Nineteenth-Century Neurologist and Endocrinologist* (Baltimore, 1946), 205-39; Merriley Borell, "Brown-Séquard's Organotherapy and Its Appearance in America at the End of the Nineteenth Century," *Bull. Hist. Med.* 50 (1976): 309–20; Michael J. Aminoff, *Brown-Séquard: A Visionary of Science* (New York, 1993), 163–73.
28. *Sci. Am. Suppl.*, 10 August 1889, 11347–48. Even the editorial directing *Scientific American* readers to the Supplement's translation cannot forgo sly puns about the potent attractions of such a treatment: "The number of elderly people who are anxious to be made young and happy again is almost countless, and there is likely to be an epidemic of desire among them to try the new medicine" (p. 80).
29. For example, "Doctors Who Disagree: The Brown-Séquard Elixir Divides the Medical Profession," *New York Times*, 23 August 1889, 2; "Another Victim of the Elixir," *New York Times*, 3 September 1889, 1.
30. *Frank Leslie's Illustrated Newspaper*, 24 August 1889, 39.
31. "The Elixir of Life," *North Am. Rev.*, September 1889, 257–64. For more on Hammond's scientific and commercial work in organotherapy, see Bonnie Ellen Blustein, *Preserve Your Love for Science: Life of William A. Hammond, American Neurologist* (Cambridge, 1991).
32. The figures in the center are Charles A. Dana (with a tag to identify him as owner–editor of the *New York Sun*) and Joseph Pulitzer (proprietor of the *New York World*, apparently recognizable without a label), who have brought the Democratic Party (see tag on the tiger's tail) in for Doctor Randall's protectionism treatment. (By chance, Randall died at age sixty-two in April 1890, less than a year after this cartoon appeared.) At the right, "Free Trade" is being carried in by two men coming from the U.S. Capitol, visible behind them in the doorway: Roger Quarles Mills, congressman (later senator) from Texas, and Henry Watterson, editor of the *Louisville Courier-Journal*. Watterson, not "Waterson"—Is the misspelling a further joke on this fellow editor?—was an aggressive advocate of free-trade ideas. Biographical information on political figures, here and elsewhere, comes from the *Dictionary of American Biography and Appletons' Cyclopaedia of American Biography*, eds. James Grant Wilson and John Fiske, 7 vols. (New York, 1887–1900).
33. G. Archie Stockwell, "The Brown-Sequard Discovery," *Sci. Am. Suppl.*, 19 October 1889, 11509–10. A further indication of popularity is the 1889 publication of a song-sheet in Chicago and Cincinnati, entitled "Brown-Sequard's Elixir: The Greatest Comic Song of the Day," words and music by J. Winchell Forbes. I wish to thank William Helfand for sharing with me a copy of this song.
34. Olmsted (n. 27 above), 209.
35. Koch proposed the use of his tuberculin lymph in 1890 exclusively as a therapy; its value as a diagnostic test became apparent only later, thanks to observations made incidentally on the first cohorts of patients.

36. See David Leibowitz, "Scientific Failure in an Age of Optimism: Public Reaction to Robert Koch's Tuberculin Cure," *New York State J. Med.* 93 (1993): 41–8 (this is a revised version of the essay for which Leibowitz received the Osler Medal of the American Association for the History of Medicine in May 1987; as a first-year medical student, Leibowitz undertook research on this topic under my supervision in the summer of 1985); see p. 43 for the image of Koch as St. George. On the tuberculin story in America more generally, see Thomas D. Brock, *Robert Koch: A Life in Medicine and Bacteriology* (Madison, WI, 1988); Mark Caldwell, *The Last Crusade: The War on Consumption, 1862–1954* (New York, 1988); and Georgina D. Feldberg, *Disease and Class: Tuberculosis and the Shaping of Modern North American Society* (New Brunswick, NJ, 1995). The Rare Book Room of the New York Academy of Medicine Library, New York, NY, holds a contemporary, but anonymous, scrapbook of newspaper clippings about the first several weeks of this episode (labeled "Koch's Tuberculin"). Leibowitz first discovered this item in the Library's general stacks and called it to my attention. It was given to the Academy by a Miss Prudden, possibly a niece of T. Mitchell Prudden—a leading public health physician in New York City, who could well have made such a compilation.
37. For his preliminary examination of the Danbury materials, I wish to acknowledge Mark C. Young, who prepared a research paper on the subject in December 1988 for a graduate history of medicine course that I taught in the Department of History, New York University. My own further research on this paper's stories was made possible through the courtesy of the Connecticut State Library, and I am grateful for their gracious loan of microfilms. I also wish to thank the interlibrary-loan staff of the Newman Library of Baruch College for their steadfast assistance with numerous requests.
38. "Away with Koch's Lymph," *Medical News*, 6 June 1891, 625.
39. A small version of this portrait appeared in the *Danbury Evening News*, 22 November 1890, 1.
40. "The Prevention and Cure of Consumption: Dr. Koch's Great Discovery," *Frank Leslie's Illustrated Newspaper*, 13 December 1890, 349; the associated article, "A Visit to Dr. Koch," appears on page 353. The same portrait had been used six years earlier in *Harper's Weekly*, 30 August 1884, 563. In 1890, it was republished in *Harper's Weekly*, 29 November 1890, 932, to illustrate the article "Dr. Koch and His Great Work" by Amos W. Wright on page 934 (with a related editorial, "Dr. Koch's Discovery," on page 923). A week later the portrait and the laboratory scene appeared together in "Cure of Consumption: An Interview with Professor Koch by Dr. Charles Hacks in *L'Illustration*," *Sci. Am.*, 6 December 1890, 358–59; since this article was a translation from the report in a French weekly, *L'Illustration*, this was perhaps the source of the American versions of the scene in *Scientific American*, *Frank Leslie's*, and the *New York Herald* of 16 January 1891. This portrait also appeared (in reverse, it seems) in *Illustrated London News* 97 (1890): 688, according to Kenneth Chew and Anthony Wilson, Victorian Science and Engineering Portrayed in the *Illustrated London News* (Dover, NH, 1993), 31. Small sketches of two pipettes, a bottle of lymph, "The Needle," and "The Injection" (into the back of a seated patient) ran in the *New York Herald*, 28 December 1890, 23.
41. "The Koch Treatment for Consumption: The Patient Sent to Berlin by Frank Leslie's *Illustrated Newspaper* Operated upon by Professor Ewald, at the Augusta Hospital, Drawn Expressly for the Newspaper by Werner Zehme, Berlin," *Frank Leslie's Illustrated Newspaper*, 21 February 1891, 47. This engraving is reproduced in Leibowitz (n. 36 above), 44.
42. The image appeared in a cluster of illustrations under the rubric "Pictorial Spirit of Leading Foreign Events," *Frank Leslie's Illustrated Newspaper*, 27 December 1890, 400.
43. This image is reproduced in Leibowitz (n. 36 above), 45.
44. Ten years earlier, Thomas Edison's neuralgia remedy, Polyform, had been mocked in the same magazine by the same artist in a centerfold cartoon: "The Decadence of the Wizard of Menlo Park—From the Phonograph to Polyform," *Puck*, 5 May 1880, 150–51. Joseph Keppler did not invent the wizard appellation: It first appeared in the *New York Daily Graphic* in 1878, according to Wyn Wachhorst, *Thomas Alva Edison: An American Myth* (Cambridge, 1981), 19, and it was still in current use in the 1890s when the cover image from the 10 January 1891 issue of *Frank Leslie's Illustrated Newspaper* was reprinted on coated stock for separate distribution as "Thomas A. Edison: The Wizard of Menlo Park." Wachhorst explains that Polyform was a mixture of morphine, chloroform, ether, chloral hydrate, alcohol, and spices (p. 32).
45. Grover Cleveland was currently out of office, having been defeated in his bid for reelection as president

in 1888; he would be elected to that office again in 1892. David B. Hill was governor of New York State and would be Cleveland's rival for the Democratic nomination in 1892.

46. *Danbury Evening News*, 23 January 1891, 1.
47. *Danbury Evening News*, 3 February 1891, 8.
48. *Danbury Evening News*, 5 February 1891, 4.
49. *Judge*, 17 January 1891, 267.
50. *Judge*, 9 January 1892, 34. In the cartoon, these labels appear on four large bottles standing on the floor, each in front of a man holding a huge hypodermic syringe. The fourth therapy mocked here is an injectable treatment for alcoholism, popularized in the 1890s across the country by an Illinois physician, Dr. Leslie E. Keeley, who offered his bichloride of gold solution first in Dwight, IL, and established residential hospitals to provide the treatment. Keeley's reputation was made nationally after it caught the interest, enthusiasm, and financial support of the temperance-minded editor of the *Chicago Tribune*, Joseph Medill; see Lloyd Wendt, *Chicago Tribune: The Rise of a Great American Newspaper* (Chicago, 1979), 303. Reports on the cure also appeared in *Harper's Weekly*, 3 October 1891, 755–56, and in the *New York Times* (about a dozen items between October 1891 and November 1892). On 18 October 1891, the *Times* devoted four full columns to "The Claims of Dr. Keeley" (p. 17). See also a series of six essays, both pro and con, under the rubric "Is Drunkenness Curable?" in three issues of the *North American Review*, September, October, and December 1891, opening with an article by William A. Hammond and closing with a reply by Keeley. The gold cure came to be widely advertised, including regular placements in *Harper's Weekly*. The *Judge* cartoon cited here was not the only time Keeley's gold cure appeared in a popular satire.
51. There are further indications that contemporaries were beginning to recognize a series. In 1889, for example, an unsigned editorial in the *Medical Age* (a Detroit paper published by George S. Davis and edited by R.W. Palmer) indicated approval of Brown-Séquard ("the claims of a scientist of world-wide reputation, made upon the strength of nearly a quarter of a century of careful honest experimentation") by condemning the rabies vaccine ("the weather-cock assertions of Pasteur, unsupported as they were, and are, by evidence, and based upon no tangible scientific fact"); this writer also acknowledged the press's role: "It is sad to think that the gentleman to whom we are most indebted for our advance in neuropathology and physiology should be the subject of ribald jests, while the emanations of the Laboratorie [sic] de Rage, based upon experiments of one day, entirely divested of control, are eagerly snapped up the day following, loudly heralded and widely disseminated" (*Medical Age*, 26 August 1889, 372). Then in 1890, when *Frank Leslie's Illustrated Newspaper* editorialized on the importance of Koch's consumption cure, the writer harked back to the Brown-Séquard elixir (6 December 1890, 326). By 1894, the series was well established, and references back to the earlier breakthroughs were becoming routine.
52. Since most of the primary sources from that era use the spelling anti-toxine, I will here adopt that now-obsolete form (instead of using antitoxin, the usual form today) in order to minimize distracting variations between quotations and my writing.
53. In the twentieth century, two exceedingly popular and dramatic accounts were chapter 6 ("Roux and Behring: Massacre the Guinea Pigs") of Paul De Kruif, *Microbe Hunters* (New York, 1926; frequently reprinted, as recently as 1996); and the diphtheria episode in the Oscar-winning Hollywood film about salvarsan directed by William Dieterle, *Dr. Ehrlich's Magic Bullet* (1940, with Edward G. Robinson and others).
54. A recent article by Paul Weindling tells the international scientific story and cites further literature: "From Medical Research to Clinical Practice: Serum Therapy for Diphtheria in the 1890s," in *Medical Innovations in Historical Perspective*, ed. John V. Pickstone (New York, 1992), 72–83. On the importance of the press and the public in Hermann Biggs's diphtheria campaign, the pioneering examination is Jean Howson, "'Sure Cure for Diphtheria': Medicine and the New York Newspapers in 1894" (unpublished graduate course paper, History Department, New York University, 1986). See also David Anthony Blancher, "Workshops of the Bacteriological Revolution: A History of the Laboratories of the New York City Department of Health, 1892–1912" (Ph.D. thesis, The City University of New York, 1979); and esp. Evelynn M. Hammonds, "The Search for Perfect Control: A Social History of Diphtheria, 1880–1930" (Ph.D. thesis, History of Science Department, Harvard University, 1993). Recent published accounts include Terra Ziporyn, *Disease in the Popular American Press: The Case of*

Diphtheria, Typhoid Fever, and Syphilis, 1870–1920 (Westport, CT, 1988); and Elizabeth Fee and Evelynn M. Hammonds, "Science, Politics, and the Art of Persuasion: Promoting the New Scientific Medicine in New York City," in *Hives of Sickness: Public Health and Epidemics in New York City*, ed. David Rosner (New Brunswick, NJ, 1995), 155–96. Hammonds's book, *Childhood's Deadly Scourge: The Campaign to Control Diphtheria in New York City, 1880–1930*, (Baltimore, 1999), appeared only after this article was in press. On the commercial developments, see Jonathan M. Liebenau, "Public Health and the Production and Use of Diphtheria Antitoxin in Philadelphia," *Bull. Hist. Med.* 61 (1987): 216–36; Louis Galambos with Jane Eliot Sewell, *Networks of Innovation: Vaccine Development at Merck, Sharpe & Dohme, and Mulford, 1895–1995* (Cambridge, 1995).

55. "The New Remedy for Diphtheria," *Harper's Weekly*, 15 September 1894, 867.
56. Ibid.
57. Ibid.
58. "The New Cure for Diphtheria, Croup, etc.," *Sci. Am.*, 17 November 1894, 308–9; the drawings are captioned "Injecting the Serum," "Preparing the Toxin," and "Drawing the Serum from the Horse."
59. As detailed below, both these particular images and their general subjects were later reprinted in other publications. These three drawings might well be based on engravings or photographs from European magazines (a common practice), but I have not yet found the antecedents. A quite different depiction of a child being injected ("Le croup guri par le docteur Roux") was published on the cover of *Le Petit Journal: Supplement Illustr*, dated 24 September 1894; this was a daily paper, with a pictorial supplement each week. (I am grateful to William Helfand for sending me a photocopy of this print in his collection.) It is also a different composition from that in the French painting by A. Brouillet, *Le vaccine du croup l'Hospital Trousseau*, now lost, but well known through a photograph made in 1895: see Andre Pecker, *La medecine Paris du XIIIe au XXe sicle* (Paris: editions Hervas, 1984), 458; a heavily cropped and unidentified reproduction may also be found in Otto L. Bettmann, *A Pictorial History of Medicine* (Springfield, IL, 1956), 306. For more on this and other French medical paintings of the era, see Richard E. Weisberg, "The Representation of Doctors at Work in Salon Art of the Early Third Republic in France" (Ph.D. thesis, New York University, 1995). Two further examples confirm the iconic character of the horses' role. A long article in the *New York Times*, 26 March 1895, 3, opens with this series of headlines: "'No. 7' A Valuable Horse. Has Furnished the Health Board with 15 Quarts of Antitoxine. Bought for $10; Worth $5,000. Gaining Flesh While Losing Blood and Does Not Appear to Be at All Dissatisfied in His New Role." Even decades later, horses are the primary image used to represent the anti-toxine discovery in Robert A. Thom's (widely reproduced) painting *The Era of Biologicals*, which shows three anonymous technicians in white jackets, pants, and hats drawing blood from two horses: see George A. Bender, *Great Moments in Pharmacy: The Stories and Paintings in the Series "A History of Pharmacy in Pictures"... by Robert A. Thom*, 2d ed. (Detroit, 1967), 173. For scholarly analysis, see Jacalyn Duffin and Alison Li, "Great Moments: Parke, Davis and Company and the Creation of Medical Art," *Isis*, 86 (1995): 1–29.
60. The traditional page of loose type composed of individual letters and separate pictorial blocks was held together in part by the rigid rules dividing the columns; any large image that broke these rules weakened the plate and increased the risk of its falling apart on high-speed rotary presses. When stereotyping was introduced (making a mold and then a cast of the plate) so that the same page could be run simultaneously on several presses, it had the secondary benefit of allowing images to break the column rules without the old danger, and images wider than one column became commonplace. Fig. 6 above shows the postage-stamp-sized images to which newspapers had formerly been restricted when they wanted to mix illustrations with text.
61. *New York Herald*, 10 December 1894, 3. Since pages 1–2 of the *Herald* were entirely devoted to classified advertising, page 3 was equivalent to other newspapers' front page.
62. *New York Herald*, 11 December 1894, 3.
63. *New York Herald*, 12 December 1894, 3.
64. That wide public appreciation of how these horses were saving children's lives might have undermined antivivisection sentiment is not easily demonstrated, but the possibility merits consideration.
65. *New York Herald*, 13 December 1894, 3.
66. The first implied the public's possible interest in the hygiene and purity of the preparation: "Every New

Horse Is Clipped" (*New York Herald*, 17 December 1894, 4). The second offered a taste of reality, showing a horse strapped down on its side: "Inoculating a Refractory Horse" (p. 4)—but the image was very calm; no struggle was evident despite the caption. The third image, "Where Fodder Is Kept" (p. 4), offered more realistic detail, but might also have raised questions of whether the paper was simply trying to fill space to keep the story big.

67. *New York Herald*, 20 December 1894, 10.
68. *New York Herald*, 23 December 1894, 6.
69. *Review of Reviews*, January 1895, 4.
70. "The New Diphtheria Cure," *Leslie's Illustrated Weekly*, 17 January 1895, 43 (text) and 46 (images), had an accurate text, but ran an alarmingly erroneous caption for the picture of treating the baby: "The Method of Injecting the Poison in Order to Obtain Serum." A few weeks later, *Leslie's Illustrated* ran another diphtheria picture (this time without a story) and used an incorrect or misleading caption again: see "The New Treatment for Diphtheria at the Hospital for Sick Children, Paris—L'Illustration" (one of several images on the Foreign Press page), *Leslie's Illustrated*, 14 February 1895, 109, which clearly shows not the new hypodermic injection, but the established intubation operation (in which a seated physician works in the mouth of a baby held on a woman's lap with an attendant standing behind the woman to hold the baby's head steady). Confirmation that this is a portrayal of intubation is offered by a 1904 painting by the French physician Georges Chicotot, *Tubage par Albert Josias entour de ses ves,* reproduced in color in Pecker (n. 59 above), 264; and by an 1895 American photograph, reproduced in Rima D. Apple, *Illustrated Catalogue of the Slide Archive of Historical Medical Photographs at Stony Brook* (Westport, CT, 1984), item 2123.
71. Henry Smith Williams, M.D., "How Antitoxines Are Developed," *Harper's Weekly*, 5 January 1895, 8.
72. This article's statement that the New York Pasteur Institute was already making anti-toxine would place it ahead of the Health Department's far better known effort. The precise relationship of the two efforts (if indeed they are distinct) is difficult to assess—but those particulars are not essential for an appreciation of visual documents widely accessible in the public sphere. For more information on the Pasteur Institutes in several American cities, see Hansen (n. 5 above), 407–8.
73. I believe that the sober take on the diphtheria cure probably derives from three factors. First, a consensus about its worth emerged quickly to unite the media, the medical profession, leaders in public health, and the public in support of the discovery and its use. With no public uncertainty about its value, there was less purchase for a satirist's bite. Second, while there was consensus on its value, there was uncertainty about how quickly and widely it could be made available, and some newspapers created a campaign, virtually a crusade, to press the government to act. Graphic art was put into service delivering the miracle therapy to the public, complemented by pleading headlines that called for action and urged the public to support the demand. The serious, almost angry, propaganda of editors and publishers pushed humor to the side. And third, the pathos of sick and dying children—in contrast to the healthy and cheery dog-bite victims of the rabies adventure—also kept the humorists at bay. (For conversations about this point and other aspects of the diphtheria story, I wish to express my appreciation to Evelynn M. Hammonds.) About the use of humor more generally, it should be noted that satire about breakthroughs was directed almost always toward the public excitement, not toward the scientists themselves—with two exceptions: (1) a very few cartoons where these breakthroughs are associated with "cranks" and patent-medicine "sure cures," and (2) antivivisection caricatures of medical professionals. An example of the former in *Judge* in 1892 was described above in the tuberculin section; for an example of the latter, see a centerfold cartoon, "Turn About Is Fair Play," with animals in an operating theater doing electrical experiments on a man, in *Life*, 12 December 1895, 384–85. *Life* ran many such cartoons; a full-page drawing from the issue of 16 March 1911 (page 534), "The Little Boy Who Never Grew Up," has recently been reprinted in Lederer (n. 6 above), 41.
74. See, for example, E.R.N. Grigg, *The Trail of the Invisible Light: From X-Strahlen to Radio(bio)logy* (Springfield, IL, 1965); Joel D. Howell, "Early Use of X-ray Machines and Electrocardiographs at the Pennsylvania Hospital, 1897 through 1927," *J. Am. Med. Assoc.* 255 (1986): 2320–23; Nancy Knight, "'The New Light': X Rays and Medical Futurism," in *Imagining Tomorrow: History, Technology, and the American Future*, ed. Joseph J. Corn (Cambridge, 1986), 10–34; J.T.H. Connor, "The Adoption and Effects of X-Rays in Ontario," *Ontario History* 79 (March 1987): 92–107; Beverly Robertson, "The

Medical Significance of X-Rays as Seen in the Contemporary Popular Media from January to April 1896" (unpublished graduate course paper, History Department, New York University, 1988); Lisa Cartwright, "Decomposing the Body: X Rays and the Cinema," *Screening the Body: Tracing Medicine's Visual Culture* (Minneapolis, 1995); Joel D. Howell, *Technology in the Hospital: Transforming Patient Care in the Early Twentieth Century* (Baltimore, 1995); Bettyann Holtzmann Kevles, *Naked to the Bone: Medical Imaging in the Twentieth Century* (New Brunswick, NJ, 1997); Charles R. R. Hayter, "The Clinic as Laboratory: The Case of Radiation Therapy, 1896–1920," *Bull. Hist. Med.* 72 (Winter 1998): 663–88. Ready access to several good images is also found in L. Pearce Williams, *Album of Science: The Nineteenth Century* (New York, 1978). Prominent examples of contemporary magazine coverage include *Scientific American* of 15 February 1896 and *Harper's Weekly* of 22 February 1896. X-ray photographs are found in several *Leslie's Illustrated Weekly* issues in early 1896, including those of 13 February, 27 February, 2 April, and 9 April. Of course, the social satirists working for *Puck* and *Judge* joined in the fun on many occasions. Visual jokes even appeared in stereoviews, such as the composite photograph published in 1896 by Littleton View Co. under the title "Our Latest in X Rays."

75. Starr's book remains the best single account of these nineteenth- and early-twentieth-century developments: Paul Starr, *The Social Transformation of American Medicine* (New York, 1982). Richard Harrison Shryock's much older textbook, *The Development of Modern Medicine: An Interpretation of the Social and Scientific Factors Involved* (1947; reprinted, New York, 1969), holds up rather well and should be recognized for its brief but clear acknowledgment of public attention to the publicity surrounding rabies vaccine and other breakthroughs. A recent overview by James H. Cassedy also acknowledges the popular enthusiasm for turn-of-the-century breakthroughs: *Medicine in America: A Short History* (Baltimore, 1991), 84, 86, 97. Also useful—in addition to Lederer (n. 6 above), and Tomes (n. 6 above)—are recent essays in *Scientific Authority and Twentieth-Century America*, ed. Ronald G. Walters (Baltimore, 1997), esp. JoAnne Brown, "Crime, Commerce, and Contagionism: The Political Languages of Public Health and the Popularization of Germ Theory in the United States, 1870–1950" (53–81), and Walters's introduction, "Uncertainty, Science, and Reform in Twentieth-Century America" (1–10). A recent study of contemporary changes in British medicine provides a useful comparison to some of the developments explored in this article: see Steve Sturdy and Rogert Cooter, "Science, Scientific Management, and the Transformation of Medicine in Britain, c. 1870–1950," *Hist. Sci* 36 (1998): 421–66.

Chapter 4

Research at the Hospital of the Rockefeller Institute for Medical Research

Olga Amsterdamska

Lecturer in Science Dynamics, Department of Sociology, University of Amsterdam, Amsterdam, Netherlands

As its creators were fully aware, at the time of its establishment the Hospital of the Rockefeller Institute of Medical Research was a unique institution. Both intellectually and organizationally, the Hospital was to be an embodiment of a new ideal of clinical medicine as a science.[1] It was to unite laboratory research with bedside investigation of disease pursued by investigator–physicians adept not only in the care of patients and the clinical study of scientific diagnostic and therapeutic methods but also simultaneously skilled in experimental laboratory research. Many of the individual elements of this new mode of medical research could be found elsewhere—in the German university clinics, in the laboratories of individual physician–researchers in England, or at the newly organized laboratories of the Johns Hopkins Hospital.[2] But the configuration found at the Rockefeller Hospital was unique. Nowhere else in 1910 could you find a well-endowed and equipped hospital devoted *exclusively* to research, using a full-time salaried staff of physicians, each and every one of whom was expected to engage in both laboratory research and bedside investigations of patients suffering from a few selected diseases. Although by the early years of the twentieth century the importance of laboratory work in clinical medicine and the importance of laboratory medical research were widely recognized, nowhere but at the Rockefeller Institute was an entire organization premised on the idea that the clinic itself must become a laboratory.

The innovations in the manner in which research was organized and conducted at the Rockefeller Hospital were not the fully foreseen outcome of a well-structured plan: the novelty emerged out of a series of not always coordinated decisions about a heterogeneous set of issues—ranging from architectural choices and personnel selections to attempts to provide the Hospital with a proper management structure and efforts to "sell" the project to its patrons, John D. Rockefeller Sr. and his son. The innovations also did not reflect a single vision of what the Hospital should become. Though committed to a common enterprise and a shared ideology of medical progress through scientific inquiry, those who were the most intimately involved in the establishment of the Hospital—Simon Flexner, Christian Herter, T. Mitchell Prudden, William H. Welch, and Rufus Cole—held somewhat divergent views about its organization and functioning, and about the manner in which research in the Hospital should be conducted. The organization that emerged out of the various discussions, negotiations, adjustments, and compromises was not a faithful embodiment of any individual's vision but the outcome of a collective project.

The structure that resulted from years of planning and construction—both as a material, one can almost say architectural, entity, and as a socio-cultural setting with its distinctive work organization, its distribution of authority and division of labor, its own set of values and standards, its own patterns of distributing resources, and its own ways of selecting and treating patients—continued to shape research conducted at the Rockefeller Hospital at least through the years of Rufus Cole's directorship. It was within the constraints and opportunities provided by this structure that researchers working at the Hospital chose and formulated the problems they addressed in their work, organized their research strategies, and conducted their investigations. The social and physical organization of the Hospital set down in these early stages of development was thus not a neutral setting equally hospitable to all formulations of clinical problems or all translations of these problems into research questions, but a prestructured environment in which some formulations and translations were preferred over others, in which some research choices were privileged while others were precluded.

This essay traces the process of planning, designing, and organizing the Rockefeller Institute Hospital in order to analyze some of the distinctive characteristics of the Hospital's unique organizational structure and to examine their consequences for the development of the research undertaken in the Hospital in its early years. What considerations governed the organizational choices made in the planning of the Hospital? What was the relationship between these choices and the various ideals and models of scientific clinical medicine current at the time? How did the various choices made in the period of planning and organizing the Hospital contribute to its later functioning as a research institution? How was the research conducted at the Hospital structured by its organization? Or, generally speaking, since the work conducted at the Hospital was supposed to focus on the study of diseases, how were these diseases made amenable to the style of research promoted in the Hospital?

One of the guiding principles of John D. Rockefeller Sr.'s philanthropy was surely his unwavering commitment to gradualism—no matter how radical the innovation that was being supported or how huge the sums eventually expanded, the beginnings had to be prudent and moderate, and the expense could increase only after the initial "investment" seemed to be paying off. The idea that the Rockefeller Institute for Medical Research would, just like the Pasteur Institute, possess its own hospital can be found in the early plans for the Institute. However, the gradualist approach meant that the laboratories were fully in operation before the original intention to build a hospital was put back on the agenda. Some of the most innovative features of the new hospital—especially its independence from the Institute laboratories and the consequent organization of hospital research—were probably an unintended consequence of this delay in the addition of the Hospital to the original Institute.

In March 1902, when the Institute was still on the drawing board, and after Theobald Smith's refusal to become the director of the future Rockefeller Institute, the scientific directors asked Simon Flexner "to consider under what circumstances he would be induced to take charge of a laboratory."[3] In his response dated April 8, 1902, Flexner specifically referred to the building of a hospital as one of the features of the new Institute.[4] He expected "a close association" between the Hospital and the Institute and thought such association would contribute to the Institute's prominence. Flexner also discussed the establishment of the new Hospital in his correspondence with Christian Herter.[5]

Flexner's ideas about the Hospital were presented more formally in the official plans for the organization of the Institute. In a May 1902 document incorporated into the minutes of the board of directors, the Hospital was portrayed primarily as an annex to the laboratories: as a setting for the investigation of a "special group of diseases" and a testing ground for the application of "such curative agencies as the Institute might develop or foster." The nature of the investigations to be conducted in the Hospital, insofar as they were to be independent of what was being developed in the laboratories, was not specified. The emphasis was on experimental work conducted in the Institute's laboratories and on creating a setting in which the findings made there could be applied and tested. The role of clinical investigations in the solution of medical problems was presented in the report as severely limited by the fact that experimental methods of research could not be used in the study of humans.[6]

Just as important as any insight into disease which clinical studies might offer was what we might call the "motivational" role of the Hospital, for the contact with patients—or rather with diseases affecting humans—was supposed to remind the Institute scientists that (treating) human disease was the ultimate aim of all their activities.

> The problems of human disease should always be close to the Institute. While the study of the diseases of lower animals is highly important both from an economic point of view and from their bearing upon the understanding of many forms of human disease, and while the work of the Institute will of necessity be largely experimental, yet intimate relation with the problems of human disease should not for a moment be lost sight of. In order that the causes and treatment of human diseases may be studied to the best advantage, there should be attached to the Institute a hospital for the investigation of special groups of diseases. This hospital should be modern and fully equipped, but it need not be large. It should attempt to provide only for selected cases of disease, and the patients would thus secure the advantage of special and skilled attendance and such curative agencies as the Institute might develop or foster. [. . .] Hospitals similar to this one suggested for the Institute are connected with the Koch Institute in Berlin and with the Pasteur Institute in Paris and with Kitasato's Institute in Tokyo.[7]

The access to patients that a special hospital would provide was considered especially important in the investigation of infection and immunity, areas that the directors considered to be central for the new Institute both because infectious diseases were seen as "threatening dangers of our present social system" and because they were ripe for scientific research from "all points of view."[8]

Although it is risky to attempt a history of events that did not occur, the original plans for the Hospital, and the analogy drawn between the future Hospital and the existing arrangements in Koch's Institute in Berlin or the Pasteur Institute in Paris suggest that had the Hospital been built at the same time as the laboratories, it might easily have become an annex to the laboratories. It might have primarily become a testing ground for the therapies and diagnostic procedures that were confidently expected to ensue from research conducted in the new laboratories and a source of motivation for scientists to keep their attention focused on problems of disease. Although the intimate relation between research and problems of human disease should not be forgotten, in the eyes of a pathologist and a laboratory man such as Flexner, the progress in medicine had to come from laboratories and experiments on animals rather than from the clinic or studies based on observation of patients at the bedside. A clinic was to be primarily a place where discoveries were to be tested and applied, not one where new discoveries were made.

The construction and organization of the laboratories kept the matter of the Hospital in suspension and it was only after the new laboratory building was inaugurated in 1906 that the issue of a hospital reappeared on the agenda of the board of directors. However, at that point, even if only to demonstrate their prudence and modesty to their patrons, the directors first considered other, less costly, possibilities such as the affiliation of the Institute with one of the large New York Hospitals, most likely the Presbyterian Hospital.

At the meeting of November 14, 1906,

> After full discussion it was the unanimous opinion of the Executive Committee that any alliance with an existing hospital would be undesirable and that the Institute adhere to its original plan of erecting and controlling its own hospital.[9]

The possibility of using existing hospital facilities by affiliation with one of the New York hospitals was also discussed several months later in a document prepared as an "Estimate for the Endowment of the Rockefeller Institute."[10] The directors reiterated that an alliance with a general hospital would not be as desirable as command over a small separate hospital. Only a hospital under the Institute's direct control would provide researchers with the opportunity to engage in "close observations through which alone are made possible discoveries as to the nature of disease or its treatment." Because in the "work of research the patients must of necessity be under the closest possible kind of control and supervision," the Institute should acquire its own small hospital rather than relying on other institutions in the city.[11]

In defending the idea that, despite receiving offers of affiliation from elsewhere, the Institute should control its own hospital, the "Estimate" emphasized the uniqueness of the new undertaking by bringing to the center of attention the opportunities for controlled and specialized clinical research that it would provide and that the existing general or even university hospitals could not. Although in 1902, the proposed hospital was being legitimized by the fact that both the Pasteur and the Koch Institutes were affiliated with clinics, in 1907 the directors instead stressed their view that "At the present time there probably exists nowhere in the world the most advantageous affiliation of laboratories and hospitals such as is here proposed."[12] Two distinct arguments ran through this and the following planning documents. On the one hand, we find here the older idea that the Hospital should be a testing ground for findings made in the laboratory. It would be a place where "facts [established in the Rockefeller Institute laboratories] could be studied in their application [. . .] to human patients." On the other hand, we find a suggestion that the new hospital itself could become a locus of quasi-experimental clinical investigations. Furthermore, the "Estimate" argues that, although until now progress in medicine has been made by "experiments upon animals,"

> all indications at present point toward a closer and *more scientific study of disease in man* as the line of investigation of the future. For such observations, patients must not only be near the laboratory, but the conditions in which they live, their food, their surroundings, etc., must be *under complete control of those who are prosecuting investigations.*[13]

Thus, advantage of the new institution would not be just access to patients for the testing of new treatments or the opportunity to observe human disease in "nature" but also the possibility of conducting clinical investigations under controlled conditions that could be made to approximate —at least to some extent—those which can be obtained in the laboratory.

The notion that the new hospital should be organized so as to promote a new style of clinical investigations at this point translated neither into any specific physical organization of the hospital nor into the organization of its staff. In the pages detailing the costs of the proposed organization of the Institute as a whole, \$92,000 is assigned to salaries for the scientific staff in the laboratories and only \$11,500 for those of the professional medical staff working in the Hospital. The envisaged staff was to consist of four physicians (two resident and two attending) and two pathologists. Clearly, the Institute's laboratories were to remain the dominant setting for research and the Hospital staff was thought of more in terms of the needs involved in providing adequate patient care than in terms of the research they were to engage in. There is also no mention of the need for any separate clinical laboratories.

On February 28, 1907, John D. Rockefeller Jr. responded to the board's "Estimate." Writing on behalf of his father, he authorized the board of directors to prepare plans and secure bids for the construction of "a small hospital to be used in connection with the laboratory of the Institute."[14] The receipt of Rockefeller's letter was noted at the meeting of April 13, 1907, and after a general discussion of the hospital plans, the formulation of specific plans for the Hospital was referred to the executive committee. The lead at this point was taken by Christian Herter, who prepared the "Notes on Plans for a Research Hospital to be Affiliated with the Research Laboratories of the Rockefeller Institute." Herter, who was intimately involved in the planning of the Rockefeller Institute from the very beginning, taught at Columbia Medical School, was one of the founders of the *Journal of Biological Chemistry,* and maintained his own private laboratory in his home in New York. Like Flexner, Herter was primarily a laboratory scientist. His research focused on chemical investigations of metabolic disorders. Although by 1906, his health was already rather precarious, it seems that at the time the Hospital was being planned, he was considered as its most likely director.[15]

Herter was eager to combine clinical investigations with laboratory work. He believed that "the closest relationship should exist between the clinical interests represented in the hospital and the experimental and laboratory interests represented in the laboratory building of the Rockefeller Institute."[16] But despite his interest in both laboratory and clinical research and his insistence on the "closest imaginable cooperation between the clinical and the most modern methods of investigation," Herter thought that these two activities would be *conducted by distinct groups of people*: laboratory research was to be primarily the task of scientists working in the Institute's laboratories, and clinical research was to be the duty of the physicians working in the hospital. Both Herter's notes and the "Outline of Plan for the Organization of a Research Hospital," which was at least partially based on Herter's document and which represented the consensus of the board of directors as of June 13, 1907, emphasized both the distinction between laboratory experiments and clinical investigations *and* the benefits that the directors were sure would accrue from the "closest possible union of the existing laboratory facilities with the facilities for clinical study to be provided by the Hospital."[17] The added value of having both clinical and laboratory studies conducted in the same hospital would thus come from collaboration and communication between the two groups of researchers: "It is believed," Herter wrote, "that the interchange of ideas between those representing the clinical side of medicine and the research workers in the laboratories would lead to the best possible results in the accumulation of knowledge."[18]

Although the idea presented here by Herter (and reiterated in the "Outline") can be seen as a direct extension of the call for a new kind of clinical investigation suggested in the "Estimate," the plans discussed during the June 1907 meetings do include a significant innovation: for the first time, it was proposed that the new Hospital should have *its own laboratories using some professional staff.* According to Herter, a physician studying patients might need some "immediate help" from "a small group of chemical, bacteriological, and microscopical workers" whose chief task would be to perform routine tests, but which would also allow the "physician in chief to be in far closer touch with the different phases of his problem than would be possible if all phases of investigation of the patients under his charge should be carried on in the large laboratory."[19] Because Herter assumed that the studies conducted by attending physicians would be different from those conducted "by means of methods and in accordance with ideas originating from the workers and under the direction of the director of the laboratories," he saw the necessity of providing the attending physicians with separate clinical labs and laboratory assistants.[20] The "Outline" reiterates and defends this position—though the decision to provide the Hospital with separate labs is presented here mainly as an architectural choice and a matter of convenience rather than a programmatic change. Despite the availability of laboratory space in the main building of the Institute, the Hospital would need its own set of "small clinical laboratories" because "the physicians in charge of the patients should be able to conduct certain routine examinations within the Hospital itself. To carry on such routine examinations in the main laboratories would involve considerable loss of energy and imperfect coordination of observations."[21] Although these clinical laboratories were envisaged mainly as a setting for routine examinations, in the summer of 1907, the entire fifth floor of the projected Hospital was set aside for the labs.

The increased role of clinical investigations projected in Herter's notes and the approved outline was also reflected in the projected budget. Although the January 1907 budget, which was part of the endowment estimate, called for some $11,500 to be spent on the salaries of the four physicians and the two pathologists working in the Hospital, by June 1907, the directors expected these expenses to amount to $24,500 (salaries of seven physicians, a bacteriologist, and a chemist).[22] The greater role being accorded to clinical investigations, and thus the shift in the responsibilities of the medical staff of the future Hospital, was reflected not only in the increase in the number of doctors but also in the directors' concern with finding an appropriate way for these physician–researchers to be affiliated with the Hospital. As long as the plan called for both attending and resident physicians to be concerned mainly with patient care, the directors expected them to maintain their own private practices, as was customary for the attending staff in general hospitals. However, the growing expectation that these physicians should also engage in clinical investigations suggested the need to keep all their outside activities to a minimum. The directors wanted to make sure that "the hospital, instead of being of secondary importance to private practice would have the first claim to the services of the appointees to these positions."[23] The arguments against allowing clinicians to engage in private practice used by the Rockefeller Institute directors were the same as those made by the advocates of full-time clinical chairs in the medical school clinics who had been promoting their plan since the 1890s.[24] Although in 1907, the Rockefeller Institute board of directors did not suggest hiring their clinicians on a full-time basis, they were clearly aware of the shortcomings of allowing for unlimited private practice. For the time being, the need to keep the Hospital affiliation central was to be implemented by offering relatively high salaries and by a careful selection of the staff.

The "Outline" adopted at the June 1907 meeting was to serve as the basis for the very detailed negotiations about the Hospital building in which the members of the Hospital committee, Herter and Holt, attempted to reach an understanding with John D. Rockefeller Sr. and his advisors such as Frederick Gates and Starr J. Murphy. Apart from detailed financial negotiations, there was much discussion about the precise size of the Hospital, the placement of the isolation ward (or pavilion) either within the main building of the Hospital or separately, and the option of leaving open various possibilities for a future expansion of the building.

The negotiations between the board and the patrons of the Institute resulted in one consequential decision that affected later policy regarding the status of clinical staff in the Hospital and the relationship between the Hospital and the patients providing "clinical material" to the researchers. In July 1907, Gates and Herter discussed the relative merits and shortcomings of the choice between supplementing the Hospital income by charging patients for the care the Hospital offered versus providing all hospital services free to all patients. Gates was initially dubious about the fact that the planning did not provide for patients paying for their care and treatment at the new Hospital. He argued that given the expected quality of the Hospital and its staff, patients would be eager to pay, and he asked whether it "would it not be safe on estimating some income [from patients paying for their treatment] at least to offset these expenses; indeed might not that income be very considerable"?[25] Herter quickly convinced Gates (and indirectly Rockefeller) that in order to maintain full commitment to and freedom of research, the Hospital should not charge fees for its services. But the decision that all patients were to receive their treatment for free brought to the fore and made more difficult the question of the attending physicians' income (which was not to be supplemented by private patients' payments for treatment and consultations in the Hospital).[26]

It was only at the end of May 1908 that John D. Rockefeller Jr. formally informed L. Emmett Holt, the representative of the board, that his father had agreed to provide $500,000 for the "purchase of land and the erection and equipment of a suitable hospital building."[27] By that time, however, Christian Herter was too sick to consider running the Hospital and the board of the Institute embarked on a search for a director.

The decision to hire Rufus Cole as director of the Hospital was made in August 1908 when Simon Flexner learned from William Welch that Cole was about to accept a professorship of medicine at the University of Michigan Medical School at Ann Arbor. With great speed, Flexner invited Cole for a discussion at his summer home in Chocorua, New Hampshire, and then rapidly contacted his colleagues on the board in order to finalize the appointment. Holt was telegraphed in London; Herter was paid a visit in his vacation house in Seal Harbor, Maine. At every step of the way, Flexner reported to Cole on the progress of his negotiations with the other directors and tried to tempt Cole into accepting the position by emphasizing the unique scientific and clinical opportunities that the new Hospital was likely to offer. Given the possibility that Cole might instead accept the Michigan position, the directors did not have much difficulty in quickly reaching a consensus on Cole's appointment.[28]

This was not the first time that Simon Flexner attempted to hire Cole. In 1901, when Flexner was still professor of pathology at the University of Pennsylvania and Cole was an assistant to William Osler at Johns Hopkins, Flexner had asked Cole to take charge of the pathological and clinical laboratories at the Philadelphia Hospital. At that time, Cole had declined Flexner's offer, preferring to remain at Johns Hopkins to work under Osler where he could retain both laboratory and clinical responsibilities.[29] Cole's decision was a result of his careful consideration of how the Philadelphia and Baltimore opportunities would affect his chances of fulfilling very definite career ambitions: Cole's goal, which he discussed at length in his letters home, was to become a professor of medicine in Chicago and to combine his teaching and research activities with a consultation practice.[30] Though actively interested and involved in laboratory research, Cole did not want to become exclusively a laboratory researcher. In 1908, when Flexner invited him for a talk in Chocorua, Cole was working under Lewellys Barker at Johns Hopkins, where he directed the Biological Laboratories and, with the invitation to the professorship in

Ann Arbor, he was about to realize his ambitions.

In hiring Cole, Flexner was obviously aware that he and the board were selecting someone who had persistently attempted to combine clinical concerns with laboratory interests. Cole was clearly not just a clinician nor just a laboratory scientist. From Cole's refusal to take the job in Philadelphia, Flexner knew that Cole wanted to maintain his clinical practice and was not interested in a career that would keep him permanently in a laboratory. But Cole's record and experience at Johns Hopkins, where he was by then both an associate in medicine with his own patients and the head of a biological laboratory devoted to research as well as to routine work, also showed that he regarded research as an activity that takes place in the laboratory as much as at the bedside. In his telegram to L. Emmett Holt, Flexner succinctly justified his and Welch's preference for Cole: "believe Cole much the best available man for our hospital because excellent clinician and excellent and successful investigator."[31] In an effort to make the offer of the directorship attractive to Cole, Flexner carefully spelled out how the Hospital would meet the aspirations of those interested in the renewal of clinical research. Noting that he had received assurances from "five of the seven directors" of the board about Cole's appointment to the directorship, Flexner wrote

> The opportunities offered by the Rockefeller Hospital are indeed unique, and can hardly fail to make the strongest appeal to one devoted, as you are, to research in clinical medicine and to promoting the best future interests of clinical medicine in this country. The conditions for scientific work and for developing men with strong laboratory interests in clinical medicine should be quite ideal. The scale of the plans for the hospital should, I think, convince you that the Directors of the Institute have endeavored to construct a model small hospital, provided with facilities for promoting discovery in medical science and for carrying on the highest type of clinical observation.[32]

Flexner's emphasis on the promise that Cole would be able to "develop the clinical and scientific work of the hospital" and that the Hospital was intended to "be made to contribute its part, and I believe a large part, in the regeneration of clinical medicine in this country," were certainly attempts to make the job offer attractive to Cole. However, in emphasizing the significance of laboratory research conducted by the clinical staff of the Hospital, Flexner was also moving away from the original notion of the Hospital as basically a convenient testing ground for research conducted in the Institute laboratories. Flexner seems to have been fully aware that the decision to hire Cole gave a new meaning to the idea of "the close union of Institute laboratories and Hospital" on which the entire Hospital project was predicated from the very beginning: laboratory and clinical research were now to be closely associated because they were to become activities of the same individuals. Whereas in Herter's plans for the Hospital, the union meant close collaboration and communication between two distinct groups of people—scientists working in the main Institute laboratories and the Hospital clinicians working in the wards—the decision to hire Cole meant, at the very least, that Hospital clinicians would be just as likely to engage in laboratory research as the laboratory scientists would be likely to work in the Hospital wards.

Immediately upon being offered the job, Cole was also offered the opportunity to modify the Hospital plans before final contracts were signed with the architect and builders. Insofar as this can be ascertained from the surviving correspondence, Cole was quite satisfied with the architectural plans and the changes he proposed were relatively minor (he proposed, for example, a different location for the Hospital laundry and was concerned with ventilation). In November

1908, Cole reviewed the plans for Hospital laboratories and the changes he proposed—trying to make sure that the various laboratories would receive proper lighting, or that the room divisions were appropriate—suggest no major differences between his ideas about the laboratories from what had been planned earlier. In continuation of the ideas presented in the plans for the Hospital dating from before Cole was hired, Cole treated the Hospital laboratories as research settings and not merely locations in which routine determinations could be made. For example, Cole never doubted that the Hospital laboratories should be equipped so as to make animal experimentation possible.[33]

In November 1908, Flexner also asked Cole to prepare a "plan of organization of the hospital," which could be "used as a basis of discussion" by the board.[34] Cole's "Suggestions in Regard to the Organization of the Rockefeller Hospital for Medical Research" appear to have been discussed at the special meeting of the board of directors held on November 28, 1908.[35] In his "Suggestions" Cole defined the task of the Hospital as the application of what he termed an "intensive method of clinical study" combining "investigative" clinical approaches with the "experimental method of the laboratory." Just as in the initial plans for the Hospital, laboratory scientists were to enrich their experience and increase their motivation by contact with patients in the Hospital wards, so now "the best results can be obtained from clinical study when those engaged [in] it have at the same time facilities for undertaking experimental work." In his plan, Cole vigorously put forward the idea that the best way to support "the closest possible connection between the Institute Laboratory and Hospital" and eliminate the "physical and intellectual barrier between the laboratory and wards" was to allow "the Hospital laboratory to be developed so far as possible as a true research laboratory, and that, moreover, the residents of the Hospital be permitted and urged to undertake experimental work on animals. . . ." Simultaneously, Cole agreed that the "closest union" might also be achieved by bringing laboratory scientists to the bedside: "Members and Assistants of the Institute engaged primarily on purely experimental work in the Institute laboratories should have full opportunity in the Hospital wards for the study of cases of the diseases which they are investigating."[36]

The idea that the most advantageous combination of laboratory and bedside research could be achieved only when physicians are able to engage in both of these activities together served Cole as a guideline for the organization of the Hospital. Accordingly, Cole argued that the visiting (or "externe") physicians should be selected and appointed on a temporary basis depending on the kinds of investigations they would like to pursue while affiliated with the Hospital, whereas the resident staff, on whom Cole wanted to place the major burden of the Hospital's operation as a research institution, should be comprised only of physicians who would "be very actively and personally engaged in medical research."[37] Cole's plan did allow for the attending (external) physicians to "be engaged in practice in New York," though he believed that "preference should be given to men who can devote all of their time to Hospital work."[38] The full-time requirement was, however, to be imposed on the residents. By the very nature of their appointments, residents would be responsible for routine care of patients. Cole insisted that each of them should also "have at least half his time free for the investigations which he should be required to undertake."[39] Given their obligation to engage both in bedside work and in laboratory research, the resident physicians were the ones who would be chiefly responsible for "the service the Hospital will render in the advancement of medical knowledge."[40] The importance of Cole's commitment to laboratory research conducted in the Hospital by its resident and external staff is also apparent if we examine the eventual staffing of the Hospital once it came into operation. Although the size and cost of the medical staff grew only moderately from the projected seven physicians in July 1907 to the eight doctors actually working in the Hospital in its first year of operation, the change in the size of the technical staff employed exclusively in the Hospital laboratories were significant.[41] In addition to a single bacteriologist and a single chemist projected in the 1907 budget, the "technical staff" in 1910–1911 also included four helpers in three different labs.[42]

Although Cole was far more specific than either Herter or Flexner or the board as a whole about the organization of the Hospital staff and insisted on the autonomy of Hospital research to a far greater extent than had been done previously, his general outlook did not differ to any significant extent from the vision presented in Flexner's letters written at the time of Cole's hiring. And significantly, by providing for the possibility that the attending physicians would engage in private practice outside of the Hospital, Cole himself did not take the radical step of proposing a full-time plan for the entire medical staff.

The decision to adopt such a full-time policy for both residents and attending physicians was in fact taken in two separate steps. At the special meeting of November 28, 1908, the board followed Cole's advice and decided that "neither the Resident Physician nor Assistant nor Interns shall be permitted to practice medicine outside the Hospital or receive fees from Hospital patients."[43] The further decision regarding externs was made only at the next "special meeting" held at the end of January 1909 and called by Flexner to consider "certain questions relating to the Hospital which had come up recently in an interview with Mr. Gates." It was at that meeting, at which Cole was not even present, that the directors "unanimously voted that the board . . . not favor permitting physicians holding appointments in the Institute to practice medicine outside or to receive fees therefore. . . ."[44] John D. Rockefeller Jr. confirmed his father's commitment to the full-time plan and to the free provision of Hospital services to its patients in his letter of February 26, 1909.[45] In this manner, the Rockefeller Institute Hospital became the first medical research institution in the United States operating according to the full-time scheme.

Although more than a year and a half would pass before the Hospital was finally inaugurated, Rockefeller's commitment to the full-time plan marked the conclusion of the period when the most consequential organizational decisions about the Hospital were taken. Much negotiation about costs, construction of the Hospital wards (especially the isolation pavilion), and hiring still lay ahead. As the negotiations with the architects and the patrons focused on ever more specific details and decisions, tempers occasionally ran high. At one point, in May 1909, Cole got so frustrated that he was on the verge of resigning, fearing that he was being made a scapegoat for cost overruns and concerned that the board of directors did not trust him to support architectural modifications he had deemed important. Eventually, compromises about some features of the building were made, and John D. Rockefeller Sr. was asked to provide an additional $100,000 for construction. Another set of negotiations and consultations led to the hiring of the Hospital business manager and of the superintendent of nursing. In June 1909, Cole went to Europe to examine hospitals in Germany, France, and England, and to purchase some laboratory equipment. However, all this activity did not alter the basic organizational and architectural features of the Hospital. The basic organizational structure of the Hospital was set by January 1909: the closest union of the clinic and the laboratory was reinterpreted to mean their union in the person of a clinician–investigator who would conduct research in both settings. To secure this goal, the Hospital was provided with a full set of laboratories, separate from the laboratories serving researchers in the Institute. The clinical staff of the Hospital was to be carefully chosen from among the very small group of young American clinicians trained in the basic sciences (or in some cases scientists—chemists or bacteriologists—without medical training). No physician working in the Hospital was to devote more than half of his time to the care of patients, and all physicians were to be fully employed by the Institute. Hospital workers were to be evaluated largely in terms of their laboratory skills and research ingenuity, and by publications in scientific journals—not in terms of their clinical acumen or bedside manner. Even though Cole consulted Flexner on most policy and hiring decisions, and occasionally Flexner expressed his opinions forcefully, it was the director of the Hospital, not the director of the laboratories, who decided about the kinds of research conducted in the Hospital and about who was going to perform it.

The "final act" in the discussion as to the respective roles of the Institute laboratories and the Hospital took place a full year after the Hospital's inauguration when, after a question raised by William Welch at a meeting of the Board of Scientific Directors, Rufus Cole was asked to put on paper his ideas regarding "the general policy of the Hospital with respect to the development of close relations between the Hospital and the Laboratories of the Institute."[46] Cole's answer was a forceful defense of the idea of the Hospital as a "definite scientific department" within the Institute as a whole, of the status of internal medicine as a full-fledged science devoted to "the study of the fundamental nature of disease" based on both experimental and observational methods, and of the need to have each Hospital clinician work in the laboratory and at the bedside.[47] Although he thought that collaboration or cooperation between scientists working in the different laboratories of the Institute should be encouraged, Cole presupposed the equality of scientists working in the Institute laboratories and those working in the Hospital, and he argued that such collaboration could only be fruitful if it was allowed to develop on voluntary basis. Significantly, while asserting the Hospital's independence and its scientific status, Cole could appeal to earlier decisions of the Institute's directors and to views he attributed to Herter and Flexner.

Histories of the development of the Rockefeller Institute Hospital often point to the differences of vision between Flexner, Herter, and Cole regarding the nature of the research that was to be conducted there. According to George Corner, the hiring of Cole marked the adoption of ". . . hospital program quite different from that which the board had envisioned earlier."[48] In 1949 Walter Palmer, who worked at the Institute from 1915 to 1917 and later became the professor of internal medicine at Columbia's College of Physicians and Surgeons, wrote to Cole about his impression of profound differences between Flexner's and Cole's visions of the Hospital's function. Praising Cole and the Rockefeller Hospital for setting an example of the new kind of clinical research, Palmer remarked that "All these years I had it fixed in mind that he [Flexner] was the one who had the desire to open the hospital as a human guinea pig laboratory for the Institute."[49] Similarly, Thomas Rivers, contrasted Herter's and Flexner's views with those of Cole arguing that

> Dr. Flexner wanted the Hospital to act as a testing ground for the ideas generated by the people who worked under him in the laboratories [. . .] Cole made it clear that the Hospital was not going to be a handmaiden to the laboratories and that he and his boys were not going to test Noguchi's ideas, Meltzer's ideas or Levene's ideas [. . .] Cole was adamant that the people who took care of the patients would do the research on them. Well, Cole won the argument hands down before he came. . . .[50]

As I have tried to demonstrate with this reconstruction of the decision-making process, drawing the contrast between Herter and Flexner on the one hand and Cole on the other hand is too simple. It is true that their visions of what kind of research should be performed in the Hospital were not identical, and it is reasonable to assume that as the director of laboratories Flexner saw the Hospital in terms of opportunities for the researchers working under his direction. In contrast, Cole, as director of the Hospital, strove for maximum autonomy. However, the structure and organization of the Hospital emerged not from any one person's argument "winning hands down," but from a lengthy social process in which a variety of considerations as well as previous commitments and decisions played a role. Thus, the independence of the Hospital from the Institute's main laboratories was as much an inadvertent result of the caution and gradualism of the Rockefellers and their advisors—and of the resulting delays in the construction of the Hospital—as of any reasoned plan to make the Hospital a separate entity. The claim that a small hospital focused on a few diseases and devoted exclusively to research would be particularly advantageous for the advancement of knowledge, because it would allow for close, quasi-experimental supervision and control of patients, was made in the context of trying to delegitimize the less expensive option of affiliating the Institute with one of the existing New York hospitals. The decision to add separate laboratories to the Hospital was prompted initially not by research considerations but by the attempts to make architectural choices allowing for the most convenient organization of patient care. The decision to offer the services of the Hospital free to its patients was prompted by concerns about the researchers' ability to select cases according to criteria of clinical research interest while maintaining the charitable profile of the Institute as a whole, but it had ramifications for relations between patients and the Hospital physician–researchers and it influenced the eventual decision to hire clinicians on a full-time basis. The role of the laboratory in clinical research did increase in importance when the decision to hire Cole was being made, but it was as much a result of Flexner's attempts to entice Cole to come to the Rockefeller as of Cole's conscious efforts to reshape the idea of clinical research. And the full-time plan itself, long considered the lynchpin of the new clinical science's success and regarded as one of Cole's main contributions to the Hospital's organization, was adopted carefully and gradually as the outcome of discussions involving Flexner, Holt, Herter, Frederick Gates, and the Rockefellers, father and son. It was in these discussions that the respective research and clinical tasks of the resident and the visiting staff were defined.

The idea that creating a close union between the laboratory and the clinic would bring forth major benefits to medical research was a notion that guided the planning of the Hospital from its very beginning. As I have tried to show, views about the kind of research organization leading to the best embodiment of this ideal of a "closest union" varied a great deal. One format suggested a union would have involved laboratory researchers colonizing the clinic by subordinating it to their needs and using it as a source of clinical material or as a testing ground for the results of their studies. Regarded in this manner, clinical medicine would be an applied science, an area where the findings of biochemical, physiological, bacteriological, and pathological laboratories would prove their practical utility. Cole, as well as other physicians who later worked in the Rockefeller Hospital, such as Alfred Cohn and Thomas Rivers, emphatically rejected this idea.[51] Alternatively, the union of lab and clinic could involve collaboration between two different types of researchers: clinical investigators working mainly at the bedside and involved in careful observational studies of disease, and laboratory researchers focused on experimental studies designed to answer basic biological— be it physiological, biochemical, or pathological—questions. The argument for such collaboration tended to assume that clinical science and practice were inherently distinct from experimental laboratory sciences. From this point of view, clinical investigation was generally considered more holistic and more focused on individual patients (with their variability, social and cultural backgrounds, and idiosyncrasies) than the laboratory-based biological sciences. By the early twentieth century, this kind of clinical investigation was also generally considered less "scientific." When Cole argued that he would prefer that physicians working at the Hospital not publish individual case studies, no matter how interesting they might be, he was forcefully rejecting this ideal of clinical investigation.[52]

The third option—the one chosen at the Rockefeller Hospital and actively promoted by Cole as well as Flexner—involved getting clinician–researchers to work both at the bedside and in the laboratory so as to advance medical knowledge by bringing disease into the laboratory and the laboratory into the Hospital. This particular option provided a powerful defense of the professional status of clinicians and clinical researchers. But how different in practice was this model of clinical science from the colonization model that the progressive clinicians explicitly rejected?[53] Was the "personal union" of the laboratory and the bedside researcher sufficient to break the methodological and practical divide between an experimentalist and a clinical observer?

Even a cursory look at the effort that the physician–researchers at the Rockefeller Hospital had to expend on the translation of clinical problems into laboratory research and vice versa—at the work that went into the development and application of instruments and techniques that could be used to study disease in both settings, or into the problems involved in matching animal models of disease with their human counterparts—suggests that the process of linking the laboratory with the bedside remained a formidable challenge.[54] However, in order to understand how this challenge was met and the consequences of this particular model of clinical science for medicine in general, we would have to look in far greater detail not at the programmatic statements of the directors of the Institute and the Hospital but at the actual research trajectories of the scientists whose mission was to realize this vision.

Endnotes

1. For the history of clinical research in the U.S., see A. McGehee Harvey, *Science at the Bedside: Clinical Research in American Medicine 1905–1945* (Baltimore, 1981); Morris Vogel and Charles E. Rosenberg, eds., *The Therapeutic Revolution: Essays in the Social History of American Medicine* (Philadelphia, 1979); Russell C. Maulitz and Diana E. Long, *Grand Rounds: One Hundred Years of Internal Medicine* (Philadelphia, 1988).
2. See Andrew Cunningham and Perry Williams, eds., *The Laboratory Revolution in Medicine* (Cambridge, 1992). On the history of the Johns Hopkins School of Medicine, see A. McGehee Harvey, *Adventures in Medical Research: A Century of Discovery at Johns Hopkins* (Baltimore, 1976); Alan M. Chesney, *The Johns Hopkins Hospital and the Johns Hopkins University School of Medicine* (Baltimore, 1963).
3. Meeting of March 2, 1902, Scientific Directors' Minutes 1901–1911, vol. 1, p. 36, Record Group 110.2, Rockefeller University Archives, Rockefeller Archive Center, Sleepy Hollow, NY (hereafter RAC).
4. Simon Flexner to William Welch, April 8, 1902, letter appended to the minutes of April 12, 1902, Scientific Directors' Minutes 1901–1911, vol. 1, RG 110.2, Rockefeller University Archives, RAC.
5. George Corner, *A History of the Rockefeller Institute, 1901–1953: Origins and Growth* (New York, 1964), 88–9.
6. "Report and Recommendations of the Directors of the Rockefeller Institute, 1901–1902," Scientific Directors' Minutes 1901–1911, vol. 1, p. 65–7, RG 110.2, Rockefeller University Archives, RAC.
7. Ibid., 65–6.

8. Ibid., 66.
9. Meeting of the Executive Committee, November 14, 1906, Scientific Directors' Minutes 1901–1911, vol. 1, RG 110.2, Rockefeller University Archives, RAC.
10. According to George Corner (*History of Rockefeller*, n. 5 above, 65), this document was prepared in the early part of 1907 by T. Mitchell Prudden. It is attached to the minutes of either the meeting of January 12, 1907 or of February 22, 1907. See Scientific Directors' Minutes 1901–1911, vol. 1, RG 110.2, Rockefeller University Archives, RAC.
11. "An Estimate for the Endowment of the Rockefeller Institute," Scientific Directors' Minutes 1901–1911, vol. 1, RG 110.2, Rockefeller University Archives, RAC.
12. Ibid., 6.
13. Ibid., 5.
14. John D. Rockefeller Jr. to L.E. Holt, February 28, 1907, folder 541, box 52, Rockefeller Boards series, RG 2, Office of the Messrs. Rockefeller (OMR), Rockefeller Family Archives, RAC.
15. "Memorial, Christian Archibald Herter, 1865–1910," December 15, 1910, Scientific Directors' Minutes 1901–1911, vol. 2, RG 110.2, Rockefeller University Archives, RAC.
16. "Notes on Plans for a Research Hospital to be Affiliated with the Research Laboratories of the Rockefeller Institute," folder 8, box 1, RG 417, Rockefeller University Archives, RAC.
17. "Outline of Plan for the Organization of a Research Hospital. Tentatively Approved by the Board of Directors at the Meeting, June 13, 1907," Scientific Directors' Minutes 1901–1911, vol. 2, RG 110.2, Rockefeller University Archives, RAC.
18. "Notes," (n. 16 above), 3.
19. "Notes," (n. 16 above), 2.
20. Ibid.
21. "Outline," (n. 9 above) 9.
22. "Estimate for the Proposed Hospital," folder 541, box 52, Rockefeller Boards series, RG 2, OMR, Rockefeller Family Archives, RAC. Although the budget is not dated, internal evidence suggests it accompanied the July 13, 1907 "Outline."
23. "Outline," (n. 9 above) 12.
24. Among the early proponents of the full-time clinical chairs were the Johns Hopkins anatomist Franklin P. Mall and his associate, Lewellys F. Barker, who brought the issue to national attention in 1902. (Later, Barker became an opponent of the plan, and when Johns Hopkins Medical School, with the help of Rockefeller money, actually instituted the plan, Barker resigned his chair). Later, Simon Flexner's brother Abraham was one of the most vocal advocates of the full-time system. See Simon Flexner and James Thomas Flexner, *William Welch and the Heroic Age of American Medicine* (New York, 1941), 300–20.
25. Frederick Gates to Christian Herter, late June/early July 1907, folder 541, box 52, Rockefeller Boards series, RG 2, OMR, Rockefeller Family Archives, RAC.
26. Christian Herter to Frederick Gates, July 7, 1907; Gates to Herter and Gates to Starr J. Murphy, July 12, 1907; Gates to J.D. Rockefeller Jr., July 5, 1907, folder 541, box 52, Rockefeller Boards series, RG 2, OMR, Rockefeller Family Archives, RAC.
27. John D. Rockefeller Jr. to L. Emmett Holt, May 26, 1908, folder 541, box 52, Rockefeller Boards series, RG 2, OMR, Rockefeller Family Archives, RAC.
28. Cable from Simon Flexner to William Welch, August 7, 1908; cable from Simon Flexner to Rufus Cole, August 10, 1908; Simon Flexner to Rufus Cole, August 12, 1908; Simon Flexner August 15, 1908; Simon Flexner to Rufus Cole, August 22, 1908, folder 1a, BC 671, Correspondence with S. Flexner, Rufus Cole Papers, American Philosophical Society, Philadelphia, PA (hereafter APS); cable from William Welch, Christian Herter, and Simon Flexner to L. Emmett Holt, no date [August 1908]; Rufus Cole to Simon Flexner, August 18, 1908, Rufus Cole to Simon Flexner, August 28, 1908, folder 1, box 1, RG 430.2, Rockefeller University Archives, RAC; Christian Herter to Simon Flexner, August 20, 1908, Christian Herter to Simon Flexner, August 22, 1908, Simon Flexner to Christian Herter, August 25, 1908, Christian Herter to Simon Flexner, September 7, 1908, folder 8, box 1, RG 417, Rockefeller University Archives, RAC.
29. Rufus Cole to his family, April 21, 1901, folder 1, Family Correspondence, BC 671, Rufus Cole Papers, APS; Simon Flexner to Rufus Cole, folder 1, Correspondence with S. Flexner, BC 671, Rufus Cole Papers, APS.

30. For example, Rufus Cole to his family, January 20, 1901, February 15, 1901, March 27, 1901, folder 2, Family Correspondence, BC 671, Rufus Cole Papers, APS.
31. Cable from William Welch, Christian Herter, and Simon Flexner to L. Emmett Holt, no date [August 1908], folder 1, box 1, RG 430.2, Rockefeller University Archives, RAC.
32. Simon Flexner to Rufus Cole, August 15, 1908, folder 1a, Correspondence with S. Flexner, BC 671, Rufus Cole Papers, APS.
33. Rufus Cole to Simon Flexner, November 10, 1908, folder 1, box 1, RG 430.2, Rockefeller University Archives, RAC.
34. Simon Flexner to Rufus Cole, November 10, 1908, folder 1, box 1, RG 430.2, Rockefeller University Archives, RAC.
35. "Suggestions in Regard to the Organization of the Rockefeller Hospital for Medical Research," folder 8a, box 1, RG 417, Rockefeller University Archives, RAC. (This document has a handwritten date Dec. 1908. Because it appears to be the document requested by Flexner on November 10, 1908, to be sent in some two weeks, and there is evidence that it is the document discussed at November 28 meeting of the board of directors, I suspect that the date is inaccurate).
36. Ibid., 2.
37. Ibid., 10.
38. Ibid., 9.
39. Ibid., 10.
40. Ibid., 9.
41. The salaries of the medical staff were at that point expected to total $20,000. In 1910–1911, these salaries amounted to $22,700 and included Cole's $7,500 salary. See "Estimate for the Proposed Hospital," [July 1907], folder 541, box 52, Rockefeller Boards series, RG 2, OMR, Rockefeller Family Archives, RAC.
42. "Budget for the Hospital for the Year May 1, 1910 to July 1, 1911," Scientific Directors' Minutes 1901–1911, vol. 2, RG 110.2, Rockefeller University Archives, RAC.
43. "Minutes of the Special Meeting of the Board of Directors, November 28, 1908," Scientific Directors' Minutes 1901–1911, vol. 2, RG 110.2, Rockefeller University Archives, RAC.
44. "Minutes of the Special Meeting of the Board of Directors, January 27, 1909," Scientific Directors' Minutes 1901–1911, vol. 2, RG 110.2, Rockefeller University Archives, RAC.
45. The letter states, "In connection with the provision for the staff and other expenses of the hospital, I may say that my present view is that the members of the staff should devote their entire time to the service of the Institute and should receive no compensation from any other source, and that the hospital would make no charge for the board of patients or for their treatment. We understand that the Institute and all departments of it are intended to serve a single purpose, and that is the advancement of medical knowledge through research." Letter from John D. Rockefeller Jr. to Board of Directors, Rockefeller Institute, February 26, 1909, folder 542, box 52, Rockefeller Boards series, RG 2, OMR, Rockefeller Family Archives, RAC.
46. "Minutes of the Annual Meeting of the Board of Scientific Directors, October 14, 1911." Scientific Directors' Minutes 1901–1911, vol. 2, RG 110.2, Rockefeller University Archives, RAC.
47. Rufus Cole to Simon Flexner [after October 14, 1911 meeting of the Board of Scientific Directors], folder 8, box 1, RG 417, Rockefeller University Archives, RAC.
48. Corner, *History of Rockefeller* (n. 5 above), 91.
49. Walter Palmer to Rufus Cole, February 18, 1949, Walter Palmer folder, Correspondence, BC 671, Rufus Cole Papers, APS.
50. Tom Rivers, *Reflections on Life in Medicine and Science. An Oral History Memoir*, prepared by Saul Benson (Cambridge, 1967), 70.
51. For example, see Rufus Cole, "Hospital and Laboratory," *Science* 66 (December 9, 1927): 545–52; Alfred E. Cohn, *Medicine, Science and Art. Studies in Interrelations* (Chicago, 1931).
52. Cole to Flexner (n. 47 above).
53. On the professional dynamics of the call for "clinical science," see Russell C. Maulitz, "'Physician vs. Bacteriologist': The Ideology of Science in Clinical Medicine," in *The Therapeutic Revolution* (n. 1 above).
54. Elsewhere, I have examined the research careers of two of the Rockefeller Hospital scientists—Oswald T. Avery and Donald Dexter Van Slyke—focusing on interactions between the laboratory and the clinic.

See Olga Amsterdamska, "Chemistry in the Clinic: The Research Career of D.D. Van Slyke," in *Molecularising Biology and Medicine: New Practices and Alliances, 1910s–1970s*, eds., Harmke Kamminga and Soraya de Chaderevian (London, 1998), 47–82; and "Between Pneumonia and DNA: The Research Career of Oswald T. Avery," in *Historical Studies in the Physical and Biological Sciences* 24 (1993): 1–40.

Chapter 5

Rufus Cole and the Clinical Approach

Jules Hirsch

Professor Emeritus and Physician-in-Chief Emeritus, The Rockefeller University, New York, NY

Rufus Cole, the director of the Rockefeller Hospital when it opened its doors in October, 1910, played a central role in the early history of medical research at the Rockefeller Institute. I am not the first to give tribute to Cole; as recently as 1992, at the inauguration of a series of lectures known as the "Tri-Institutional Biomedical Forum," special attention was given to him. Maclyn McCarty's talk on "The Early History of Clinical Investigation at the Rockefeller Institute," drew particular attention to Cole's contributions to the development of patient-oriented research.[1] McCarty's essay ended with these words:

> There are a host of problems still facing us in medicine that cannot be relegated for solution to the basic science laboratory without continuous reference to bed side study of the manifestations and characteristics of disease in patients. Furthermore, the testing of new therapeutic procedures and theories of pathogenesis will certainly require return to the clinical setting. We will need to devise ways to reverse the current trends away from patient-oriented clinical research in order to recapture something more like the spirit that prevailed at the Rockefeller Hospital during its formative years.

I hope to extend McCarthy's observations by providing additional details of Cole's approach to medicine and his unique contributions to the development of clinical science.

Illness has often changed the course of events by affecting the lives of important individuals. The tale has been told many times, how the Reverend Frederick Taylor Gates—a prime advisor to John D. Rockefeller Sr.—read William Osler's *Principles and Practice of Medicine* and became convinced that an institute studying the nature of human disease should be a priority for Rockefeller munificence.[2] Gates was made aware of Osler's *Textbook of Medicine* by Elon Huntington, the son of a physician who was a member of the Central Baptist Church in Minneapolis, where Gates had been pastor from 1880 to 1885. Young Elon lived with the Gates family in Montclair, New Jersey while studying medicine in New York. Gates once asked him to suggest a textbook that he might read to become more familiar with medicine and the Osler book was Elon's recommendation. What may have fired Gates' curiosity about medicine was told by Simon Flexner on May 15, 1929, at a special meeting held at the Rockfeller Institute to honor Gates' memory.[3] Flexner spoke after John D. Rockefeller Jr. and William Welch, and noted that

> the project of an Institution for Medical Research, which as Mr. Rockefeller and Dr. Welch have explained, originated in Reverend Gates' mind, grew out of a personal experience. Mr. Gates had told me about this. He had a very dangerous illness when he was in the prime of life. Escaping with his life, he decided to acquaint himself with the state of medical knowledge existing at the time and to read the Osler textbook. Perhaps personal illness may have played a role in kindling his interest in medicine and from that interest a desire to found a research institute.

Another illness that may have shaped the early history of the Rockefeller Institute was the untimely death in 1901 of the first Rockefeller grandchild from scarlet fever. Soon afterwards, the decision was taken to expand the Rockefeller endeavor in medicine.

Undoubtedly, Cole recognized, as we all do, that illness can have profound consequences, but he came to believe that the study of medicine in a new and scientific way might have an even greater impact. Cole became a protagonist of the idea that the study of human illness can be a central driving force for the development of scientific biology.

Cole grew up in small town Ohio, the son of a physician. Accompanying his father on calls to patients gave him the boyhood resolve to study medicine. After undergraduate study at the University of Michigan, he enrolled and completed one year at the Medical School of the University of Michigan. He then had the good fortune to visit Chicago during the World's Columbian Exposition where a special exhibit describing the recently opened Johns Hopkins School of Medicine so impressed him that he left Michigan and enrolled at Johns Hopkins, completing his medical studies in 1899 at the age of twenty-seven. Thereafter, he joined the house staff at Hopkins and came under the influence of Osler. Osler's approach to medicine has been well described by G. Canby Robinson, Cole's first resident physician at the Rockefeller Hospital:

> Osler was a great physician and a preeminent teacher, but he was not an investigator in the present-day sense of the word. He was primarily interested in the manifestations of disease in patients, and his great skill and experience in observing and interpreting these manifestations made him a peerless diagnostician. His statistical method of studying the symptoms and physical signs of disease gave him the special knowledge required to predict the outcome of an illness and made him especially skillful in prognosis. He was not deeply interested in the study of the essential problems of disease requiring prolonged laboratory and experimental investigation; he was concerned with outward manifestations rather than with the broad biological significance of disease.[4]

In 1905, Osler left Johns Hopkins to become the regius professor at Oxford University. His successor, Lewellys Barker, differed sharply from Osler in his views of medicine and medical education. Barker had a great deal of laboratory experience, but much less clinical experience than Osler. He wisely made Rufus Cole, Osler's resident physician, his own first resident physician assuring that the Oslerian tradition of clinical excellence would be maintained.

Osler and Barker were both Canadians, and products of the University of Toronto, but they had been students twenty years apart, Osler in the 1870s and Barker in the 1890s. Barker had come under the influence of Franklin Paine Mall, the head of anatomy at Johns Hopkins and one of the first American educators to agitate for the essentiality of laboratory-based scientific investigation to understand human disease. In 1885, Mall entered Carl Ludwig's laboratory in Germany and became convinced by Ludwig that clinical medicine should be taught in a university setting and that its faculty should have a seamless relationship with both bedside and laboratory. Barker was deeply affected by Mall and became a major spokesperson for Mall's views. He also developed enduring friendships with the other major medical leaders of the day, among them, Simon Flexner.

On February 29, 1902, Flexner wrote to Barker soliciting his advice as to whether he should become the first director for the newly formed Rockefeller Institute for Medical Research in New York.[5] He ends his letter as follows:

> You know me better than any other person, even, perhaps, better than I do myself. You have seen me in many moods and as "naked" as at birth. Tell me what your advice is—freely and without reserve and 'from the heart.' Anything you say I will understand.

Five days later, Barker urged Simon Flexner to accept, writing as follows: "The only three men who could be considered for the position are Theobald Smith, Herter, and yourself and in my opinion you have more of the desirable qualities than either of the other two because you know enough to get the strongest men available around you and to give them a free hand and all the credit." Later that year on August 26, Barker wrote Flexner again, emphasizing his belief in the centrality of investigations: "We are at the point where, if ever, undergraduate teaching must be made an appendage and investigation the main work of the university departments in medicine. May we strike the right path."

Since Barker had spent so much time in the laboratory and so little time at the bedside, his resident physician, Rufus Cole, became the bridge between the laboratory with the clinic. As head of the Department of Medicine at Johns Hopkins, Barker restructured the teaching of clinical medicine by creating three divisions for investigation: chemical, physiological, and biological divisions. Cole, although untried in research, was made head of the Biological Division. He was given three small rooms equipped for ordinary bacteriologic investigations, as done at that time. There were two centrifuges reaching a speed of 3,000 rpm, sterilizers, and incubators, and access to an animal house. Having research as an integral part of the Department of Medicine was considered by many to be a radical departure. The great battle of full-time, research-oriented, departments of medicine versus part-time teaching by "pure" clinicians had begun. Osler, even from afar, continued to protest against having physicians who were not full-time practitioners as central members of the department.[6] But Barker remained unshaken in his effort to bring to fruition Mall's dream of making clinical medicine a scientific discipline taught by full-time investigator–clinicians.

Cole flourished in the new environment. Corner described Cole's work at that time and in his summary states that Cole carried on his pioneer studies of typhoid bacilli in the blood stream, studies which constituted the first systematic clinical laboratory research at the Johns Hopkins Hospital."[7] G. Canby Robinson gives further details:

> He studied typhoid fever, then a prevalent disease, with particular interest in the isolation of the typhoid bacillus from the blood of patients. Isolation of bacteria from the circulating blood of patients was then a relatively new and rare procedure, and Cole's work, among the first of its kind, served to establish the blood culture as a routine clinical procedure one which threw much light on the nature of typhoid fever and other diseases and became generally accepted as a means of making definitive diagnoses. Previous to this time practically all hospital laboratory work was concerned with the diagnosis of disease; Cole's work was a study of the disease itself. His activities in developing this new concept constitute his outstanding contribution to American medicine."[8]

Cole had seen illness firsthand when he accompanied his physician father during his medical studies, and had a personal brush with a severe illness. Describing his relationship to Osler he wrote "At one time I was also his patient, for he looked after me during my senior year in the Medical School at Johns Hopkins, when I was ill with typhoid."[9] Cole always admired Osler, but he recognized that Osler was not the type of experimentalist needed for the next developments in medicine.

At Hopkins, Cole became a stellar example of Barker's new scheme for making an inseparable mixture of investigation, clinical observation, and teaching in a full-time department of medicine. When Cole was developing his research skills, Osler's approach to medicine was still in the ascendancy elsewhere. But at Johns Hopkins, Cole and other physician–scientists demonstrated what a full-time post-Oslerian department could be. Close knowledge of Osler's approach as garnered by Gates and as experienced by Cole made these two deeply respectful of clinical observation, but at the same time they had become strongly committed to the concept that full-time physician–investigators should be the primary teachers and leaders of medicine.

Rockefeller Sr. and Reverend Gates had considered developing a medical school at the University of Chicago that would be exemplary of full-time scientific medicine. But the incorporation of Rush Medical School, a traditionally clinical type of school, into the University of Chicago, seemed to have preempted this possibility. Over time as full-time university-based departments of medicine developed at premier medical schools and eventually at the University of Chicago as well, it became apparent that there was a need for a special institute that would train young physicians to become the leaders of the "full-time" medical schools. Cole fulfilled this need with great distinction at the Rockefeller Hospital in the Rockefeller Institute of Medical Research and, by the end of his career, roughly half of the full-time chiefs of internal medicine in America were Rockefeller Hospital alumni.

When the Rockefeller Hospital was being built, it was believed that Christian Herter, a distinguished clinician and experimenter, would become its first head, but he died prematurely of a disease that may have been *myasthenia gravis.* The waxing and waning in severity of his illness carried with it the hope that he might finally improve, and that may have delayed the appointment of a successor to Herter. When the inevitable occurred, two candidates headed the list: one was Theodore Janeway and the other was the young Rufus Cole. Janeway was a respected physician of the Oslerian type. On the other hand, Cole was, as already described, an example of Barker's new type of physician–scientist. The choice of Cole to head the Hospital was therefore a selection of the route espoused by Barker, and before him by Mall and Ludwig: thus the Rockefeller commitment to the new science of patient-oriented research was made. Janeway's talents were put to other duties. He served the new Rockefeller Institute as a member of its board of scientific directors, while continuing to teach and practice at the College of Physicians and Surgeons of Columbia University.

The victory of the full-time system of physician–scientists as the major teachers of medicine held sway for most of the twentieth century. It only began to be dismantled in recent decades by the assault of healthcare schemes, and the entry of academic medicine into the business of healthcare as opposed to its role in the scientific inquiry of the nature of health and disease.

Cole's ideas on scientific medicine were central in shaping the plans for a hospital at the Rockefeller Institute for Medical Research. In 1901 before Cole's involvement, the exact directions to be taken at the Rockefeller Institute were uncertain. At first, active support of research at other sites was tried. On May 10, 1902, the board of directors of the Rockefeller Institute, meeting at 14 West 55th Street under the chairmanship of Dr. Welch, reviewed the activities of the first year of its existence. Twenty-three applications for financial aid had been selected for funding. All were in support of the amelioration and understanding of human disease. The directors frankly stated "it is not possible this early to form a just estimate of the value of the work accomplished in these specific lines during the first year."[10] Although they recognized that many valuable researches in medicine could not be carried on in the United States because of the lack of facilities and funds, and therefore supported researchers at home and abroad, they were nonetheless "united in the conviction that the highest aims of the Institute cannot be secured [by grants] alone."[11] They concluded that a new institution with scientific workers together under a single roof would be required for unity of research on human disease and they therefore resolved that the Rockefeller Institute should be constructed. They urged that

> the problems of human disease should always be close to the Institute. While the studies of the diseases of the lower animals is highly important, both from an economic point of view and from their bearing upon the understanding of many forms of human disease, and while the work of the institute will of necessity be largely experimental, yet intimate relation with the problems of human disease should not for a moment be lost sight of. In order that the causes and treatment of human disease may be studied to the best advantage, there should be attached to the institute a hospital for the investigation of special groups of disease.[12]

In May 1906, the first building on the campus, the present Founders Hall, was opened as the Laboratory Division of the Rockefeller Institute. Continued attention was given to the building of a hospital. In 1908, when Cole became interested in what type of hospital might be developed, he prepared a memorandum for the board of directors, describing a close connection between clinical observation and scientific laboratory work characteristic of his work at Johns Hopkins under Barker. He noted that "only the best results can be obtained from clinical study when those engaged upon it have at the same time facilities for undertaking experimental work on animals along parallel lines."[13] Although Cole's views were accepted at the time, their consequences were to be tested only after the opening of the hospital. The hospital was completed and officially inaugurated on October 17, 1910. On October 26, the first patient was admitted.

Cole, with the advice and aid of Flexner, put together a young, vigorous staff for the hospital. Cole himself wished to work on acute lobar pneumonia and selected Alphonse R. Dochez and Henry Marks as his assistants. Dochez had been at the Rockefeller Institute since graduating from the Johns Hopkins Medical School in 1907, and Cole arranged for his transfer from the laboratories to the hospital. Marks had graduated from Harvard Medical School and was trained at the Massachusetts General Hospital. Francis W. Peabody and George Draper, both to have brilliant careers in scientific medicine, also joined the group.

In these early days, an international flavor came to pervade the hospital, and has remained a permanent feature of the Hospital and the University. Francis R. Fraser and Arthur Ellis, early members of the Hospital resident staff, became leaders in British medicine after their training under Cole. Florentin Medigreceanu was a particularly colorful visitor from abroad. He was, in the words of Michael Heidelberger, "an impressively black-bearded Rumanian."[14] Heidelberger, recalling the early years in the Hospital noted that

> In the spring of 1912, we had a baseball game on an empty lot in front of the buildings. Van Slyke pitched for the hospital and I did the same for the labs. Medigreceanu managed to get as far as second base and then on the next hit nearly broke up the game by running back to first.[15]

Unfortunately, Medigreceanu returned to a less amiable environment in Europe and his talented life ended during the World War I.

The camaraderie and lifelong commitment to medical excellence and medical science that developed in these men from all nations is most notable. Their lives at the Hospital had been both productive and happy. G. Canby Robinson noted that

> Life in the hospital was full of joy. A few patients in whom we had special and intensive interest; laboratories such as none of us had ever before seen in any clinics; varied interests both within and without the realm of medicine; the East River with its great span of light at night, and its lapping water; a blazing hearth about which we gathered after dinner—all these things made the setting in which friendship deepened and true sympathy thrived.[16]

The deep commitment to medicine of Cole and his young colleagues and their intense desire to provide a scientific basis for clinical observations was put to the test in the summer of 1911 when a poliomyelitis epidemic flared in New York City. (The results of these first studies in the new hospital were published in June 1912 as a monograph of the Rockefeller Institute under the title *A Clinical Study of Acute Poliomyelitis* by Francis W. Peabody, George Draper, and A.R. Dochez.) Cole wished his men to probe deeply into those laboratory investigations that would provide scientific underpinning to the clinical aspects of poliomyelitis. I have elsewhere described the differences of opinion that developed on the propriety of physicians undertaking in-depth laboratory work.[17] Cole spoke eloquently on their behalf when he informed the board of scientific directors in 1911 that

> men who are studying disease clinically have the right to go deeply into its fundamental nature as their training allowed and in the Rockefeller Institute Hospital every man who was caring for patients should also be engaged in more fundamental study. It has required some effort and energy to get the men to adopt this view, but they are now convinced of its soundness and he hoped that some of them, at least, might share in the revolution, or evolution of clinical medicine that was bound to come.[18]

Such apparent differences of opinion between Cole and Flexner on what the nature of the Hospital should be, were resolved over succeeding decades. In a memorial piece written after the death of Simon Flexner on May 2, 1946, Cole commented that

> largely due to the influence of Dr. Flexner, it was provided that the physicians in the hospital should not only have charge of the treatment of the patients, and observe the superficial characters of disease, but that they themselves should at the same time be actively engaged in investigating the underlying phenomena. Besides making important contributions to knowledge, this hospital has developed many physicians who have later become Professors of Medicine, here and abroad, and who have carried the spirit of scientific investigation into many medical clinics, and have influenced many students of medicine.[19]

Flexner and Cole worked together to assemble a hospital staff that demonstrated the importance of bringing clinically trained individuals into a setting where continued clinical observation and laboratory work were blended in inquisitive minds attempting to reconstruct the pathogenesis of disease states.

The careful selection of those of unusual ability became a major element in the success of the Institute. There is perhaps no better example of the artistry practiced by Flexner and Cole in their selections than the case of Oswald Theodore Avery. Avery, a young physician graduated from the College of Physicians and Surgeons of Columbia University in 1904, found employment at the Hoagland Laboratory in Brooklyn. For its day, this was a rather sophisticated laboratory of bacteriologic research. Avery became interested in the pathogenesis of tuberculosis in humans and was examining the incidence of bacteremia with the tuberculosis organism and also how secondary infections came about in tuberculosis. During the course of this work, he developed an interest in the chemical fractionation of the bacterium to evaluate the chemical causes of the tissue response to infection. His publications caught Cole's eye and he was brought to the Institute in 1913 to continue his chemical explorations as applied to the *pneumococcus*. Thirty-one years later, he published a classic of molecular genetics, demonstrating that a chemical substance in the *pneumococcus*, namely DNA, could induce transformation of the nature of the *pneumococcus*. Three decades before publication of Avery's work on pneumococcal transformation, Cole commented on his good fortune in finding him. At the twentieth anniversary of the Hospital on May 8, 1931, Cole was given a gift of 460 scientific papers in 13 bound volumes, all work done in the second 10 years of the Hospital. In his gracious acceptance he noted

> But as imposing as these volumes are, they do not contain all the contributions of the Hospital. Some of my discoveries, probably the most important ones, are not here. Some of you are my most valued discoveries. For instance, shortly after the Hospital opened I came across a paper by a man of whom I had never heard. The work so impressed me by its evidence of accuracy and care, the conclusions were so logical and straightforward and it was written in such a clear, lucid manner that I decided the writer must be a man of great ability. I found that he was working in a laboratory in Brooklyn and at once I rushed over to see what manner of man he was. As soon as it could be arranged, I offered him an opportunity to work in the Hospital of the Rockefeller Institute and Dr. Avery has been with us ever since. That was really a great discovery.[20]

When in 1946, Avery was awarded the Kober Medal of the Association of American Physicians for his distinguished work, he recalled how important his colleagues at Rockefeller Institute had been. He stated "Cole picked these men and all I had to do was pick their brains."[21] Cole gave the Hospital a special approach to scholarship in clinical medicine, and then made certain that those who were given the opportunity to become physician–scientists at the Hospital had been appropriately selected.

Rather than expressing unalloyed jubilation at this great triumph, Cole remained deeply concerned about the future of clinical science. Five remarkable talks given on the occasion of various special events were published in *Science* and collectively constitute a document expressing Cole's concerns.[22] Cole predicted that the science born of blending medical observations and laboratory experiences into a unitary science of clinical medicine might have lesser interest and lesser impact than the development of the laboratory sciences alone. He foresaw the time when laboratory work would be so dominant that clinical medicine would become only a testing ground for ideas coming from elsewhere. Cole's prophecy has been fulfilled. The scientific medicine that he and his colleagues created 100 years ago seems to have been made redundant by new sciences of biomolecular medicine. Moreover, the coup de grâce devastating clinical science today is the pressing need for healthcare delivery, which has been assumed by medical schools to the detriment of careful observations of disease and, thereby, of learning from nature's experiments.

Illness and its effects on important individuals and thus on history is inevitable, but it will take additional efforts to return to a deeper consideration of illness with systematic study by trained observers who, as physician–scientists, will draw on their clinical experiences as well as laboratory sciences to answer fundamental biologic questions. The lesson taught by Cole is that careful selection of motivated physicians, working in a clinical environment, protected from the day-to-day demands of medical practice, can enrich medical science and direct us to new frontiers in biological science. If we still believe this approach has merit, the memory and commitment to the convictions of Cole may strengthen our resolve and light the way.

Endnotes

1. Maclyn McCarty, "The Early History of Clinical Investigation at the Rockefeller Institute," Occasional Papers of the Tri-Institutional Biomedical Forum, Rockefeller University Hospital (New York, 1992).
2. George W. Comer, *A History of the Rockefeller Institute* (New York, 1964), 23.
3. Addresses to Honor the Memory of Frederick Taylor Gates, May 15, 1929, folder 495, box 65, Friends and Services series, Record Group 2, Office of the Messrs. Rockefeller (OMR), Rockefeller Family Archives, Rockefeller Archive Center, Sleepy Hollow, New York (hereafter RAC).
4. G. Canby Robinson, *Adventures in Medical Education* (Cambridge, 1957), 84.
5. Abner McGehee Harvey, "Rufus Cole and the Hospital of the Rockefeller Institute," *Trends in Biomedical Research, 1901–1976. Proceedings of the Second Rockefeller Archive Center Conference, December 19, 1976.* A Rockefeller Archive Center Publication. (Sleepy Hollow, NY, 1977), 13–24.
6. Michael Bliss, *William Osler: A Life in Medicine* (Oxford, 1999), 387.
7. Comer, *History of Rockefeller* (n. 2 above), 93.
8. Robinson, *Adventures* (n. 4 above), 86.
9. Rufus Cole, "Dr. Osler: Scientist and Teacher," *Archives of Internal Medicine* 84 (1949): 54–63.
10. Minutes of the Board of Directors of the Rockefeller Institute for Medical Research, 10 May 1902, RG 110.2, Rockefeller University Archives, RAC.
11. Ibid.
12. Ibid.
13. McGehee Harvey, "Rufus Cole" (n. 5 above), 21.
14. Michael Heidelberger, "Early Days at the Rockefeller Institute," *Trends in Biomedical Research 1901–1976, Proceedings of the Second Rockefeller Archive Center Conference, December 10, 1976.* A Rockefeller Archive Center Publication. (Sleepy Hollow, NY, 1977), 47–51.
15. Ibid.
16. Robinson, *Adventures*, 84.
17. Jules Hirsch, "The Role of Clinical Investigation in Medicine: Historical Perspective from the Rockefeller University," *Perspectives in Biology and Medicine* 41 (1997): 108–17.
18. Comer, *History of Rockefeller* (n. 2 above), 107.
19. Rufus Cole, "In Memoriam: Simon Flexner," *Bulletin of New York Academy of Medicine* 22 (1946): 546–52.
20. McCarty, "Early History" (n. 1 above).
21. Oswald T. Avery, "Acceptance of the Kober Medal Award," *Transactions of the Association of American Physicians* 59 (1946): 43.
22. Rufus Cole, "The Modern Hospital and Medical Progress," *Science* 64 (1926): 123–30; Rufus Cole, "Hospital and Laboratory," *Science* 66 (1927): 545–52.
23. Rufus Cole, "The Inter-Relation of the Medical Sciences," *Science* 67 (1928): 47–52. Rufus Cole, "Progress of Medicine during the Past Twenty-five Years as Exemplified by the Harvey Society Lectures," *Science* 71 (1930): 617–27.
24. Rufus Cole, "The Practice of Medicine," *Science* 88 (1938): 309–16.

Chapter 6

Innovation in Modern Surgery: Alexis Carrel and Blood Vessel Repair

Shelley McKellar

Assistant Professor, Department of History, University of Western Ontario, Social Science Center, London, Ontario, Canada

Until recent times, surgery was regarded as a treatment of last resort, one associated with pain, blood, and almost certain death. This changed as a result of numerous innovations and advances in surgery during the late nineteenth and twentieth centuries. By 1900, anesthesia and antisepsis had become accepted practices in surgery, enabling surgeons to combat the pain and infection associated with their craft. An increasing number and range of surgical operations were being performed successfully, and heralded as being curative. Leading surgeons of the period, such as Theodor Billroth, Victor Horsley, and William Halsted among others, were boldly operating in the abdomen and the cranium. New surgical treatments for a range of medical conditions emerged, including intestinal obstructions, gastric cancer, ulcers, thyroid surgery, problems of the face and neck, and orthopedic surgery. Healing by the knife was gaining legitimacy, and before long, no organ or cavity in the body was necessarily deemed to be beyond the purview of the surgeon.[1] The perception of physicians, patients, and society about what was surgically possible and desirable in the treatment of disease was changing.[2]

Yet despite the improved management of pain and infection in surgery, bleeding continued to be a problem for the surgeon.[3] To combat fatal hemorrhaging (excessive blood loss), practitioners cauterized and ligated (tied off) bleeding arteries and veins. When main arteries were tied off, this often meant that the blood supply to the limbs was cut off, and that the leg or arm would turn black with gangrene, forcing the surgeon to amputate. The preferred alternative to ligation would be to repair the damaged vessel to restore blood circulation: how difficult could it be to suture blood vessels? By 1900, several surgical researchers in Europe and the United States were exploring this question and presenting various experimental methods of suturing blood vessels, but no one had developed a successful clinical technique. Beginning in 1901, French surgeon Alexis Carrel (1873–1944) tackled this problem, first in his laboratory in France and later at the Rockefeller Institute for Medical Research in New York, and subsequently was successful in developing the essential techniques for suturing blood vessels, which is still taught to surgical residents today.[4]

Blood vessel repair marked a turning point in the expansion of the therapeutic role of surgery and in the surgical concept of what was possible, rousing excitement among researchers, medical practitioners, and society. This essay focuses on Carrel's innovations in blood vessel repair that contributed to improved vascular procedures, including transfusion, in the early decades of the twentieth century and laid the foundation for later successful heart operations and transplant surgery. For this work, Carrel was awarded the Nobel Prize for Physiology and Medicine in 1912. Carrel's experimentation with blood vessel repair and organ transplantation also contributed to the public imagination and acceptance of new possible and desirable surgical treatments. Sensational media reporting announced the dawn of a new surgical era based on Carrel's experimental procedures; however, successful routine clinical application of this research was delayed for another 30 to 40 years.

Alexis Carrel: From France to America

Alexis Carrel was born near Lyons, France on June 28, 1873. He was the eldest of three children in a bourgeois Roman Catholic family. His father, a well-to-do textile manufacturer, died when Alexis was only five years old, requiring the family to adopt a more modest lifestyle. The young Alexis received a Catholic education, attending a Jesuit day school and college, and was a good, but not outstanding, student. He received a baccalaureate in letters and science, and then began his medical studies. From 1896 to 1900, Carrel gained his practical training in various hospitals in Lyons, principally the Hotel-Dieu, and served as an army surgeon with the Chasseurs Alpins (the mountain infantry). During this period, he also conducted laboratory work where he demonstrated great technical ability in dissection and operative surgery. In 1900, Carrel was awarded the MD degree from the University of Lyons, and for the next two years taught anatomy and experimental surgery in the Faculty of Medicine. Despite several attempts, however, Carrel was not successful in passing the difficult hospital exams necessary for a surgical appointment during this period.[5]

On the occasion of his second failed attempt, Carrel was almost 30 years of age. He had financed his medical studies with a modest inheritance from his grandparents. A humble individual, he had simple manners and tastes. He was a short, stocky man, with a round face and the distinctive pince-nez glasses he wore throughout his life; his eyes were small and piercing—one brown and one blue—and radiated the intensity of his personality. He was a serious, somber man who spoke with a soft, contained voice. He possessed a creative mind, ready to explore new possibilities and generous with his time to intelligently discuss new ideas. This innate curiosity drove much of his research work, which he tackled with great energy and self-confidence. He was firm in his convictions, refused to procrastinate, and was frustrated by those who did otherwise. He could be friendly and charming, but was not overly social—he disliked interruption or distraction to his work. He could also be tactlessly blunt and demonstratively irritated with individuals he deemed to be wasting his time. At this point and time in his young career, Carrel was particularly angry and bitter toward his French colleagues.[6]

By 1903, Carrel had been unsuccessful in securing the coveted hospital appointment in Lyons and he became frustrated by the rigid system of seniority and patronage; for Carrel this was a considerable professional and psychological setback. Undoubtedly a contributing factor to his lack of success was his earlier statement concerning a Lourdes miraculous healing. Miracles had no place in the scientific mind, yet Carrel reported to the Lyons medical community that the tuberculous peritonitis (an inflammatory disease of the walls of the lining of the abdomen and pelvis) of a young girl, near death, inexplicably resolved itself after the sprinkling of sacred water on the girl's stomach.[7] Refusing to declare it a miracle, Carrel rationalized the episode as evidence that there were organic and mental processes still not understood by the medical profession. He credited most religious healings to the power of suggestion. Still medical men criticized him for being gullible and for declaring the girl cured from the pilgrimage. The Lourdes case damaged his credibility within the Lyons medical community, and Carrel gave up any hope of acquiring a hospital appointment in the city.[8]

In the spring of 1904, Carrel left France and traveled to Canada. Several historians have suggested that Carrel considered leaving medicine to take up farming or ranching in North America.[9] Fortunately, he never seriously pursued either. Shortly after arriving in Montreal, at the Second Medical Congress of the French Language in North America, Carrel delivered a paper and gave a demonstration on his experimental blood vessel repair work that he had begun in Lyons.[10] It was an opportune occasion to present his work and to explore research possibilities in Canada and the United States. Dr. Carl Beck, professor of surgery at the University of Illinois, attended that conference and invited Carrel to join his surgical practice in Chicago.[11] But Carrel was a researcher, not a clinician. Instead, Carrel accepted a position in the Hull Physiology Laboratory at the University of Chicago. In Chicago, Carrel was provided with adequate laboratory space and equipment, and worked with Dr. Charles Guthrie, a young physiologist. Carrel could now direct his attention to what he liked best—conducting surgical research—work that would earn the expatriate a Nobel Prize in the near future.

Blood Vessel Repair and a Nobel Prize

Several historians suggest that Carrel's interest in vascular surgery resulted from the 1894 assassination of French President Sadi Carnot who died of a hemorrhage from a knife wound that severed a portal vein.[12] At that time, surgeons were unable to repair severed blood vessels, and in frustration, they stated that nothing could be done to save President Carnot; perhaps this influenced Carrel. More likely, the promising experiments of Mathieu Jaboulay, under whom Carrel interned during his medical studies in Lyons, persuaded him that vascular procedures were indeed within surgical reach. At this time, Jaboulay was one of only a few researchers working on the challenge of repairing blood vessels to restore circulation as an alternative to ligature. In 1896, he published one of the first papers describing an experimental technique to perform an end-to-end anastomosis (joining) of blood vessels.[13] The next year, American researcher John Murphy reported the successful repair of a lacerated femoral artery.[14] In Germany, surgeon E. Payr explored the possibility of substituting magnesium tubes for arterial segments in repairing damaged vessels.[15] Despite using different techniques or materials, their common challenge was thrombosis (or blood clot formation) at the site of anastomosis as a result of injury to the inner lining of the vessel wall. Technically, if they succeeded in suturing the vessel together, it later became obstructed (or closed) due to clotting. They queried their different suturing techniques, should the sutures be continuous or minimal? should the sutures only penetrate the outer layer of the vessel wall? or should a tube be used to connect the ends of the blood vessel? There was no consensus of opinion regarding the correct way to reunite blood vessels and all techniques remained experimental.[16]

Within this context, while still in France, Carrel conducted preliminary experiments in blood vessel repair from 1901 to 1904. He reviewed, evaluated, and modified the divergent techniques and understanding of vascular surgical procedures. He realized immediately that a successful suture technique demanded manual dexterity, gentleness in handling the sensitive vascular tissue, and strict aseptic conditions. He experimented with different size needles and varying suture materials; in the end, he adopted very fine needles and thread to suture vessels that were less than a matchstick in diameter. With practice, his manual dexterity improved. Carrel partially attributed this to the embroidery lessons he received from an embroidress in Lyons.[17] His experiments were predominantly end-to-end anastomosis of arteries to veins in dogs, which produced mixed results. Sometimes the vessels remained patent or open, other times they became obstructed with blood clots—not unlike the results of others in this new field of research. Carrel's research conditions in his French laboratory were also far from ideal, and often infection compromised his experiments.[18] Refinement of his blood vessel suture technique would be performed in the United States.

In 1904, Carrel left France for North America, where he was soon installed at the Hull Physiology Laboratory at the University of Chicago. There, Carrel enjoyed improved research conditions and several years of productive experimental work. Most significantly, he refined the triangulation method of anastomosis, which became known as the Carrel method. This triangulation technique of suturing altered the circular form of the vessel into a triangle, thus allowing the surgeon to sew three straight lines, which is a more effective suturing method. Three sutures were placed 120° apart, on the circumference of the cut circular ends, and then two of the sutures were pulled in opposite directions. The surgeon sutured this straight line, a third of the circumference, before he repeated this step for each of the other two thirds. Carrel performed a continuous stitch with the smallest of short round needles using fine silk thread coated with petroleum jelly. The petroleum jelly rubbed off in the tiny puncture holes, and smoothed over the inner layer of the vessel wall. These "everted" sutures left the inside of the vessel thread-free, thereby minimizing endothelial injury (or injury to the inner lining of the blood vessel) and clotting. Carrel also used narrow linen bands instead of forceps again to minimize blood vessel damage. In describing his suture technique, he wrote,

> A rigid asepsis is absolutely essential for success . . . The dissection of the vessel is not dangerous if the wall of the vessel is not crushed or roughly handled with metallic forceps or other hard instruments . . . it is necessary that these clamps (vascular) be smooth-jawed and not too strong in the spring . . . by using very sharp, round needles, only extremely small wounds are made . . . great care is taken not to include fragments of the connective tissue layer in the lining of suturing, and to obtain a smooth union and approximation of the endothelial coats."[19]

Typically, surgeons at this time used large absorbable sutures and forceps, which contributed to blood vessel trauma and clotting. Carrel's "everted" suture technique produced repeated successful results.[20]

Once Carrel had refined the suture technique and was able to suture vessels together successfully, he practiced excising and reattaching vessels, and transplanting blood vessels and organs. The blood vessel repair method made this possible—in fact, it was the next logical step to Carrel. In 1905 and 1906, Carrel and Guthrie began grafting veins in arteries, a promising, possible treatment for aneurysms. They also experimented with replantation and transplantation of several organs and limbs, including the thyroid gland, the kidney, the leg, and the thigh.[21] These experiments tested the feasibility of reestablishing blood circulation and viability of these organs. In dogs, the organs and limbs were removed and reattached after a short period, usually within a matter of hours. With the exception of the thyroid gland replantation, all dogs died of infection, but Carrel viewed the experiments as successful because circulation was reestablished in all cases. In his transplant experiments, Carrel explored auto-, homo-, and heterotransplantation of kidneys, renal glands, intestines, hearts, lungs, thighs, and ovaries in cats and dogs. Again, this work focused on the viability of dissecting organs and vessels and reattaching these body parts to suitable vessels of the same or another animal. In many cases, the organs were not transplanted into the true anatomical positions, such as the kidney and heart, which were more or less grafted to vessels in the neck.[22] Carrel's results were far from conclusive as he experienced problems of infection and organ rejection.[23] He also claimed that he was unaware of Emerich Ullmann's kidney transplant success in Vienna reported in 1902, but did acknowledge the ongoing work in the field of Carl Beck in Chicago, Hopfner in Berlin, and Floresco in France.[24]

At this time, Carrel was among the few pioneers who demonstrated such imagination, vision and creativity in surgical research and who presented encouraging results. He had developed the technical essentials of vascular surgery by devising a suture technique that reduced trauma to the inner wall of the vessel, managed the problem of clotting, and was reproducible by other surgeons. The introduction of this suture technique—in fact, the beginning of vascular surgery—marked a key turning point in the surgical concept of what would now be possible. Carrel showed the medical community how vascular surgery translated into larger surgical possibilities like replantation and transplantation of organs and limbs. In particular, Carrel's work drew the interest of several leading surgeons in America, most notably Harvey Cushing of the Johns Hopkins University in Baltimore.

In the fall of 1905, the Society of Clinical Surgery met in Chicago. Cushing, writing directly to Carrel, requested a private demonstration: "I would much rather see one of your experiments and your methods of suture, etc., than go to our prescribed meeting."[25] Carrel was pleased to do so, for he had long admired Cushing's "progressive mind" and looked forward to meeting the man.[26] It marked the beginning of their lifelong friendship. Carrel first met Cushing in 1905 as well as many other leading surgeons at an intended private meeting, which turned into a large crowd including Drs. Rudolph Matas, George Crile, John Murphy, and others who were investigating related vascular procedures.[27] Carrel described the demonstration to Guthrie this way:

> Harvey Cushing is a splendid fellow very intelligent and broadminded . . . Saturday Matas, Cushing and Crile came to the laboratory, but unfortunately about twenty other people, Monro, Lecont, Murphy, etc. came also. It was overcrowded and it was impossible to see anything. Everything must be cleaned before it will be possible to operate again. We operated on a dog. Crile was making the [anesthesia]. Within five minutes, the dog was dead! It was very funny . . . Now everyone knows our experiments. I have been very glad of this occasion to know these three men, Cushing, Matas and Crile for they are very good and interesting.[28]

Cushing later apologized for the "invasion of unexpected guests," and years later they joked about Crile spoiling the procedure by over-anesthetizing the subject.[29]

This demonstration reaped huge benefits for Carrel, providing exposure for Carrel and his work to a larger American medical audience, notably the leaders of the experimental surgical community. Back in Baltimore, Cushing reported favorably on Carrel's work to Drs. Halsted and Kocher.[30] George Crile went back to Cleveland and, within months, applied Carrel's method of vessel anastomosis successfully in his work on blood transfusion. To Carrel, he wrote, "The method seems to me to be quite perfect and I hope your own results are satisfactory. Should you venture in this part of the country, I would be very glad to have you visit me."[31] The surgical community wanted to know more about Carrel's work. Professional invitations, requests for reprints, and inquiries about private visits to Carrel's lab began to pour in. In the spring of 1906, Carrel traveled to Baltimore at the invitation of Cushing to demonstrate and deliver a paper on his work before the Johns Hopkins Hospital Medical Society. Despite delivering his paper in broken English, which embarrassed Carrel, his work was well received and later published.[32]

The year 1906 was difficult for Carrel, not least because he found himself in the awkward position of needing an income. His position in Chicago did not include a stipend or salary. Although Carrel told people that he was glad to be able to work in a laboratory, he felt that he was "nothing" at the university and that the laboratory equipment was poor.[33] He was frustrated by his financial situation, his experiments were difficult and necessitated his full attention, and so he preferred not to teach or practice surgery. Carrel even considered leaving the United States. In a letter to Cushing, Carrel wrote of his predicament:

> My plans for next year are not yet fixed. I would remain in University of Chicago only if I could establish there the teaching of Surgical Physiology and make my researches in good conditions. But it is entirely impossible. Perhaps I will go to Central America. Perhaps I will stay in Chicago and operate on human beings instead of on dogs. From a business stand point, it would be excellent. But, as I hate medical practice, I would like better to make little money in doing scientific work than a great deal in doing surgical operations.[34]

Cushing set to work to bring Carrel to Baltimore on a Rockefeller Institute grant.[35] Undoubtedly, he recognized the potential impact of Carrel's work to surgery, and he used his connections in an attempt to keep Carrel's research going.

On Carrel's return to Chicago from his address to the Johns Hopkins Hospital Medical Society, Cushing arranged for Carrel to meet with Simon Flexner, director of the Rockefeller Institute for Medical Research, in New York. This meeting changed Carrel's viewpoint, and as it turned out his future career plans, regarding the conduct of research in the United States. In rare praise of scientific men and laboratories in America, Carrel wrote this to Cushing:

> In New York I greatly admired the Rockefeller Institute and the Director Dr. Flexner. The set-up of the Rockefeller Institute is both very simple and very practical. It will without doubt constitute an excellent center for scientific research. I was intensely pleased to make the acquaintance of Dr. Flexner, who gave me the impression of being an absolutely remarkable man. I am really extremely grateful for your introduction to him.[36]

Cushing responded with similar praise of Flexner and the Rockefeller Institute. He stated,

> I quite agree with all that you say in regard to Flexner. He is a very unusual type of man, and the only person in the country, I believe, who could undertake the work that he is doing at the Rockefeller with any probability of making a success of it. We have not in this country a great many men of the type of those who have with such self-sacrifice spent their years at work in the Pasteur Institute in Paris. Flexner, however, is of the same stamp.[37]

In expanding the work and staff of the Rockefeller Institute, Flexner searched for men with ideas, regardless of specialties, and he was impressed with Carrel's research achievements and imagination.[38] Within weeks, Flexner notified Carrel that the Rockefeller Institute would fund his research, not in Baltimore, but at the newly opened Rockefeller laboratories in New York.[39] Carrel immediately accepted the offer.

The first of its kind in America, the Rockefeller Institute provided Carrel with the ideal research environment for his surgical research. In comparison with contemporary university laboratories, Carrel enjoyed large research quarters, new equipment, and substantial support (equipment and assistance) for this work without the distraction of teaching or private practice. Although an academic position or a surgical practice would have garnered a higher income, Carrel was happy to devote his time entirely to research.[40] Nevertheless, several academic surgeons tried to attract Carrel to their university laboratories. On several occasions, Dr. George Crile promised Carrel the ideal research position in his new laboratory in Cleveland, doubling his Rockefeller stipend, arguing that, unlike the Rockefeller Institute, the nearby hospital offered the opportunity for Carrel's work to move from the laboratory to the clinic more quickly.[41] Carrel politely declined. At the Rockefeller Institute, he was given great autonomy to organize the surgical rooms as he liked–such as dark operating room walls and dark operating clothes to reduce glare—and to train, in Carrel's words, "absolutely ignorant assistants"[42] without interference from Flexner, who supported all of Carrel's requests.[43] At the Rockefeller Institute, Carrel demanded absolute sterility in his laboratory, from disinfected instruments to full-garbed assistants, to avoid contamination of his various experiments. Most of his staff were skilled technicians, who Carrel closely directed and demanded unquestioning service.[44] He realized his fortunate position, stating that "From a scientific standpoint, the Rockefeller Institute appears to me as an ideal place where it is possible to make successfully experiments quite impossible elsewhere."[45] His only complaint was that the Rockefeller Institute was located in New York. He wrote Guthrie that

> New York is an unpleasant city. All is overcrowded. When I came back from Canada I had to get settled in New York. I was so disgusted by the city that I settled as far as possible from it. I advertised, and I found a nice private family in Larchmont, on the shore of the Ocean, where I settled. It is in the country. I live in a small cottage, and it is very nice. But the trouble is that I have to take a little trip every morning (15 minutes walk, 40 minutes railroad, 10 minutes elevated railroad, 10 minutes walk). After that I am in the Rockefeller Institute, where I stay generally from 9 a.m. to 4 or 5 p.m.[46]

Carrel found living in New York expensive, over-crowded, and noisy. Nonetheless, he remained there virtually for the rest of his scientific career, changing accommodations many times, and returning to France each summer for his vacation. New York was livable for Carrel because of the Rockefeller Institute and the excellent research facilities therein.

Once installed in his new laboratory, Carrel returned to his research. Between 1906 and 1910, Carrel focused on further refining his vascular suture technique and exploring various organ transplantation procedures.[47] He transplanted arteries and veins in cats and dogs, concluding that his suture technique was a safe and constantly successful method. Blood vessels could be sutured without danger of thrombosis and occlusion (clotting).[48] He studied the preservation of blood vessels in cold storage to determine the conditions under which vessels could remain viable outside the body. He then experimented with transplanting these preserved vessels.[49] He again attempted transplantation of the thigh from a dead dog to a living one, but with no greater results than his previous work. He performed kidney transplants from cat to dog, dog to cat, even rabbit to cat. He successfully performed numerous auto-transplant experiments, replanting one kidney after a double nephrectomy. But his homotransplantations and heterotransplantations, following the same techniques, consistently yielded unsuccessful results. This led Carrel to conclude that organ replantation in an individual dog, such as a thyroid gland or kidney, was feasible; however, transplantations between animals of the same species and of different species failed. Carrel suspected differences in the chemical physiology of the individual animals contributed to organ degeneration.[50] The surgical technique of transplantation had been devised, but he had not overcome the biological problem. In 1910, Carrel also began exploring intrathoracic surgery.[51] He experimented with patching the aorta, resecting a segment of the vena cava, and attaching shunts between the apex of the left ventricle and the aorta, among other cardiac procedures without stopping the heart. He even attempted elementary coronary artery bypass operations without success.[52]

In 1912, Carrel was awarded the Nobel Prize for Physiology and Medicine for his work in suturing blood vessels and transplanting organs. His friend, Dr. Carl Beck, had nominated him. At the time, the 39-year-old Carrel was the youngest Nobel laureate and the first researcher in America to be awarded this honor.[53] The award celebrated his technical achievement of blood vessel repair and organ transplantation and for the expansion of the therapeutic role of surgery. As the presenting member of the Nobel Committee stated,

> You have successfully performed daring and extremely difficult operations. By means of all these experiments you have stretched the limits of human surgical intervention and proved once again that the development of applied science, which operative medicine is, is based on the lessons learned from animal experimentation.[54]

Congratulatory telegrams and letters to Carrel reiterated this same point—Carrel's ingenuity had opened new surgical possibilities.[55] Carrel's work contributed to the reconceptualization of surgical treatment in this period. Lifesaving vascular procedures, heart operations, and transplant surgery successfully performed on animals in the laboratory would soon be performed clinically. Or so the public envisioned.

The Impact of Carrel's Work

Before 1912 and the award of the Nobel Prize, Carrel's more "sensational" work received sporadic attention by the public press. The nature of this reporting by the public press tended to be promotional and celebratory of the Rockefeller Institute, medical science, and, in particular, society who would benefit from these new surgical advances. Reporters presented Carrel's work, not as experimental or limited to animals per se, but as new procedures ready to save human lives. In reporting medical advances in this way, the press shaped patterns of public expectation, enthusiasm, and meaning. Sensational media reporting announced the dawn of a new surgical era in which fit Carrel's work on blood vessel repair and organ transplantation. This stirred public imagination and expectation for surgical solutions to previously untreated medical conditions.

In 1908, in response to the Rockefeller Institute's announcement of Carrel's success with transplantation of kidneys in cats,[56] bold headlines read: "Kidneys? Borrow a Cat's—Doctors Say They Can Transplant the Vital Organs Now," and "Transfer of Vital Organs Coming."[57] Reporters stated "It was not a far cry to the time when it may be possible to transplant one of the vital organs from an animal's body to that of a human." Trumpeting Carrel's work as an important breakthrough, reporters went so far as to suggest that modern surgery was close to revolutionizing medicine. "The substitution of healthy organs for the diseased parts of the human body will be made possible through the new experimental surgery and vivisection and will revolutionize modern medicine," stated one article in the *New York Tribune*.[58] The concept of spare parts surgery took hold among the public, appearing more feasible as Carrel continued to present promising results from his experimental research.

The press had a field day when Carrel presented a paper at the meeting of the American Philosophical Society in Philadelphia in December 1908 on his success in transplanting a leg from a dead dog to the stump of a living dog. In this paper, Carrel presented his results from several experiments, including the successful preservation of arteries for surgical use, the joining of blood vessels between two humans for direct transfusion, and the transplantation of a kidney (preserved in cold storage for 60 days) into a cat.[59] But what captured the attention of reporters was the image of a female fox terrier frisking about on the leg of a dead male companion.[60] The headlines read: "New Limbs for Old and New Vital Organs," "Doctor Can Do Most Anything Now-A-Days," and "New Surgery Ready to Apply Results to Making Over Humans."[61] To the Academy of Medicine in Paris, French surgeon Samuel Pozzi who recently visited the United States praised the work of Carrel and the Rockefeller Institute. He said that "he had returned to France wonder-struck over the marvelous results obtained by Carrel in grafting and transplanting arteries, veins, ears, kidneys, and other organs . . . It is tremendous surgical progress," he stated, "opening the way to an era of new surgery."[62] The next day, the French press, obviously less awestruck and impartial, ran a cartoon showing one man's preference for the transplantation of wheels rather than limbs to his lower body, which he claimed was more stylish and practical.[63]

The medical press attempted to downplay the publicity by stating that the transplant operation (limbs or organs) was hardly within the range of practical surgical procedures. Since the time of John Hunter's famous experiment of the successful grafting of human teeth into a rooster's comb in the eighteenth century, many others have tried similar experiments.[64] Teeth, skin, bones, nerves, blood vessels, and now kidneys had all been reported as transplantable experimentally. Similarly, Carrel's work in the transplantation of limbs remained extremely experimental, not really a clinical possibility anytime soon. As one reporter of the *Medical Press and Circular* wrote regarding Carrel's dog with the new transplanted leg, "Its chief purpose in life at present seems to be to give a delightful opening to the raging propaganda of the anti-vivisectionists."[65] Still, the public press continued to celebrate Carrel's work. The *New York Scientific American* reported that "Clearly the day is not far off when the perfect organs of a man who in life had been free from disease may be kept in cold storage after his death and used to replace diseased organs in living men."[66]

Fueling this public sentiment or hope for the viability of spare parts surgery, Carrel's work in tissue culture earned similar headlines in the press. His study of cultures of living tissues began in earnest in 1911 at the Rockefeller Institute.[67] Carrel worked toward devising a technique of keeping living cells alive outside the body to study the reparative and growth process of cells.[68] This was intended to further his research toward improving and hastening the healing of wounds. What if human tissues and even whole organs could be cultivated artificially to be substituted for diseased parts of the body? (In terms of this research, what most people remember is Carrel's '"chicken heart culture," frequently reported in the popular press, and which "lived" for 34 years.) In 1912, Carrel reported to the American Medical Association that he was working on preserving tissues and organs after death and encouraging growth of new cells for viability for transplantation. He was harvesting, even growing, spare body parts for surgery. The press headline "Human Hearts, Eyes and Bones on Sale for Surgeons' Use" reported,

> It was not generally known until today that there is a sort of department store where one may obtain properly "canned" and labeled parts of a human heart, nerves, blood

> vessels, spleen, many of the smaller glands, the cornea of the eye, various bones of the body and cartilage to be used in repairing diseased human frames.[69]

Carrel's surgical procedures were experimental, and not yet ready to move from the laboratory to the clinic, despite public demand. For example, first, his blood vessel suturing technique and grafting procedures were only just beginning to be reproducible and used by American surgeons in the early twentieth century.[70] Second, regarding his work in organ transplantation, technically he was able to perform transplant surgery in animals, but he had not overcome the biological problem of rejection. All of Carrel's work was creative, imaginative, but most of it was not clinically acceptable. Nevertheless, after the 1912 Nobel Prize announcement, Carrel's work gained greater notoriety and legitimacy. He began to receive increasing correspondence from desperate individuals inquiring about the experimental procedures. A man from Detroit, Michigan volunteered for a limb transplant operation. "I wear two artificial legs," he wrote Carrel. "One stump above the knee and the other below. I have for a long time believed it possible to graft limbs on to take the place of those I have lost."[71] A New York doctor sent this request to Carrel.

> An acquaintance of mine from South Dakota wrote me saying he understand[s] that there is a most wonderful man in New York who can transplant human parts and make them grow . . . Would it be possible for him or his associates or you or some one in New York to find and implant an external ear on a seven month old baby girl successfully? About what will it cost?[72]

People, especially desperate individuals, wanted to believe in Carrel, who the press had dubbed "The Wizard Surgeon," and the possibility that his work was clinically feasible.[73]

In fact, the clinical application of Carrel's research was delayed for another 30 to 40 years. Whereas the public may have quickly accepted Carrel's work, his proposed surgical procedures were not so quickly endorsed or adopted by practicing surgeons. Carrel's suture technique, specifically his triangulation method, was described and illustrated in surgical textbooks during the 1910s, such as Horsley's *Surgery of the Blood Vessels* (1915) and Da Costa's *Modern Surgery* (1919).[74] Although endorsed by the medical profession as a recognized, improved method of blood vessel repair, the procedure was complicated, difficult, and required trained assistants, as noted by Horsley in *Operative Surgery* (1924).[75] During World War I, when blood vessel repair would have saved limbs, even lives, it was not a feasible operation because of the septic conditions of the battlefield. After the war, the majority of surgeons had difficulty reproducing Carrel's successful results due to either infection or blood clotting problems. Still, practitioners recognized blood vessel repair as a new, promising surgical therapy to better treat their patients.[76] With the introduction of heparin (an anticoagulant) in the 1930s and antibiotics in the 1940s, clotting and infection difficulties were managed more effectively and vascular surgery expanded further.

Carrel was not a clinician: he was an experimental surgeon. He moved rapidly from one experimental procedure to another. He liked to prove something to his own satisfaction, and was not concerned with the need to prove it to others.[77] It was up to them to reproduce his results. At the Rockefeller Institute and its hospital, laboratory research and clinical application were separate functions exercised by different sets of medical practitioners.[78] Carrel worked on animals, not on humans. In many cases, only the most talented surgeons were able to repeat

Carrel's successes clinically. What bothered Carrel was the medical mindset regarding surgery at the period. He wrote this to Cushing:

> I like very much your ideas about surgery and surgeons and general medicine. It is to be hoped that your broad conception of medicine be understood by a great many physicians. It would be very useful, indeed, to teach them that surgery is a little more than a simple trade and that it is not a thing to be made a show of before a crowded amphitheater. It would be very important for the production of great discoveries in surgical therapeutics, for instance, that the term medicine be understood by the investigators in its Hippocratic sense. It is difficult to imagine how enormous are the untried possibilities of research. However this immense field remains almost unexplored because the investigators are very often "enfermés" [confined] in their specialty as in a jail. They have no general scientific ideas, and of course they are deprived of the "imagination créatrice" [creativity] of bold hypothesis and new experiments.[79]

In his publications, Carrel was rightly cautious in advancing any absolutes regarding the clinical application of his work. When he presented his papers or discussed his ideas with colleagues, he often clearly stated that his new operations "may have an almost immediate interest for the surgeons."[80] He expected them to carry his work into the clinic on their own, without realizing their individual limitations or clinical difficulties.

Surgeons were interested in Carrel's new procedures and Carrel readily presented his work in medical journals, at professional meetings, and through laboratory demonstrations. Carrel perfected the required surgical techniques, and other therapeutic and diagnostic advances (such as heparin, antibiotics, and angiographs) allowed the majority of surgeons to perform his and other vascular procedures even more successfully. In time, Carrel's surgical innovations in the laboratory were accepted in the clinic. For example, in the 1950s, blocked arteries in the limbs were being replaced; in the next decade, coronary artery bypass procedures were performed successfully.[81] In 1962, a 12-year-old boy's severed right arm was grafted back on, becoming the first successful replantation of a limb.[82] In the 1940s, British researcher Peter Medawar identified the need for immunosuppressive drugs in transplantation, and in 1954 in Boston, Joseph Murray and J. Hartwell Harrison performed the first successful human kidney transplant.[83] Carrel's work represented a critical first stage: a blood vessel repair technique that allowed surgeons to control bleeding and restore circulation by sewing vessels together. This led to grafting segments of arteries and veins, to bypassing blocked coronary arteries, and even to organ transplantation. As one medical practitioner stated, "There are few innovations in cardiac and vascular surgery today that do not have roots in his work. The epithet, father of 'vascular surgery,' is justly applied to Alexis Carrel."[84] More important than being the father of vascular surgery or the first to sew blood vessels together successfully, Carrel and his successes in the laboratory contributed to altering the perception of physicians, patients, and society about what was surgically possible and desirable in the treatment of disease in humans. As the twentieth century progressed, younger researchers would negotiate even further the surgical limits challenged by Carrel.

Conclusion

Carrel's research was not limited to vascular surgery. During World War I, Carrel's interest in the healing of wounds took priority as he was appalled by the badly infected war wounds of

Allied soldiers. In collaboration with chemist Henry Dakin, Carrel devised a new wound irrigation procedure using a strong antiseptic solution, known as the Carrel–Dakin technique.[85] An effective method of disinfectant in wartime to battle massive infection, the complicated procedure was not adopted into civilian practice where infection was more controllable. In future wars, infection was fought with sulfa drugs and, later, antibiotics. During the 1920s and 1930s, Carrel's time was spent on tissue culture and organ perfusion experiments. With Charles Lindbergh, the well-known aviator of the *Spirit of the St. Louis*, Carrel worked on an apparatus (a perfusion pump) to keep isolated organs, such as the heart, liver, kidneys, thyroid glands, and ovaries, alive outside of the body.[86] The pump was not an artificial heart, as dubbed by the press, for it was not a system for cardiopulmonary bypass.[87] Nonetheless, it was showcased as such at the 1939 New York World's Fair. In that same year, the 65-year-old Carrel was forced into mandatory retirement from the Rockefeller Institute. Frustrated, he wrote Cushing, "It is the first time, I believe, that a man who has received the Nobel Prize has been compelled to give up scientific research when the research is most promising."[88] He closed his New York laboratory soon thereafter, and returned to France.

Carrel spent the remaining years of his life in France, where he worked to set up a research laboratory. During World War II, Carrel accepted the offer of the Vichy government to subsidize his Institute of Man, a long-time dream. In 1941, the Fondation Francaise Pour L'Etude des Problemes Humains was sanctioned by law and charged with ". . .researching all practical solutions and proceedings with all demonstrations in view of improving the physiological, mental and social conditions of the population."[89] It was intended to be a research center where experts from all disciplines would assemble to solve various human problems. Early work at the Institute ranged from the problems of children to the psychology of work to mental telepathy and extrasensory perception. By this time, French society and most scientists characterized Carrel as a Nazi sympathizer and collaborator. Earlier, Carrel had written a non-medical, controversial book, entitled *Man the Unknown*, which outlined his views on the ills of society and the needed remedies. It caused a stir at the time of its publication in 1935 and again during World War II when individuals cited passages on Carrel's support of eugenics as evidence of Nazi collaboration. His fascist political leanings and his racist and elitist views concerning Jews, women, intelligence, eugenics, and other subjects make Carrel a controversial figure. Leaving the mystic and philosophical side of Carrel's character to the philosophers, Carrel's earlier medical contributions, notably his blood vessel repair work, were largely overshadowed in the later years of his life. In 1944, at the age of 71, Carrel suffered a fatal heart attack. He was survived by his wife of 31 years; they had no children. Less than a year after Carrel's death, the Institute of Man was dissolved.[90]

Despite the controversy that surrounded Carrel in his later years, most obituaries published in the medical and popular press respectfully described the scientist's earlier contributions to surgical research.[91] Simon Flexner characterized Carrel's work as "novel and original . . . There can be no doubt that he possessed the essential intellectual perceptions, as well as the delicate skilled hands, of the master surgeon, which fitted him for the exacting work he had undertaken."[92] At a time when surgeons still grappled with bleeding and infection, Carrel presented techniques to manage both these aspects, most notably repairing blood vessel damage. Blood vessel repair was Carrel's most important contribution, demonstrating that suturing arteries and veins together was achievable. He next went on to devise procedures of blood vessel grafting, coronary artery bypass, limb replantation, organ transplantation, and more.

His experimental work, despite not moving immediately from laboratory to clinic, presented the medical community and the public with new possible and desirable surgical treatments. It stimulated public imagination and medical interest in these areas. Blood vessel repair marked a key turning point in the surgical concept of what was possible. Early twentieth century surgical limits were pushed back and whole new surgical fields were developed. What could and would be done in cardio-thoracic, vascular, and transplant surgery was founded on much of Carrel's experimental work.

I am grateful for all questions and comments from audience members at the Rockefeller University Centennial History Conference, specifically informal discussions with Bert Hansen, Olga Amsterdamska, Carol Moberg, and Hannah Landecker. In addition, Toronto colleagues Margaret Derry, Allison Kirk-Montgomery, and the Institute for the History and Philosophy of Science and Technology colloquium audience offered helpful comments and insights on a similar paper. I thank Professor Michael Bliss for directing me towards the Carrel-Cushing correspondence in the Harvey Williams Cushing Papers, Yale University Library. Interpretations, errors, and omissions in this article are mine. Funding for this research was provided in part by a Rockefeller Archive Center grant.

Endnotes

1. Roy Porter, *The Greatest Benefit to Mankind: A Medical History of Humanity* (New York, 1997), 597–605.
2. Jacalyn Duffin, *History of Medicine* (Toronto, 1999), 231–4.
3. Ulrich Trohler, "Surgery (Modern)," in *Companion Encyclopedia of the History of Medicine,* eds. W.F. Bynum and Roy Porter (London, 1993), 984–94.
4. Steven G. Friedman, *A History of Vascular Surgery* (New York, 1989), 75, 88.
5. Biographical Sketch, folder 1; Biographical Sketch, folder 19, box 44, Alexis Carrel Papers, Special Collections Division, Georgetown University Library, Washington, DC (hereafter GU).
6. Biographical Sketch, folder 19, box 44, Carrel Papers, GU; W. Sterling Edwards and Peter D. Edwards, *Alexis Carrel: Visionary Surgeon* (Springfield, Illinois, 1974), 8; Charles A. Lindbergh, "A Tribute to Alexis Carrel," in *Papers of the Centennial Conference at Georgetown University, June 28, 1973,* eds. R. W. Chambers and J. T. Durkin (Washington, DC, 1973), 29–33.
7. The girl entered a convent and lived another 34 years. Friedman, *History of Surgery* (n. 4 above), 76.
8. See Carrel's account, *Voyage to Lourdes,* quoted in Edwards and Edwards, *Alexis Carrel* (n. 6 above), 17–21.
9. Theodore I. Malinin, *Surgery and Life: The Extraordinary Career of Alexis Carrel* (New York, 1979), 16; Edwards and Edwards, (n. 6 above), 21.
10. Alexis Carrel, "Les anastomoses vasculaires, leur technique opératoire et leurs indications," 2e *Congres des Medicin de Langue Francaise de l'Amérique du Nord,* (Montreal, 1904).
11. Carl Beck to Carrel, no date, box 40, Carrel Papers, GU.
12. Malinin, *Surgery and Life* (n. 9 above), 4; Edwards and Edwards, *Alexis Carrel* (n. 6 above), 8.
13. M. Jaboulay and E. Briau, "Recherches experimentales sur la suture et la greffe arterielles," *Lyon Medical,* 81 (1896) 97–9.
14. John B. Murphy, "Resection of Arteries and Veins Injured in Continuity: End-to-end Suture, Experimental and Clinical Research," *Medical Record* 51 (1897): 73–88.
15. Erwin Payr, "Zur Frage der Circulaeren Vereingung Von Blutgefaessen mit Resorbibaren Prothesen," *Langenbecks Archiv der Klinische Chirurgie* 70 (1900): 67-9.
16. Friedman, *Vascular Surgery* (n. 4 above), 30.
17. Edwards and Edwards, *Alexis Carrel* (n. 6 above), 13.
18. Alexis Carrel, "Anastomose bout a bout de la jugulaire et de la Carotide Primitive," *Lyon Medical* (1902): 114.
19. Alexis Carrel, "The Surgery of Blood Vessels, Etc.," *Johns Hopkins Hospital Bulletin* (January 1907): 18–28.
20. Alexis Carrel, "Anastomosis and Transplantation of Blood-Vessels," *American Medicine* 10 (1905): 284–5.
21. For more on the relationship between Carrel and Guthrie, see Samuel P. Harbison, "Origins of Vascular

Surgery: The Carrel-Guthrie Letters," *Surgery* (August 1962): 406–18.
22. Alexis Carrel and Charles C. Guthrie, "Functions of a Transplanted Kidney," *Science* 22 (1905): 473.
23. Alexis Carrel, "The Transplantation of Organs: A Preliminary Communication," *Journal of the American Medical Association* 10 (1905): 1645–6.
24. Carrel, "Surgery of Vessels" (n. 19 above), 18–28.
25. Harvey Cushing to Carrel, 2 October 1905, box 41, Carrel Papers, GU.
26. Alexis Carrel to Harvey Cushing, undated, folder 272, reel 11, series I Correspondence, Harvey Williams Cushing Papers, Manuscript and Archives, Yale University Library, New Haven, CT (hereafter Yale).
27. Murphy, (n. 14 above), 73; Rudolph Matas, "An Operation for the Radical Cure of Aneurism, based upon Arteriorrhaphy," *Annals of Surgery* 19 (1903): 119–21; William Halsted, "The Partial Occlusion of Blood Vessels, Especially of the Abdominal Aorta," *Bulletin of the Johns Hopkins Hospital* 17 (1905): 346; Rudolph Matas, "The Suture in the Surgery of the Vascular System" (address delivered at the Meeting of the Medical Association of Alabama, 1905).
28. Carrel to Guthrie, 9 October 1906, quoted in Samuel P. Harbison, "Origins" (n. 21 above), 414.
29. Cushing to Carrel, 24 October 1905, box 41, Carrel Papers, GU; Cushing to Carrel, 27 June 1935, box 41, Carrel Papers, GU.
30. Carrel to Cushing, 12 November 1905, folder 272, reel 11, series I Correspondence, Cushing Papers, Yale.
31. George Crile to Carrel, 26 November 1906, box 41, Carrel Papers, GU.
32. Carrel, "Surgery of Vessels" (n. 19 above), 18–28.
33. Carrel to Cushing, 13 December 1905, folder 272, reel 11, series I Correspondence, Cushing Papers, Yale.
34. Carrel to Cushing, 22 February 1906, folder 272, reel 11, series I Correspondence, Cushing Papers, Yale.
35. William Welch to Cushing, 28 March 1906, box 41, Carrel Papers, GU; Cushing to Carrel, Announcement of Scholarships and Fellowships of the Rockefeller Institute, no date, box 41, Carrel Papers, GU.
36. Carrel to Cushing, 6 May 1906, folder 272, reel 11, series I Correspondence, Cushing Papers, Yale.
37. Cushing to Carrel, 8 May 1906, box 41, Carrel Papers, GU.
38. George W. Corner, *A History of The Rockefeller Institute, 1901–1953: Origins and Growth* (New York, 1964), 74–6.
39. L. Emmett Holt to Carrel, 14 May 1906, box 42, Carrel Papers, GU.
40. "The Developments of the First Twenty Years of the Rockefeller Institute," 295–96, box 3, volume 14, Record Group 439, Scientific Reports of the Laboratories, Rockefeller University Archives, Rockefeller Archive Center, Sleepy Hollow, New York (hereafter RAC).
41. Crile to Carrel, 8 January 1907, 7 February 1907, 28 February 1907, box 41, Carrel Papers, GU; Stewart to Carrel, 30 January 1907, 4 February 1907, box 45, Carrel Papers, GU.
42. Carrel to Guthrie, 14 November 1906, in Harbison, "Origins," (n. 21 above), 413.
43. "Men work here," Flexner wrote, "in a dozen different branches of biological sciences, can I be an authority on them all? No, no, give them perfect freedom; let them search where and how they will; help them in every way you can, but do not pretend to be master over them." Quoted in Corner, *History of Rockefeller* (n. 38 above), 58.
44. Ibid, 153.
45. Carrel to Cushing, 26 January 1907, folder 272, reel 11, series I Correspondence, Cushing Papers, Yale.
46. Carrel to Guthrie, 14 November 1906, in Harbison, "Origins," (n. 21 above), 413.
47. Reports of Dr. Carrel, 1907, 1908, 1909, 1910, RG 439, Scientific Reports of the Laboratories, Rockefeller University Archives, RAC.
48. Alexis Carrel, "Further Studies on Transplantation of Vessels and Organs," *Proceedings of the American Philosophical Society* 52 (1908): 677–96; Alexis Carrel, "Latent life of arteries," *Journal of Experimental Medicine* 12 (1910): 460–86.
49. Alexis Carrel, "Heterotransplantation of Blood Vessels Preserved in Cold Storage," *Journal of Experimental Medicine* 9 (1907): 226–8.
50. Alexis Carrel, "Transplantation in Mass of the Kidneys," *Journal of Experimental Medicine* 10 (1908): 98–140; Alexis Carrel, "Results of Transplantation of Blood Vessels, Organs, and Limbs," *Journal of the American Medical Association* 52 (1908): 1662; Alexis Carrel, "Remote Results of the Replantation of the Kidney and the Spleen," *Journal of Experimental Medicine* 12 (1910): 146; Alexis Carrel, "The Ultimate Result of a Double Nephrectomy and the Replantation of One Kidney," *Journal of Experimental*

Medicine 14 (1911): 124; Alexis Carrel, "The Transplantation of Organs," *New York Medical Journal* 98 (1914): 840.

51. In 1909, Carrel began to use endotracheal anesthesia, developed by Samuel J. Meltzer and his assistant John Auer at the Rockefeller Institute. Endotracheal anesthesia contributed the development of chest and heart surgery by allowing the lungs to be ventilated with the thoracic cavity open. Edwards and Edwards, *Alexis Carrel* (n. 6 above), 44–8.
52. Alexis Carrel, "Experimental Surgery of the Thoracic Aorta by the Method of Meltzer and Auer," *Journal of the American Medical Association* 55 (1910): 28–31; Alexis Carrel, "On the Experimental Surgery of the Thoracic Aorta and Heart," *American Journal of Surgery* 23 (1910): 83–5; Alexis Carrel, "Permanent Intubation of the Thoracic Aorta," *Journal of Experimental Medicine* 15 (1912): 389–92; Alexis Carrel, "Experimental Operations on the Orifices of the Heart," *Annals of Surgery* 29 (1914): 1–4; Alexis Carrel, "On the Technique of Intrathoracic Operations," *Surgery Gynecology and Obstetrics* 19 (1914): 226–28.
53. Carrel was the third surgeon to receive the Nobel Prize in Medicine and Physiology, after Theodor Kocher (1841–1917) of Switzerland, who received the Nobel Prize in 1909 for thyroid surgery, and Allvar Gullstrand (1862–1930) of Sweden, who received the Nobel Prize in 1911 for ocular dioptrics. Since Carrel, there have been other surgeons who have received the award: Robert Barany (1876–1936) of Austria for vesicular disease in 1914; Frederick Banting (1891–1941) of Canada for insulin in 1922; Walter Hess (1881–1973) of Switzerland for midbrain physiology in 1949; Werner Forssmann (1904–1979) of Germany for cardiac catheterization; Charles Huggins (1901–present) for his work in oncology in 1966; Joseph Murray (1919–present) for his work in transplantation in 1990.
54. "Alexis Carrel: Nobel Prize for Physiology and Medicine, 1912: Address by Professor Jules Akerman, Member of the Medical Nobel Committee," *Transplant Proceedings* 4 (August 1987): 9–11.
55. Correspondence, 1912, box 41, Carrel Papers, GU.
56. Carrel, "Transplantation" (n. 50 above), 98.
57. Press Clippings, folder 4, box 72, Carrel Papers, GU.
58. *New York Tribune,* January 2, 1908.
59. This paper was later published as "Further Studies on Transplantation of Vessels and Organs," *Proceedings from the American Philosophical Society* 52 (1908): 677–96.
60. The dog with the transplanted leg (attached below the knee) died of pneumonia 22 days after the transplant operation. Postmortem examination showed that circulation had been restored and the bones had united fairly well. It is unknown why rejection did not occur; blood and tissue-type matching were not done. In Carrel's mind, this was the first experiment (of which more were to follow but without this success) to show that the functions of a transplanted limb could be normally re-established. See Carrel, "Further Studies" (n. 59 above), 684–6.
61. Press Clippings, folder 94, box 72, Carrel Papers, GU; Press Clippings, folder 95, box 72, Carrel Papers, GU.
62. Press Clippings, folder 71, box 72, Carrel Papers, GU.
63. Press Clippings, folder 68, box 72, Carrel Papers, GU.
64. John Kobler, *The Reluctant Surgeon: A Biography of John Hunter* (New York, 1960), 141–2.
65. Alexis Carrel, *The Medical Press and Circular*, 23 June 1909. Antivivisectionists targeted Carrel and his experiments for the following three reasons: (1) the lack of utility of most of the experiments from the viewpoint of practical application to man; (2) the intense suffering of the victims; and (3) the non-use of anesthetics to allay or prevent such suffering. Their cause temporarily lost momentum in 1909 when a blood transfusion, based on Carrel's blood vessel grafting and suturing techniques and administered by Carrel at the Rockefeller Institute, successfully saved the life of an infant with the blood of her father. The infant suffered from melena neonatorum, in which blood oozes from the whole surface of the digestive tract from mouth to lower intestine. The father was an active antivivisectionist protester in New York. See "Vivisection Editorial," *The Southern Christian Advocate*, 24 March 1910); and Corner, *History of Rockefeller* (n. 38 above), 76–7.
66. *New York Scientific American*, 5 December 1908.
67. Reports of Dr. Carrel, 1911, RG 439, Scientific Reports of the Laboratories, Rockefeller University Archives, RAC.
68. For more information on Carrel's research on tissue culture, refer to the work of Hannah Landecker,

who argues that Carrel's surgical training influenced the development of tissue culture. See Chapter 7 in this book.

69. Press Clippings, folder 310, box 72, Carrel Papers, GU.
70. Cushing commented on the "scattered cases" in the literature that used the Carrel suture technique. Cushing to Carrel, 27 January 1907, box 41, Carrel Papers, GU.
71. H.M. Kent to Carrel, 16 October 1913, box 45, Carrel Papers, GU.
72. W. Sohier Bryant, MD, to Carrel, 25 February 1913, box 45, Carrel Papers, GU.
73. Press Clippings, folder 65, box 39, Carrel Papers, GU.
74. J. Shelton Horsley, *Surgery of the Blood Vessels* (St. Louis, 1915), 31–79; John Chalmers Da Costa, *Modern Surgery*, 8th ed. (Philadelphia, 1919), 503–7.
75. J. Shelton Horsely, *Operative Surgery*, 2nd ed. (St. Louis, 1924), 96–101.
76. I thank Bert Hansen for his comments on this particular point, as well as his essay (see Chapter 3 in this book.
77. Charles A. Hufnagel, "Alexis Carrel: Contributions to Surgery," in *A. Carrel Papers of the Centennial Conference at Georgetown University, June 28, 1973,* eds. R. W. Chambers and J. T. Durkin (Washington DC, 1973), 84–107.
78. Certainly laboratory staff, including Carrel, looked forward to the testing and application of their ideas clinically in the Rockefeller Hospital by the hospital staff. Carrel did not have operating privileges in the Hospital, and Hospital staff pursued their own clinical research projects that may or may not have coincided with laboratory research projects at the Rockefeller Institute. For more on this, see Corner, *History of Rockefeller* (n. 38 above), 91–2; and Olga Amsterdamska, Chapter 4 in this book.
79. Carrel to Cushing, 30 June 1906, folder 272, reel 11, series I Correspondence, Cushing Papers, Yale.
80. Carrel to Cushing, 5 March 1906, folder 272, reel 11, series I Correspondence, Cushing Papers, Yale.
81. Harris B. Shumacker Jr., *The Evolution of Cardiac Surgery* (Bloomington, IN, 1992).
82. R.A. Malt and C.F. McKhann, "Replantation of Severed Arms," *Journal of the American Medical Association* 110 (1964): 716–22.
83. Porter, *Greatest Benefit* (n. 1 above), 615, 620, 623.
84. Friedman, *Vascular Surgery* (n. 4 above), p.82.
85. A. Carrel, H. Dakin, J. Daufresne, P. Dehelly, and M. Dumas, "Traitement abortif de l'infection des plaies," *Bulletin de la Academie Nationale de Medicine* (1915): 361–8; A. Carrel and G. Dehelly, *The Treatment of Infected Wounds* (New York, 1916).
86. Alexis Carrel and Charles A. Lindbergh, "Culture of Whole Organs," *Science* 80 (1935): 621; Alexis Carrel and Charles A. Lindbergh, *The Culture of Organs* (New York, 1938).
87. Schumacker, *Evolution* (n. 81 above), 248.
88. Carrel to Cushing, 17 March 1939, box 41, Carrel Papers, GU.
89. Friedman, *Vascular Surgery* (n. 4 above), 82.
90. Edwards and Edwards, *Alexis Carrel* (n. 6 above), 109–23; Malinin, *Surgery and Life* (n. 9 above), 110–23.
91. Press Clippings, box 44, Carrel Papers, GU.
92. Simon Flexner, "Alexis Carrel (1873–1944)," *Year Book of the American Philosophical Society* (1944), 344–9.

Chapter 7

Building "A new type of body in which to grow a cell": Tissue Culture at the Rockefeller Institute, 1910–1914

Hannah Landecker
Assistant Professor of Anthropology, Rice University, Houston, TX

Through the discovery of tissue culture we have, so to speak, created a new type of body in which to grow a cell.[1]

Alexis Carrel of the Rockefeller Institute for Medical Research and his assistant Montrose Burrows together coined the term "tissue culture" and in 1910 began a series of highly publicized experiments in which they showed that all kinds of tissues—including embryonic, adult, and cancerous—could not only be kept alive outside of the body, but would actually undergo cell division and growth in vitro. Growth and reproduction of cells and tissues outside of the body, rather than their mere survival, became the defining characteristic of tissue culture. Carrel dominated the practice of tissue culture for many years and laid down the early principles of its materials and methods, although several other laboratories took on the technique as their main research task.[2]

Despite early enthusiasm for the potential promise of the methodology, it was plagued with a number of difficult technical problems and obstacles to the quantitative study of biological phenomena. Before the introduction of antibiotics, it was a difficult task to keep cultures of tissues from dying of bacterial infection. Many efforts were made to find a synthetic medium in which to grow the cells and to make the studies of cell nutrition and metabolism more precise, but until the 1950s, Carrel's discovery that all cultures would diminish and perish without the addition of the ill-defined substance, embryo extract, held true. Practices and materials were idiosyncratic from laboratory to laboratory. Carol Moberg has detailed how, in 1946, with the establishment of a professional group called the Tissue Culture Commission (and later the Tissue Culture Association), practices and materials were standardized one by one.[3] These factors led to the rapid dissemination of a more standardized practice of tissue culture in all branches of biological research and instead of being a research goal in itself, to which a laboratory had to commit major resources in terms of labor and materials, it became a technique used to many different ends.

Alexis Carrel occupies a special position within the history of the development of tissue culture. It became common after his death in 1944 to blame a perceived downturn in the use of tissue culture in the 1930s on Carrel's eccentricity and emphasis on the difficulty of the method. Aside from several rather hagiographic biographies and a general recognition of his fundamental contributions to surgery, there exist fairly widespread judgments that he was (a) a mystic; (b) a vain man who stole the limelight for tissue culture when it did not properly belong to him; (c) a hindrance rather than a positive force in the further development of tissue culture after its initial establishment; and, later in life, (d) a fascist or at least a Vichy-collaborating eugenicist.

Figure 1. Alexis Carrel. Undated portrait. Alexis Carrel Papers, Rockefeller Archive Center.

In 1954, a journalist for *Collier's* magazine, after interviewing four eminent American tissue culture researchers for an article about the technique in modern medicine, summed up their opinions of Carrel as follows:

> A brilliant man . . . Dr. Carrel made valuable contributions to the science of tissue culture. But many of his contemporaries criticized him on the grounds that he treated tissue culture as an occult art (he insisted his assistants wear flowing black robes and hoods in the laboratory) and promised all kinds of advances in the conquest of disease—promises he was never able to keep because of the limited techniques then used. The whole tissue-culture field suffered in the 1930s because of his eccentric behavior.[4]

Not much has changed since 1954. In 1979, historian Jan A. Witkowski concluded that although Carrel was a pioneer of tissue culture and its "chief publicist," his mode of operation and publication convinced his contemporaries that tissue culture was a complicated and extremely difficult technique.[5] His dominance in the field coupled with his emphasis on the difficulty of the technique actually discouraged further progress in the field. Witkowski takes his cue from the judgments of scientists such as E. N. Willmer, who in an introduction to a 1965 manual of tissue culture wrote that "Tissue culture, although a delicate and exacting technique and one in which vigorous asepsis is absolutely essential, gained a spurious and unfortunate reputation for difficulty and almost for mysticism."[6] In a similar but even more sarcastic judgment of an enthusiastic developer of plant tissue culture, P. R. White stated that tissue culture manuals needed to be written just to rectify the damage Carrel had done to the perception of the subject:

> I have sought to strip from the study of this subject its former atmosphere of mystery and complication. The gray walls, black gowns, masks and hoods; the shining twisted glass and pulsating colored fluids; the gleaming stainless steel, hidden steam jets, enclosed microscopes and huge witches' cauldrons of the "great" laboratories of "tissue culture" have led far too many persons to consider cell culture too abstruse, recondite and sacrosanct a field to be invaded by mere hoi polloi![7]

This is a picture of a vainglorious scientist of dubious character and eccentric tastes, whose greatest talent was opportunism and whose work was an active deterrent to progress in a scientific field. It simultaneously gives too much and too little credit to Carrel. It portrays him as having single-handedly endowed an entire field of practice that he supposedly dominated for decades with an enduring air of occult mystery; but at the same time, it assumes that his dominance was without scientific or technical foundation, and due only to opportunism and mysticism. None of these accounts pays sufficient attention to what he and his many assistants and technicians actually did in the laboratory; how this led to the establishment of a practice called tissue culture; the medical–surgical context of his other work at the Rockefeller Institute; and the interesting and enduring connection between tissue culture and what might be called the aesthetics of Carrel's laboratory. Furthermore, Carrel succeeded where others with the same idea had failed in attempting to follow embryologist Ross Harrison's lead into a more general method of cultivation of tissues outside of the body. Neither opportunism nor mysticism can account for Carrel's role in the establishment of tissue culture, his continued dominance in the field, or his influence in shaping its terminology, aims, uses, technologies, and protocols.

However, this is neither a biography nor a defense of Carrel. Instead, it is a detailed history of the development of tissue culture technology in Alexis Carrel's Experimental Surgery research group at the Rockefeller Institute between 1910 and 1914.[8] To understand the creation of a "new type of body in which to grow a cell," it is essential to understand the context of the old type of body on which Carrel had been operating for many years as well as the creation of an experimental system based on life outside of the body. This implies a framing theory of the body and of its relation to the interventions of surgery and the technology of the laboratory.

The importance of Carrel's training and work as a surgeon, as well as his scientific audience that included the medical community, shaped the development of tissue culture in three important ways. First, assumptions and discoveries of the qualities of plasticity, regeneration, and fluidity of living tissues were intrinsic to the practice of surgery at this time. Second, the importance of technical details such as asepsis, temperature and humidity regulation, and maintenance of circulation were transferred to the practice of tissue culture. And finally, tissue culture bore the medical stamp of the underlying goal of therapeutic intervention in the human body.

I will connect Carrel's surgical practices both to his technical success with growing tissues outside of the body, and to the desire to access the internal life of the body. The technique of tissue culture was, as one of Carrel's assistants put it, the creation of "a new type of body in which to grow a cell," an artificial, technological, transparent body that would take over the functions of the obfuscating animal body that had been cut away. The life manifested by the cell in this "new type of body" would in turn reconfigure the concept both of the cellular life and the body.

I will only briefly address Carrel's career in surgery up to 1908 because this is comprehensively covered in this volume by Shelley McKellar. The detail lies in the description of Carrel's adaptation of tissue culture to his own purposes and questions, and the kinds of opposition and challenge he encountered from other scientists. This is contrasted with another experimental system that Carrel was trying to establish at the same time as tissue culture, and which he saw as being fully continuous with that work—something he called a "visceral organism." As an experimental method, it did not turn out to be as promising or productive as tissue culture, Carrel abandoned it after a few years, and no one else took it up. However, it does starkly illustrate the desire behind the first development of tissue culture: to attain "autonomous life" for parts of the body in order to externalize and analyze the internal phenomena of the body.

Experimental Surgery

The historian of medicine Christopher Lawrence has observed that "Surgical practices . . . are never mere empirical procedures. Even the most simple of them employ a theory of the body and disease, either explicit or implicit."[9] This apt observation is part of a historiographic survey of the history of surgery, but unfortunately it is made in the course of a lament on the lack of histories of surgery that go beyond surgical practices as ever-increasing technical innovations. Thus, there is not much in the way of secondary literature in which to contextualize Carrel's successful innovations in blood vessel surgery and the "theory of the body and disease" that lay behind his practices, which were recognized from the beginning as performances of great dexterity and delicacy. In Carrel's early career, during which he did the surgical work for which he won the Nobel prize in 1912, he displayed a profound technical respect for the delicacy of tissues, a dedication to strict asepsis, and a faith in the power of local regeneration of cut or wounded areas of the body. Given this power of regeneration, if the proper respect was paid to limiting damage by knife and infection, the underlying assumption was one of the extreme plasticity of living tissues to heal and rebuild, sometimes in drastically new configurations.

At the beginning of his career, Carrel's work focused on vascular surgery and transplantation —of the kidney, thyroid gland, ovaries, or limbs. All operations were based on the surgical possibility of cutting and reconnecting blood vessels. By excising a body part and sewing it right back into place, he could demonstrate that a procedure was surgically possible. If the same procedure failed when trying to transplant an organ from one individual's body into another body, the problem could be designated a biological one, not a surgical or methodological one. He could also surgically interfere with blood flow, and by rearranging the circulatory system perform such interventions as reversing the direction of blood flow.[10]

After appointment to the Rockefeller Institute in 1906, Carrel continued his work on transplantation, although it was becoming clear that the most perfect of surgical techniques would not result in long-term success in transplanting organs between individuals or species. The operations could be declared a "success" in that animals that had their own organs or limbs cut out and sewn back in could recover completely. Some of Carrel's articles were illustrated with photographs of these repaired cats or dogs leaping in the air or begging for food. Those who received organs from other individuals would heal and the transplanted organ would function, with the kidneys expressing urine or a transplanted blood vessel allowing blood flow. However, these animals would inevitably die after a number of weeks, with rare exceptions. It was not known at this time why an individual could heal back together with its own parts and live on as before, while a foreign organ could not be incorporated in this way. What was surgically conclusive was still biologically inconclusive:

> The grafting of a kidney or a spleen on the renal or the splenic vessels has become an easy and safe operation. Vascular or uretal complications occur very exceptionally, and, after the operation, the animals remain generally in good health. *From a surgical standpoint the problem of the graft of organs can be considered as having been solved.* But, from a biological standpoint, no conclusion has thus far been reached because the interactions of the host and of its new organ are still practically unknown. The study of these interactions was very difficult because the complications which followed the operation were of widely different kinds.[11] (emphasis added)

This distinction Carrel draws in this quote between "the surgical standpoint" and "the biological standpoint" was prevalent in his work on transplantation and vascular surgery in his early years at the Rockefeller Institute. The operations "worked," in that it was not the surgical wound itself that brought on death, but some undefined complication happening within the body. This distinction led Carrel to pursue the unsolved biological questions once having attained self-proclaimed success on the surgical front.[12] The claim to have *solved* the problem of the graft of organs was no humble one; but the fact remained that except in limited circumstances, organ transplantation still did not work. Carrel turned more and more toward this question of what happened in the body after the sutures were done and the animal was closed up and healing. This can be seen for example in his introduction to a paper on patching the aorta with tissue taken from the abdominal wall (peritoneum):

> This operation was developed with the view of studying two points, surgical and biological, of the problem of regeneration of arteries in mammals. Can an opening through the walls of a large artery be safely occluded by a piece of peritoneum? How can an artery use heterogeneous anatomical elements in order to redintegrate itself and by what method will the function recreate the organ?[13]

Arterial patches of this sort seemed to function well, though when examined later upon reopening the animal, they were still distinguishable from the surrounding arterial tissue. The question that remained was how "heterogenous anatomical elements" could recombine, i.e., what was the basis of the body's apparent plasticity, or "by what method" did peritoneum gain qualities of arterial wall just by having to serve as an artery?

In reporting on all his diverse surgical ventures, Carrel stressed the ability of the body to heal and remake itself. Rejoined ends, years later, could hardly be detected in healed arteries, while the artificially introduced patches or transplants became populated by muscle cells, or thickened in response to the blood pressure in the artery. Even in the transplants that ultimately failed, the reattached organs functioned and the surgical wounds healed. However, surgical success was not adequate in that it did not address the ultimate failure of most transplants. Furthermore, Carrel wanted to do more than patch up an injury, he wanted to direct its healing biologically. It was as if, after perfecting surgical anastomosis in the earliest years of his career, surgery by itself became too easy.

Despite the successes of aseptic surgery, Carrel felt that surgery itself needed to be taken to another level. It was not enough to protect a wound against infection and leave the rest to nature. One had to intervene at a more fundamental level than prevention and patching. "Would it not be feasible," he asked, "to act on the processes of reparation themselves and to activate them?"[14] He called for the development of methods of stimulation of the growth of cells, for the inhibition or the activation of the proliferation of select tissues, and for the artificial production of bone growth. This proactive approach to wound healing, or cicatrization, would be a "new evolution of surgery," an evolution that required the discovery of "the laws of redintegration of tissues of mammals."[15] In light of these ambitions, the title "Experimental Surgery" expands from trying out new types of surgery or operative techniques, to experimentation aimed at intervening in the healing process itself:

> We have no right to believe that the treatment of wounds has reached its ultimate perfection. We must investigate whether or not it is possible to advance farther. In the treatment of wounds, we content ourselves by protecting the tissues against infection, and we leave to Nature the care of cicatrization. Would it not be feasible to act on the processes of reparation themselves and to activate them? The wounds which now heal in a few days could possibly be caused to heal in a few hours . . . The development of methods of stimulation of the growth of epithelial cells, for the inhibition or the activation of the proliferation of connective tissue, and for the artificial production of osteogenesis, etc. would greatly improve the therapeutics of the ulceration of the skin and of the lesions of the peripheral nerves, bones, and many other tissues and organs. This new evolution of surgery depends on the laws of redintegration of tissues of mammals . . . From a metaphysic standpoint it would be interesting to discover *why* a wound heals. But from a scientific standpoint, it is infinitely more important to know *how* it heals, because it would then be possible to find what stimuli start the complex mechanisms of the regeneration of the tissues. Therefore, the physiologic phenomena of cicatrization must be investigated.[16]

This was no less than a call to reconfigure the aims of surgery, also reflected in the name of Carrel's laboratory—not just surgery but *experimental* surgery. This implied surgery could be practiced like other experimental life sciences (e.g., experimental physiology or embryology) that sought through experimentation to elucidate the mechanism of life processes. It was not enough to cut and sew and practice asepsis; Carrel wanted to experiment with the aim of intervening directly in the process of wound healing itself, to accompany every operation with an artificially enhanced reparation, and to outdo the body itself at the healing process. This call, coming two years before his rise to scientific prominence with the Nobel Prize, went largely unheeded, mostly because there was very little to offer in the way of evidence that anyone was anywhere near finding "what stimuli start the complex mechanisms of the regeneration of the tissues."

In his experiments on wound healing at the Rockefeller Institute before taking up tissue culture, Carrel made wounds by excising pieces of skin from the backs of dogs. He used black animals, or stained the edges of the wound black with ink, in order to distinguish new growth from old skin. Despite the ambitious call for discovery of the laws of redintegration, and the development of modes of intervention, Carrel's first public communications on the subject were strictly descriptive. The healing process was divided into periods of quiescence, granulation, epidermization, and cicatrization.[17] The effort to make these healing stages clearly visible was already present in these experiments, but very crudely. As well as painting the edges of the wound with ink, Carrel used paraffin dressings for their semi-transparency, which made it possible to "see with certainty . . . the edge of the wandering epithelium" in the healing process.[18]

Carrel also tried applying different substances to these cutaneous wounds, such as ground up tissues of different types. For example, he found that "thyroid gland pulp deposited on cutaneous wounds of the dog brought about the formation of exuberant granulations."[19] However, other than limited observations about the relation of the rate of healing to the size of the wound, or observations of the effect of added substances such as ground thyroid gland, the method of making wounds in animals did not allow any specific access to the process of healing. In addition, many of the biological questions left unanswered by his surgical results concerned not the surface of the body but what happened deep inside, in organs and vessels, and the interaction of the body's fluid internal environment and its solid tissues in these locations.

It is in the context of these questions as to how wounds heal and tissues regenerate after surgical intervention that Carrel heard embryologist Ross Harrison speak about his work on growing isolated pieces of nerve tissue outside of the body. It was in these terms of seeking cellular "laws" that he framed his first publications on the reasoning behind pursuing in vitro methods. He argued that the pursuit of the "still unknown laws of generation, growth and evolution of cells," necessitated the development of new experimental methodology. The "cultivation of adult tissues outside of the body" was described in Carrel and Burrows' initial publication of results as a general "future method" applicable to the "laws of cellular physiology."[20]

Montrose Burrows, who had graduated from the Johns Hopkins University in 1909 with a medical degree and had come to the Rockefeller Institute to work with Carrel as a junior fellow, went to Harrison's laboratory in the spring of 1910 for a number of months to learn Harrison's technique of growing isolated embryonic frog tissue. Carrel was apparently so enthusiastic that he wanted to go himself, but Simon Flexner advised that Burrows be sent.[21] Burrows adapted this method to mammalian tissues, using embryonic chicken cells, confirmed Harrison's observations of nerve outgrowth from isolated nerve cells, and made his own observations about the nature of the heartbeat from a culture of heart muscle cells. Burrows returned to the Rockefeller Institute in the autumn of 1910, and within weeks, he and Carrel published a paper in the *Journal of the American Medical Association* announcing the possibility of "Cultivation of Adult Tissues and Organs Outside of the Body."

This paper was the first to speak of "cultures" of tissues, explicitly noting the choice to name them this way: "The cultures of the different tissues—*as we shall call them*—contain common characteristics."[22] Harrison had referred only to "preparations," or "specimens" in referring to the objects made of tissue, lymph, and glass slides; though he did refer to the nerve tissue as being "under cultivation" and of lymph as a "culture medium," many of these terms were borrowed from bacteriology.

Harrison's research emphasis had been completely different from Carrel and Burrows' attention to the general possibility of growing tissues outside of the body. Harrison emphasized not the preparation in itself, but what it allowed one to say about the specific question of nerve outgrowth. The titles of his publications indicate this emphasis: "Observations on the Living Developing Nerve Fiber" (1907) and "The Outgrowth of the Nerve Fiber as a Mode of Protoplasmic Movement" (1910). His 1908 Harvey Lecture was entitled "Embryonic

Transplantation and the Development of the Nervous System." In contrast, Carrel and Burrows made the method into the experimental question an end in itself. Their articles, with titles such as "Cultivation of Sarcoma Outside of the Body," made the cultures of tissues living outside of the body the central object of interest.

More than a simple difference in terminology, this difference in emphasis signals the establishment of the phrase "tissue culture" as a thing separate from other techniques and objects of biology. As Harrison observed years later in 1927, the phrase quickly came to signify both a technique and a field of knowledge.

> The expression "tissue culture," which has come into such general use . . . is in some degree a misnomer, for it fails to convey in full the idea it represents. Moreover the use of the phrase might be taken to imply that this method of research—in reality a technique—is an object in itself, whereas it is but a means of investigating the properties of cells under conditions not previously available. *What was originally the designation of a method has in fact come to connote the field of knowledge it has brought to light.*[23] (emphasis added)

This merging of method and field of knowledge actually happened almost immediately, and was due to Carrel's rapid, spectacular, and controversial establishment of an arena of experimental possibility around in vitro life. Tissue culture technique would eventually become a more invisible means to an end (investigation of properties of cells), but first the development of the technique was in itself the goal of the experiments and was in itself an investigation of the properties of cells. Working out how it was technically possible to maintain cells alive in vitro was itself a profound alteration to the way of observing and analyzing cellular phenomena, and even the recognition of what the properties of cellular life to be investigated were in the first place. Maintaining cellular life was not distinguishable from investigating its properties, in particular in the beginning, when it was not clear what was in fact possible to do with isolated living cells, or for that matter, what exactly it was that scientists were seeing in their cultures.

Between the first paper of 1910 and 1914, when Carrel went to work in a hospital on the French front in World War I, he published approximately forty articles in four languages (English, French, German, and Portuguese) on tissue culture, and many more on surgery. The first papers were concerned with the simple possibility of growing tissues outside of the body, with descriptions of a methodology that differed only slightly from Harrison's original hanging-drop preparations. Then Carrel began to alter the technique in fundamental ways. This began with the introduction of serial cultivation, and rapidly moved on to changes such as the culture of large batches of tissue on glass plates and the attempt to grow pure cultures of one type of cell. Methodological experimentation also included varying the composition of the medium and the type of tissue grown (adult, embryonic, and cancerous). In addition, Carrel tried to relate what was happening in vitro to cellular life in vivo; he showed that tissue culture cells produced antibodies upon addition of an antigen to the medium, just as one might inject an animal to provoke an immune response.

Experimental System

At first, tissues in culture were clearly related to particular bodies, or at least to the bodies of particular disciplines. In Harrison's work, it was the developing embryonic body of development and differentiation; for Carrel, it was what one could call the "surgical body" of wound healing and transplantation. However, the development of the technology to grow tissues outside of the body, and their ensuing manifestation of surprising and extravagant qualities of life such luxurious growth and endless reproduction, meant that tissue culture increasingly took on a "life of its own" as it was developed into a quite separate artificial body with different characteristics from the animal body.

On October 15, 1910, Carrel and Burrows published the first of four closely-spaced publications in the *Journal of the American Medical Association* on tissue culture. From the very beginning, they cited Harrison's "beautiful work" as the "starting point" of their researches, but in adapting the technique, they changed it profoundly. On the surface, the technique was the same: a fragment of living tissue was placed in a hanging drop preparation and maintained for a period of time. However, a number of substitutions meant that the method was fundamentally changed. Carrel and Burrows substituted adult tissues for embryonic ones, mammalian for amphibian, and blood plasma for lymph. Perhaps the most profound change was the act of making secondary cultures by taking fragments of the original culture and placing them in new plasma. They called this "reactivation and cultivation in series." This changed the time-scale of experiment, from one-time preparations that lived for days or weeks, to a potentially endless series of preparations each made from the other. The relation of in vitro tissue to the original body of the animal was therefore also different: the researcher did not return to the body each time he made a culture, but could make cultures from other cultures already living outside the body.

Only two weeks later, Carrel and Burrows reported on the "Cultivation of Sarcoma Outside of the Body." This was a further substitution: cancerous tissue for normal tissue. They used a sarcoma that Carrel's colleague Peyton Rous had been studying in chickens. They reported that Rous had been propagating the sarcoma "from generation to generation for more than a year," which means that Rous had been transplanting bits of the tumor from one chicken to another for a year, growing new tumors in new chickens and, in a sense, doing serial cultivation of the tumor tissue in the bodies of the chickens. It is possible that this suggested the serial cultivation of the tissue outside of the body; it was also common practice in bacteriology to make new cultures from old ones. They observed that cancerous tissues started to grow much more quickly than normal tissues, which usually stayed fairly inert in the first hours or even days in culture, and only after some time started to move and divide.

The next substitution was to replace chicken sarcoma with human sarcoma, attained from a patient having a sarcoma removed from her leg. The fourth paper varied both the tissue type and the medium it was grown in. The growth of normal and sarcomatous chicken tissue was compared in normal blood plasma and plasma taken from chickens with tumors. They found that the "plasma of a sarcomatous animal acquires the property of inhibiting the growth of sarcoma taken from another animal," concluding that this must be due to "substances produced by the organism as a reaction against the tumor." Furthermore, embryonic spleen tissue grew faster in sarcomatous than in normal plasma.[24]

These papers, which set out the possibility of growing all kinds of tissues outside of the body for the medical and biological public, were very different from Harrison's publications on the developing nerve. They had no specific questions to answer. Instead, the very possibility afforded by the general method of tissue culture was their subject and conclusion. They contained extensive descriptions of what the cells looked like, and a few results such as the comparison of the effect of different media on different tissues, but for the most part they stressed the following points. First, it was possible to grow all kinds of embryonic and adult tissues, normal and pathological—and importantly, also human tissues—outside of the body.

> The main results of these observations can be summarized in a few words: Adult tissues and organs of mammals can be cultivated outside of the animal body. The cultivation of normal cells would appear to be no more difficult than the cultivation of many microbes.[25]

Second, this life and its growth was "luxuriant," with the cells growing in states of "wild vegetation, which lasted as long as the plasmatic medium was in good condition."[26] This growth could be "reactivated" at will by simply making a second culture from the first. Third, all of these tissues could be grown in isolation "under known conditions"—conditions that could be varied at will. Not only would this give access to information about normal tissues, but it promised to be important in the analysis of pathogenic processes: "it may render possible the cultivation of certain micro-organisms in conjunction with living tissue cells . . . Then it will be of great value in the study of the problem of cancer."[27] Finally, the growth of the cells grown in this way could be constantly observed over time, and phenomena such as cell division could be "directly seen": "The purpose of the present article is merely to show that all the details of the living cells can be observed at every instant of their evolution."[28]

In the space of four months, Carrel and Burrows had transformed Harrison's method for the short-term growth of living embryonic tissue into a generalized method for the cultivation of all kinds of tissues: embryonic and adult; amphibian, mammalian, and human; and normal and pathological. In four publications that together totaled only seven journal pages in the *Journal of the American Medical Association* (results that were simultaneously published in French in the *Comptes Rendus des Séances de la Societé de Biologie*), they outlined the possibility of serial cultivation of these tissues outside of the body in media of known composition, and their use in the analysis of cancer and other pathogenic phenomena afforded by the ability to observe the cells "at every instant of their evolution."

The speed at which Carrel and Burrows were able to produce these results (the first of which were published only three weeks after the experiments were begun at the Rockefeller Institute) was due in part to the context of Carrel's surgical laboratory. Conditions of strict asepsis were already in place; Carrel was not a bacteriologist, but practiced aseptic technique in surgery with considerable fervor as it had proved to be an essential element of successful operations. He and his technicians were already adept at rapid, delicate manipulations of living tissues. The successful anastomosis of vessels depended on their gentle handling and protecting them from being chilled, drying out, or getting infected, and the same principles applied to small fragments of living tissues.

Everything in Carrel's laboratory was designed to facilitate the careful handling of surgically manipulated living tissues. The laboratories on the top floors of the Rockefeller Institute were lit by natural light from skylights, and the walls were painted gray. All wore black gowns when carrying out operations. Although this setting had the effect of appearing to outsiders fabulously strange, it also decreased reflected light in the operating room and optimized visibility of the operating field and tissues.[29] The memories of Raymond Parker, who started out with Harrison, and ended up working with Carrel for nine years, provides some access to the quality of this setting. He wrote to his colleague John Paul, who was writing an article "Fifty Years of Tissue Culture," that

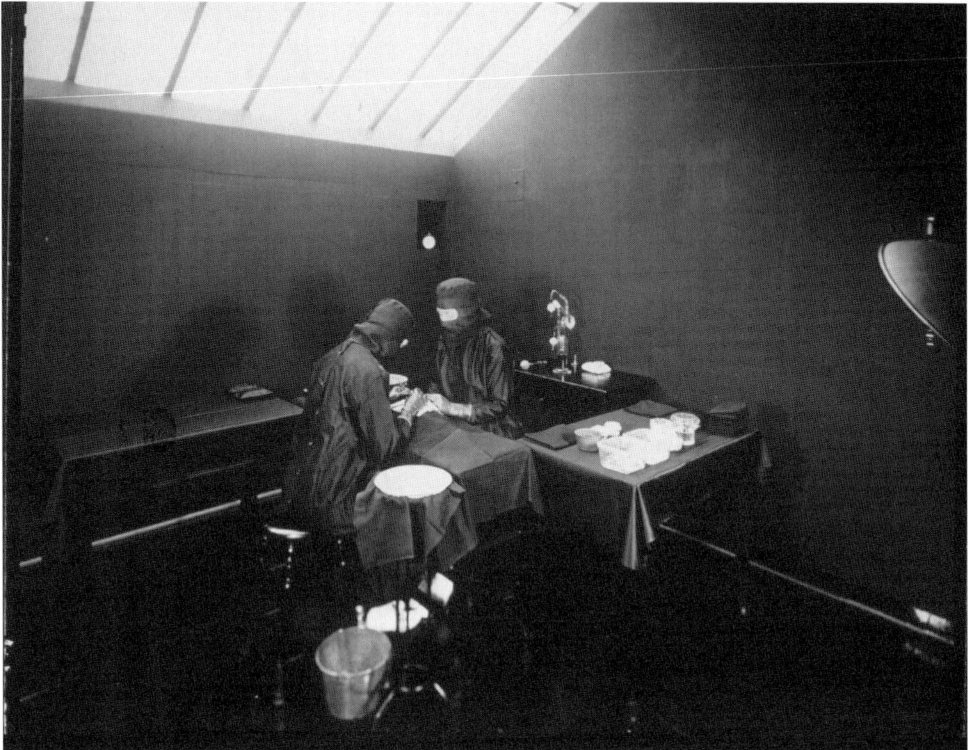

Figure 2. Tissue culture work being done in the Carrel Laboratory of the Rockefeller Institute for Medical Research. Undated. Alexis Carrel Papers, Rockefeller Archive Center.

> you must remember that Carrel was primarily a surgeon, that tissue culture was always incidental to surgery in his laboratory, and that tissue culture was done in the same open rooms, under the same conditions. Because these rooms were not cooled, and were conditioned mainly by the New York sun that poured in through skylights, the only lighting, he had to do something about masks and gowns . . . he and his staff wore hoods that were made of fine muslin and covered the entire head. Because these hoods were long and loose, exhaled air escaped downwards, instead of through the mask and into the work. These masks are now commonplace in surgery. He also chose loose, light-weight gowns. True, the hoods and gowns, the table coverings and the floors were black; and the walls were gray. There was no glare or reflected light; culture material and fine anatomical detail could be seen with ease. This was the era of 'hospital white' operating rooms and even restaurants. But Carrel saw no reason why elementary cleanliness could not be achieved without unnecessary eyestrain . . . But these unusual surroundings, when seen for the first time by casual visitors, did engender the feeling that the man must be a little odd.[30]

The layout of the rooms and the traffic between them was strictly choreographed, to maintain the cleanliness of the operating room, and to ensure that tissues never had to be carried a long way to an incubator. Nonetheless, the tissues were carried in a small electric incubator while being transferred to the larger incubator. No detail of the process was without this kind of attention. Attention entailed labor, which was supplied in both assistants and technicians. Assistants were mostly young men just out of medical school or graduate work in science, who were short-term visitors to the Institute on fellowships. They would either be appointed to longer-term positions at the Institute, or move on to other jobs elsewhere after a few years. Burrows, for example, stayed for a few years and went on to a position at Cornell University. Many of Carrel's technicians were long-term employees, and many of them were women. Raymond Parker reports that the "smooth-working order" of the laboratory was "developed and supervised by a wonderful battle-axe, Miss Irene McFaul, a Canadian nurse who ran Carrel and the rest of us."[31] Thus, a highly organized laboratory staffed with assistants already familiar with operations on living tissue and strict asepsis was in place when Carrel took up tissue culture. Burrows had already learned and practiced Harrison's technique in Harrison's laboratories at Yale for several months. Positive results in the form of "luxuriantly" growing cultures were practically instantaneous. Contemporary commentators were quite aware of the link between Carrel's surgical background and his success in growing tissues. An anonymous editorial in *Scientific American* questioned whether the method could be successful in less dextrous hands:

> We note also that in the handling and changing required in the various techniques the cultures were exposed to many accidents, chiefly to microbian infection. One wonders (from a practical viewpoint) how many more accidents and how much more infection there would be under manipulations less skilled than such as Carrel's.[32]

The establishment of a "new type of body in which to grow a cell" was performed in a technical environment set up to tend to the body in surgery. Maintaining body temperature is one good example of this attitude toward caring for the body under manipulation. Albert Fischer, who worked with Carrel in the 1920s reports that Carrel regarded the cooling of tissue cells from warm-blooded animals as being very harmful, and prescribed strict precautions for the prevention of any cooling of them for a long period of time: "He and his associates in the early days of tissue cultivation visited the laboratory several times at night in order to check the temperature of the incubators. At first they even went so far as to have all manipulations performed in the incubator."[33]

These details show the importance of the context of the surgical laboratory to these early successes. However, the publications on tissue culture were not the same sort of "surgical results" as Carrel's other publications on transplantations and open chest operations. Neither were they within a particular genre of experimental biology or part of a particular debate. They were published in a field of inquiry that was completely and utterly open. Knowledge about the growth of any kind of tissue outside of the body and its interaction with any kind of artificially provided conditions of growth was new, because tissues had never been grown and observed like this before. This openness was partly due to Carrel's emphasis on possibility, which rendered the very possibility of tissue growth outside of the body a result in itself.

Burrows left the Rockefeller Institute in 1911 to accept an appointment at Cornell University; even without him, Carrel continued to produce publications at a furious rate. Most of these focused on the technique itself and the effects of altering any of the method's elements, the protocol, or equipment. Importantly, these technical alterations were perceived to simultaneously yield important information as to the nature of the cells and the best way to keep them alive; their structural or functional features were seen to be revealed by their reaction to culture vessels and media. The most significant of these was the claim that subculturing could lead to "permanent life" of tissues. The attempt to refine the methods of tissue culture and the resulting observations on the nature of cellular life occupied most of Carrel's attention.

Permanent Life In Vitro: Tissue Culture as a Cell–Medium System

The fundamental separation of the body of the organism from the excised tissue culture was achieved most powerfully by the effort to make life in vitro "permanent," a quality that cells did not possess in the body. By the fall of 1911, one year after beginning experiments with tissue culture, Carrel was able to keep tissues alive and growing for anywhere from three to fifteen days. He was not satisfied with this. He had already shown that a tissue could be, as he put it, "reactivated" by taking it out of its initial plasmatic medium, washing it in physiological solution, and putting it in fresh plasma. This was one of the first changes to Harrison's method that he had tried. Now he changed the term from "reactivation" to "rejuvenation" in describing the promise of subculturing:

> It may easily be supposed that senility and death of tissues are not a necessary phenomenon and that they result merely from accidental causes, such as accumulation of catabolic substances and exhaustion of the medium. The suppression, then, of these causes should bring about the rejuvenation of the arrested culture and thus increase considerably the duration of its life . . . The rejuvenation consists in removing from the culture substances that inhibit growth and in giving to the tissues a new medium of development.[34]

This technique of rejuvenation involved taking coagulated plasma containing the original fragment of tissue and the surrounding new cells and washing it in Ringer's solution, and then placing the fragment in new plasma. The moment chosen for this transfer was the time at which the rate of growth decreased or "large granulations appeared in the cytoplasm of the cells," indicating the onset of "senility." With these experiments, Carrel extended the life of embryonic chick tissues to thirty-seven days, showing that "The rejuvenation of cultures of tissues is possible. They show also that, under the conditions and within the limits of the experiments, senility and death are not a necessary but merely a contingent, phenomenon."[35]

He had already moved from reactivation to rejuvenation; by 1912, he had proceeded to "regeneration" and "permanent life" in describing the increasingly elaborated procedure for maintaining life for increasingly long periods of time in vitro. He attempted to actually set up a system of "artificial circulation" in which tissue fragments were grown on cellulose through which a slow stream of serum moved, but this proved to be too complicated. It was easier to move the cultures from medium to medium than to establish a circulation system for the cultures. This he did by growing the tissue fragments in plasma on tiny pieces of silk veil. The silk veil "skeleton" could easily be removed from the hollow slide and placed in a tube of serum for washing, and then transferred back into fresh plasma. He also performed this without the silk, washing the culture at a low temperature. When the old culture was placed in new medium, the cells would wander out from the old plasma into the new plasma, and the center would eventually die. The results were far from precise; Carrel described the rate of growth being affected by "the nature of the medium, its osmotic tension, the way in which the plasma was cut, the amount of old plasma left around the cells, the form of the culture, and the frequence [*sic*] of the passages."[36] Furthermore, the size of the cultures was erratic and influenced by many mechanical disturbances such as the folding of the plasma clot during handling, and it was difficult in general to tell if the mass or the density of the culture was changing. However, the main point of the communiqué was again a sense of possibility: permanent life outside of the body. This was illustrated in particular with several cultures of embryonic heart cells, where the resuscitation of the cultures could be observed in the ability of the fragments of heart muscle to beat.

> Cultivation of the Heart (Experiment 720-1) On January 17, 1912, a small fragment of the heart of an eighteen day old chick fetus was cultivated in hypotonic plasma. The fragment pulsated regularly for a few days and grew extensively. After the first washing and passage on January 24 the culture grew again very extensively, but there were no rhythmical contractions. On January 29 and February 1, 3, 6, 9, 12, 15, 17, 20, 24, and 28, the culture underwent eleven washings and passages. It became surrounded by fusiform cells and many dead cells. There were no pulsations. After the twelfth passage the culture did not grow at all. Then the tissue was dissected and the old plasma was completely extirpated. A small central fragment was removed, washed and put in a new medium. On March 1 it was pulsating at a rate that varied between 60 and 84 per minute. On March 2 the pulsations were 104 at 41°C., and on March 3 80 at 40°C., but on March 4 the pulsations were very weak and stopped altogether at 2 P.M. On March 5 the culture underwent its fourteenth passage, and the pulsations reappeared immediately.[37]

I include this excerpt of the results section of "On the Permanent Life of Tissues Outside of the Organism," because it lends a very material sense to the power of regeneration that Carrel was claiming for his method of serial cultivation. Although he cultivated all kinds of embryonic tissues, he chose heart tissue to illustrate the possibility of endlessly renewed life, with its highly manifest liveliness: the rather uncanny ability to pulse, stop pulsing, and start again over the space of several days. Although at the time of publishing this paper, the tissues had lived for only two months, he used their continued life as evidence for the possibility that "the length of the life of a tissue outside of the organism could exceed greatly its normal duration in the body, because elemental death might be postponed indefinitely by a proper artificial nutrition."[38] Figure 3 shows a typical drawing (by Louis Schmidt, the Rockefeller Institute artist and photographer) of a cell culture.

What Carrel failed to communicate in this highly optimistic appraisal of the chances of suppressing death in vitro, was the fact that though the cells continued to multiply at each subculture, the cells themselves often got smaller and smaller with each transfer. Thus, although the tissue lived longer and manifested those important signs of life (movement and multiplication), it ceased to increase in mass. He only let this be known after he found a methodological solution to both erratic growth patterns and the lack of increase in mass of the cells. He found that the addition of extracts made of ground up tissues, in particular ground up embryonic tissue, solved the problem.

Carrel termed these embryonic tissue extracts "embryo juice." Apparently inspired by the thyroid gland pulp that had made skin wounds on dogs heal faster in his experiments of 1907 and 1908, he ground up adult and embryonic tissue with sand in a mortar. He added saline solution, put the tubes in cold storage, and centrifuged them. Next, the supernatant solution was filtered through paper and added to the cultures. He found that embryonic extracts "activated" growth in these cultures much more than extracts of adult tissues, although spleen

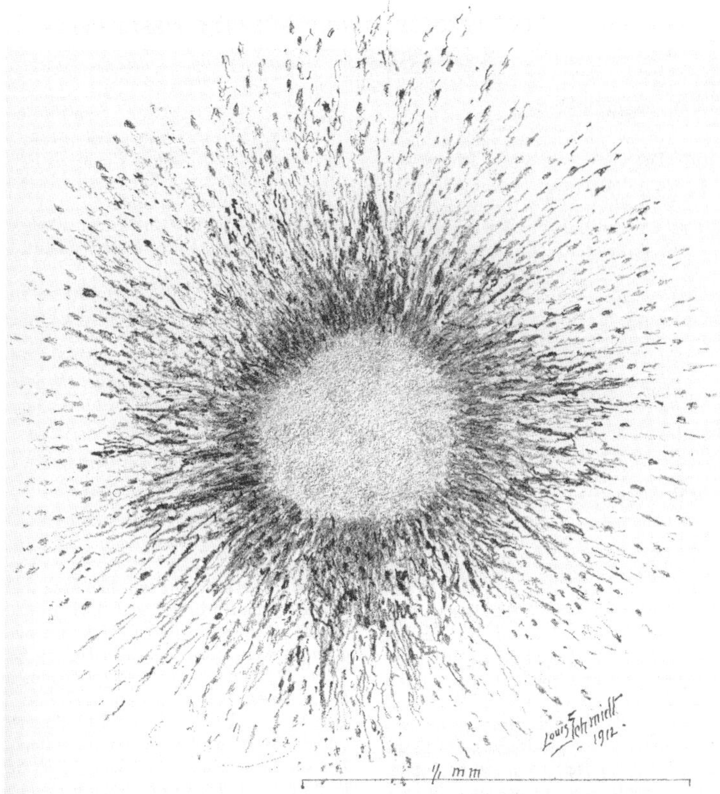

Figure 3. A drawing of a 50-day-old embryonic chicken tissue culture, from Carrel's 1913 announcement "On the Permanent Life of Tissues Outside the Organism," published in the *Journal of Experimental Medicine*.

tissue and cancerous tissue were also growth activators. He took the rate of growth by measuring the ring of new tissue around the original fragment with a micrometer. He found that fragments of tissue, as long as they were approximately the same size and taken from the same tissue of animals of the same age, would grow at the same rate in his new culture medium of two parts plasma and one part embryo juice.

The search to find a nutritive medium that would keep cells alive and growing without diminishing in size was, like other technical changes, also interpreted as an increase in knowledge about the nature of cells in general. By 1913, Carrel was declaring a "constant relation" between "the rate of growth and the composition of the medium." Having discovered this relation, it opened up a new field of investigation, cell–medium interaction, described as follows:

> Certain cell phenomena of the higher animals, such as multiplication, growth, and senility, might now be investigated profitably. Since the time of Claude Bernard it has been known that the life of an organism is the result of the interactions of the cells of which it is composed and of their milieu intérieur. But the nature of the interactions has not yet been ascertained; for in order to discover the laws by which they are regulated it would be necessary to modify the humours of the organism and to study the effect of

> these modifications on the growth of the tissues. This could not be done on account of the lack of a proper method; but this investigation is now rendered possible because of a technique which permits strains of connective tissue cells to multiply indefinitely in vitro, like microorganisms.[39]

By putting fragments of tissue of "known activity" in different media, and putting tissues of different activity in media of the same composition, he wrote that he had found the scientific method appropriate to analyzing the milieu intérieur. One could modify the activity of cells by purposefully modifying the medium, or one could analyze the medium for the changes induced by the cells living in it. The "known composition" of the medium was rather misleading: "embryo juice" was hardly a clearly delineated substance of known composition. However, all attempts to use purely synthetic media for culture, such as saline solutions, had resulted in limited life spans for the tissues. It seemed that "embryo juice" was the key to the prolonged, even indefinite life that Carrel was now claiming for his cultures.

The discovery of workable nutritive medium for the prolonged maintenance of in vitro life was thus bound up claims for tissue culture as a methodology for the external study of the body's internal interactions between tissues and fluids inside organs and muscles. By September 1913, Carrel had now maintained the original embryonic chicken heart culture for sixteenth months of "independent life" over 190 passages. It had stopped pulsing after 104 days, but continued to proliferate at a rate equal to fresh connective tissue taken from an eight-day-old chick embryo. "It appears, therefore, that time has no effect on the tissues isolated from the organism and preserved by means of the technique described above."[40] After the chicken heart culture had lived longer than the life span of the average chicken, the final terminological shift was made from permanent or indefinite life to immortality. Thus, the possibility of immortality was introduced into tissue culture.

This claim to have achieved permanent life reinvigorated the initial skepticism in France which had been temporarily put to rest. The newspapers even reported an event that normally would not make the papers: a debate in the French Academy of Medicine over the possibility of a scientific claim's truth. Under the heading "Paris Doctors Ask Proofs of Carrel," the *New York Times* on June 23, 1912, followed the "warm controversy" started in the Academy of Medicine by Carrel's friend and surgical colleague F. Pozzi, presenting the results of the ongoing chicken heart culture, a report which gave "special prominence" to the double claim that the heart tissue not only continued to beat, but showed growth and new cell division as well.[41]

> Several members of the Academy however attack Dr. Carrel's assertions, declaring them to be too marvelous to be taken on trust without evidence of a most convincing kind. The leaders among those holding this skeptical attitude are Professors Pouchet and Chantemesse, who are well-known authorities on biological and medical questions. The former, who is Director of the Laboratory of the Hygiene Commission, stated in an interview that Dr. Carrel's experiments were so extraordinary that he was personally unable to believe in them without having actually seen them. The photographs of living tissue, exhibited at the lecture were not sufficient, he thought, to justify a belief here in such epochmaking discoveries.

The French scientists also felt that tissue culture and its life outside the body contradicted contemporary understandings of life and death and the "properties of living tissue," to the extent that they had to "see with their own eyes" the movement and growth of the tissue, not just the photographic representation of a culture.

> That fragments of hearts should after remaining for a certain time apparently dead, afterward resume life involved, he continued, a complete upheaval in the ideas of European scientists on the properties of living tissue. This was entirely different from merely finding a method of inducing fragments of flesh to grow on another living organism. In conclusion Dr. Pouchet declared that this question was of such vital importance to science that a deputation of French biologists must visit the Rockefeller Institute and see with their own eyes whether Dr. Carrel's assertions were well founded or not.

While Carrel had a constant stream of visitors, no such official deputation ever came, as many in the French medical and biological community began to try tissue culture for themselves, and by 1913 evidence was forthcoming in the form both of many French scientists who had attained some success in growing tissue cultures, and of films of embryonic chick cells grown with Carrel's technique.

Carrel attempted to bring quantification and precision to his studies, in that times, measurements, and temperatures were always rigorously noted. Thousands of different cultures were produced in his laboratory in these years, meticulously cared for and watched. However, it was a curiously vague exactitude; there were growth-activating substances and growth-retarding ones. Observations on the effect of hypotonic medium led to some observations of the effect of osmotic pressure on the rate of healing of tiny pieces of in vitro epithelium with miniature wounds made in them. The appearance and movement of cells was watched and recorded in punishing detail, but the descriptors were as vague as "fusiform" (shaped like a spindle or cigar, tapered at the ends), "round," or "ameoboid" cells. In an apparent attempt to bring more accuracy to the method, Carrel described a technique by which he made "pure" cultures of one type of cell, a method also enabled by the discovery of effective continuous subcultivation. A fragment of tissue often contained several different types of cell—in culture, they would spread out and move through the medium. Working with a microscope, one could then cut out a piece of the plasmatic medium containing only one or a few types of cells, and continue to subcultivate until it was possible to isolate a single "type" of cell, even though there was some debate about what cell types meant in the in vitro context.[42]

This lack of specificity was not necessarily some particular shortcoming of Carrel himself, though it is clear that he was extremely fond of making sweeping pronouncements about the nature of cellular life, without too much concern for detail. There was great disagreement about exactly what it was that cells were doing in culture, what exactly it was that scientists were seeing when they saw things in culture. This confusion was due to great extent to the fact that cells simply looked very different, alive and in plasmatic medium, than in the static histological sections of previous modes of identification. This in turn led to decades of argument about what exactly cultured cells were, or what kinds of scientific questions they could be used to investigate.[43]

Tissue Culture as Proxy Body: Making Antibodies In Vitro

In characteristic style, Carrel spent little time thinking about doubts, confusions, and challenges, but continuously worked on renovating the tissue culture apparatus and testing the system for different experimental potentials. For example, the attempt to make in vitro tissues produce antibodies was part of the establishment of the fact that a living tissue culture could be used as a proxy body in an experiment. From the very beginning, Carrel was dissatisfied with the hanging drop technique. Sealed in a hollow slide, the drop of fluid and the growing tissue could be observed under the microscope easily enough, but was not very amenable to manipulation or measurement. One of his first innovations was to try to grow much larger cultures of tissues. This he did by mincing up tissues and spreading them, with plasma, on the surface of large black glass plates, which he placed in glass boxes sealed with paraffin and half-filled with water to maintain the humidity inside. These early attempts were frustrated by frequent bacterial infection, the inability to analyze the fluids exuded by the culture, and finally, the difficulty of adapting the culture vessels to any kind of microscopic observation.[44] Even in this fairly mundane extension of the principles of growing tissues outside of the body, Carrel's manual dexterity is as evident as in descriptions of his ability to perform surgeries. In describing the method, he calls for the division of embryonic chicken tissues by hand with a scalpel into fragments of half or one-tenth of a millimeter in diameter "care being taken not to crush the tissues."

Carrel had fine-tuned this method by 1912 by adding a silk veil support for the tissues, so that they could be removed from the box, washed, and placed in a new medium. He also attached a kind of catchment receptacle to collect the fluid exuded by the culture, and used a different kind of glass plate whereby the culture could be observed microscopically. He suggested that these large cultures were superior to small hanging drop cultures in that they provided much more tissue for further analysis. One could cut up the cultures into small pieces, take them up in a pipette, place them in a centrifuge tube, and centrifuge them, leaving a supernatant fluid that represented the "substances that develop in the medium during the life of the tissues."[45]

With the help of Hideyo Noguchi, a Rockefeller Institute pathologist, Carrel and another assistant, Ragnvald Ingebrigsten, used mass cultures to show that tissues cultured in vitro would produce antibodies. They cultured guinea pig bone marrow and lymph glands in guinea pig plasma mixed with goat red blood cells. On the third day of culturing, they observed that guinea pig leukocytes phagocytosed the red blood cells. When the team produced serum by cutting up the cultures and centrifuging them, the serum was able to hemolyze (break down) any goat red blood cells added to it. Control cultures, which had not been exposed to goat cells, did not produce goat-hemolyzing serum. The conclusion: "tissues living outside of the organism react against an antigen by the production of an antibody."[46]

This experiment demonstrated the potential of the tissue culture system: not just growth, development, and cell division could be seen happening outside of the body, but isolated tissues would have an immune reaction to a foreign antigen. Previously, antibodies were made by injecting an animal with an antigen, waiting a few days, and collecting the animal's blood. Just as with other experiments where an intervention was made, the body was closed up for a time, and then reopened to see what had happened; the actual process of antibody production was an internal and hidden one. With tissue culture, not only did the tissue stand in for the body, it made it clear that antibody production was a cellular phenomenon, and one that could be made to happen within an artificially simplified and controlled system.

The potential for studying disease processes and immune responses was enormous. Many others recognized this potential immediately. Paul Ehrlich, in introducing the first book-length publication on tissue culture, Albert Oppel's 1914 *Gewebekulturen und Gewebepflege im Explantat*, enthused,

> This new field of research is of particularly profound meaning for the prevention, treatment, and healing of the illnesses of man and animals. Tissue research and tissue culture enables the exploration of changes taking place not only under normal circumstances but under experimentally changed conditions. Thus, can the influence of pathogens, poisons and injury of all kinds and the life phenomena, resistance phenomena etc. taking place in living tissues be directly observed under the microscope.[47]

In France at the Pasteur Institute, Constantin Levatidi in 1913 immediately seized on the method as useful for growing viruses of polio and rabies:

> Given that, in the conditions realized by the method of Burrows-Harrison, modified by Carrel, certain cellular elements live and even multiply in vitro . . . it occurred to me to use this method for cultivating certain viruses which do not multiply in the usual milieux. [48]

Also in 1913, Levatidi used Carrel's technique of mass culturing to watch the effect of ultraviolet rays on embryonic heart and kidney cells. The Russian immunologist Alexander Maximov began publishing the results of experiments done with culturing lymph tissue in 1917.

Thus, while Carrel himself contributed little more to the study of antibodies and antigens in vitro, or the effects of viruses and bacteria on living cells, he was, quite characteristically, the first to see and confidently pronounce the potential within this developing experimental system. Again, the emphasis was on a *possibility* rather than a narrowly focused experimental question because it was possible to grow living tissues outside of the organism. Furthermore, it was possible to produce antibodies from these cultured cells. Therefore, it was possible to use tissue culture in place of the animal body in studying immune reactions.

The Visceral Organism

At the same time that Alexis Carrel was developing methods of tissue culture in the period 1910–1914, he was also performing increasingly dramatic surgical procedures and was trying to develop a new experimental system for the physiological analysis of internal organs, a system he called a "visceral organism." As Raymond Parker reminded his colleagues in 1958, "tissue culture was always incidental to surgery" in Alexis Carrel's laboratory. I now return the focus back to surgery as a way to characterize the more general impetus behind early tissue culture work; i.e., the creation of a living apparatus in order to scientifically manipulate life processes separated from the bounds within which life was formerly understood to be contained. Although the visceral organism theory did not prove (unlike tissue culture) to be minutely productive, it shows how the subject of "experimental surgery" in this period focused on less than whole organism. In addition, both Carrel and his contemporaneous commentators saw the visceral organism, the transplantations, the preservation of arteries and tissues in petroleum jelly, and tissue culture as all of a piece, and furthermore understood them in relation to the larger project of the technological supplementation of life and suppression of death.

The visceral organism was in Carrel's view a logical extension of the proven ability to keep small pieces of tissue alive outside of the body.

> Up to the present only fragments of tissue have survived in vitro. Since the survival of entire organs outside of the body would undoubtedly have important physiological

> uses, I began in June, 1912, to develop a technique by means of which a system of organs could be made to live and functionate when separated from the other organs.[49]

This work he described as the development of a "technic by which a system of organs could be caused to live in vitro."[50] Basically, this method consisted of surgically removing en masse the heart, lungs, liver, stomach, intestine, kidneys, and spleen of a cat, and keeping this intact system alive in an incubator.

The visceral organism was immersed in a tin box filled with physiological solution, covered with silk, and a glass cover. The tubes used for ventilation were fixed through one end of the box, and artificial respiration was carried on by a continuous current of air interrupted ten times a minute. The intestine was pulled through a glass and rubber tube at the other end of the box. The severed end of the intestine was stitched to the rubber tube, making an "artificial anus." The box was put in an incubator at the appropriate body temperature for a cat, after which the "normal condition" of the viscera could be observed,

> The pulsations of the heart and the circulation of the organs were normal. The intestine emptied itself through the artificial anus by regular peristaltic contractions. When the intestine was empty, bile and intestinal juices were evacuated. In an experiment in which the stomach was full of meat at the time of death, normal digestion occurred.[51]

The life of the visceral organism was maintained for up to thirteen hours and fifteen minutes after the death of the cat from which it originated, death being announced by irregularities in the pulsation of the heart followed by it suddenly ceasing to beat altogether. Carrel experimented with various combinations of organs kept in the system, the kinds of solutions and containers, and also with a variation of the procedure that resulted in a "reduced organism": this was a double amputation through the neck and the abdomen, in other words, the head and the back end of the animal were cut off.

Despite the specificity of description of the methodology and observations, the purpose of making such a thing was left vague: "The technique will probably be progressively modified and adapted to the various problems of pathology, physiology, and biological chemistry, for the study of which the visceral organisms can be used."[52] Carrel seems to have collaborated in some measure with several Rockefeller colleagues, including Samuel Meltzer, in figuring out how to keep the lungs ventilated, and Dr. Van Slyke in measuring the absorption by the truncated intestine of amino acids injected directly into it. Carrel's lack of specificity as to the purpose of these cat-in-a-box preparations, except to say that they would be particularly useful for studying the "internal secretions and substances which modify the growth of tissues," implies that he was doing these experiments for the most part to see if they could be done, with the confidence that "important" experimental uses would naturally follow.[53] The most explicitly stated goal was to attain "autonomous life" for isolated organs or systems of organs. The emphasis throughout all of Carrel's writing about the visceral organisms was on the ability to recreate "normal" conditions for a sustained period of time once the functions of circulation and respiration were artificially provided. Once the internal organs were suspended and sewed into the box and thus physically joined to the apparatus, one could watch through the glass cover all the manifestations of life: pinkness, peristaltic contractions, heart beat, digestion, and excretion.

Although this course of experimentation was an unequivocal dead end, on which Carrel published two papers, and which he abandoned after 1913, the venture to create a visceral

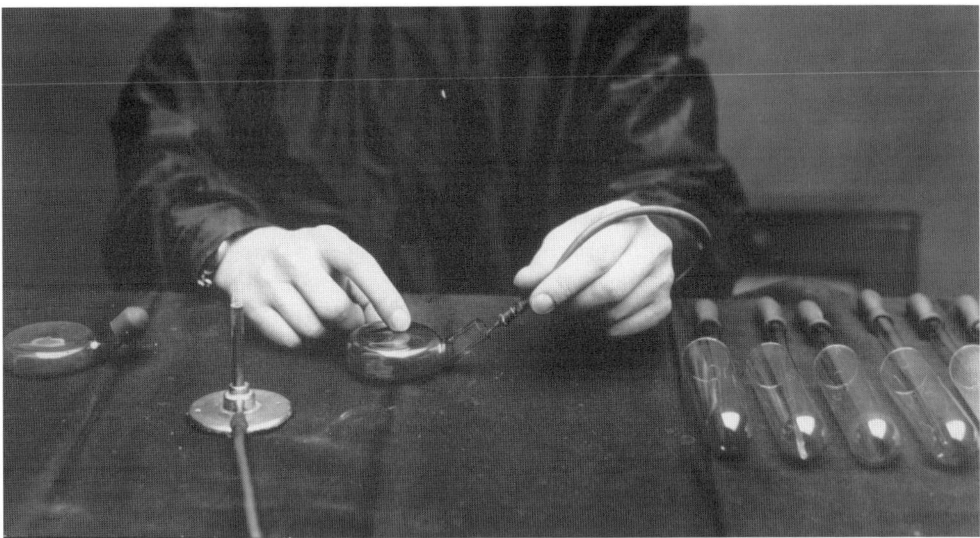

Figure 4. This undated photograph shows the hands of a technician manipulating the specially designed "Carrel flask" and the aspiration device Carrel designed in the 1920s and widely used into the 1950s. Alexis Carrel Papers, Rockefeller Archive Center.

organism was of a piece with the general attempt to maintain the life of the organism "without itself" that also included tissue culture. It was not an attempt to create life de novo, but to make life or living tissues an integral part of a technological system that would both make life processes visible and suppress death. Death was a feature of the whole organism, but not necessarily of its parts. By reducing the whole to parts and attaching those parts to a mechanical apparatus, the death of the whole could theoretically be avoided. Carrel never really progressed with the visceral organism because he depended on blood transfusions from living animal bodies into the apparatus to maintain its life, and these animals subsequently died soon thereafter with a sudden cessation of life processes. In the beginning, tissue culture was a similar venture to maintain life and suppress death, but on a smaller scale. If the visceral organism was a "reduced" animal, then tissue culture was a further reduction in scale.

Conclusion

By 1914, tissue culture had been established as both a technique and a field of knowledge about the life and disease of cells in vitro. Although many other researchers tried their hand at Ross Harrison's technique of cultivating living tissues in hanging drop preparations, it was Alexis Carrel who established tissue culture as an experimental method of universal application for the large questions of cellular growth, movement, aging, division, malignancy, the interaction of cells and medium, and the production of antibodies. Central to this was the establishment of the possibility of "permanent life" for tissues in vitro, giving rise to the possibility of an immortal or continuous experimental subject abstracted from the perishable bodies of individual animals and humans.

These developments should be understood within the medical–surgical context of Carrel's laboratory: both the conceptual context of questions of circulation and wound healing, and the technical context of asepsis and dexterity. The establishment of a "new type of body in which to grow a cell" was performed in a technical environment set up to tend the body in surgery—and to experiment with the bounds of experimentation on the body using the techniques of surgery. Tissue culture's very form and protocols were shaped by surgery's attention to the maintenance of circulation, humidity, and other factors essential to maintaining life of the *opened* body. Although I have only been able to address the beginning years of tissue culture here, Carrel later designed a set of techniques, tools, and glassware that simulated the body's conditions of circulation, warmth, nutrition, and asepsis, and were central to tissue culture technique before World War II. The early influence of the surgical body on the shaping of this now ubiquitous tool of basic biological research should be understood as a piece of the larger history of the interface between medical–surgical practices, and laboratory research into life and disease processes.

Endnotes

1. Eduard Uhlenhuth, "Changes in Pigment Epithelium Cells and Iris Pigment Cells of Rana pipiens Induced by Changes in Environmental Conditions," *Journal of Experimental Medicine* 24 (1916): 689–99.
2. Warren and Margaret Lewis at the Carnegie Institute for Embryology for example did much work in trying to develop synthetic media by using tissue culture to study cell organelles and intracellular processes such as mitochondrial activity and pinocytosis. Later, George and Margaret Gey of the Johns Hopkins University concentrated on growing human tissue cultures, particularly cancerous tissues.
3. Carol Moberg, "Keith Porter and the Founding of the Tissue Culture Association: A Fiftieth Anniversary Tribute, 1946–1996," *In Vitro Cell Developmental Biology* 32 (1996): 663–9.
4. Bill Davidson, "Probing the Secret of Life," *Collier's*, 14 May 1954, 81. Davidson interviewed George Gey, John Biesele, Charles Pomerat, and Wilton Earle for the article.
5. Jan A. Witkowski, "Alexis Carrel and the Mysticism of Tissue Culture," *Medical History* 23 (1979): 279–96.
6. E. N. Willmer, introduction to *Cells and Tissues in Culture,* ed. E. N. Willmer (New York, 1965), 1–17, quoted in Witkowski, *Medical History* (n. 5 above), 280.
7. P. R. White, preface to *The Cultivation of Animal and Plant Cells* (New York, 1954), p. vi, quoted in Witkowski, *Medical History* (n. 5 above), 281.
8. The choice to look at his work carefully and in detail reflects my belief that the development of tissue culture simply cannot be fathomed without an engagement of the work done in his laboratory at the Rockefeller Institute. There has been too facile an assumption that an unquestionably elitist, arrogant, and eccentric man with professed eugenic opinions and dubious ties to the Vichy regime during World War II could not have been a "good" scientist and his work cannot have been scientifically valid or important. In addition, there has been an assumption that because he professed belief in miracles, the possibility of extrasensory perception, and was an avid reader and friend of the philosopher Henri Bergson, he was a "vitalist," another way of dismissing his work and writing without considering it and its effects. The history of decades of tissue culture practice have been dismissed with him.
9. Christopher Lawrence, "Democratic, Divine and Heroic: The History and Historiography of Surgery," in *Medical Theory, Surgical Practice: Studies in the History of Surgery*, ed. Christopher Lawrence (New York, 1992), 15.
10. Alexis Carrel, "The Reversal of the Circulation in a Limb," *Annals of Surgery* 43 (1907): 203–15.
11. Alexis Carrel, "Remote Results of the Transplantation of the Kidney and the Spleen," *Journal of Experimental Medicine* 12 (1910): 146–50.
12. It should also be noted that other than the assistants whom Carrel himself hired, his colleagues at the Rockefeller Institute were much more inclined toward studies of the pathological and biological side of medicine, and not toward surgery. This no doubt influenced Carrel's framing of the questions he saw himself pursuing. In 1906, the Institute had begun to set up laboratories under the direction of Samuel J. Meltzer (German-trained physiologist), Hideyo Noguchi (trained by Simon Flexner at the University

of Pennsylvania), Phoebus A. Levene (German-trained biochemist), and Eugene L. Opie (Johns Hopkins–trained pathologist famous for demonstrating association of diabetes with damage to the islands of Langerhans in the pancreas). Peyton Rous joined them in 1909, and Jacques Loeb in 1911. See George Corner, *A History of the Rockefeller Institute, 1901–1953* (New York, 1964) for a complete listing of these men, their backgrounds, and their projects.

13. To redintegrate means to restore something to a state of wholeness, completeness or unity; to renew, re-establish, in a united or perfect state. In the nineteenth century and early twentieth century, it was a term often used to refer to the regrowth of parts of animals that regenerated after injury or amputation. Alexis Carrel, "Peritoneal Patching of the Aorta," *Journal of Experimental Medicine* 12 (1910): 139–44.
14. Alexis Carrel, "The Treatment of Wounds," *Journal of the American Medical Association* 55 (1910): 2148–150.
15. Ibid., 2148.
16. Ibid., 2148.
17. These were the words Carrel used to describe, respectively, a period of very little change in the appearance of the wound, the appearance of "granulations" on the surface of the wound, the growing of new epidermal skin, and the formation of a scar.
18. Carrel, "Treatment" (n. 14 above), 2149.
19. Alexis Carrel, "Artificial Activation of the Growth in Vitro of Connective Tissue," *Journal of Experimental Medicine* 17 (1913): 14–9.
20. Alexis Carrel and Montrose Burrows, "Cultivation of Adult Tissues and Organs Outside of the Body," *Journal of the American Medical Association* 55 (1910): 1379–81.
21. Corner, *History of Rockefeller* (n. 12 above), 125.
22. Carrel and Burrows, "Cultivation" (n. 20 above), 1379.
23. Ross Harrison, "On the Status and Significance of Tissue Culture," *Archiv für experimentelle Zellforschung* 6 (1927): 5–6.
24. Alexis Carrel and Montrose Burrows, "Artificial Stimulation and Inhibition of the Growth of Normal and Sarcomatous Tissues," *Journal of the American Medical Association* 56 (1911): 32–3.
25. Alexis Carrel and Montrose Burrows, "Cultivation" (n. 20 above), 1381.
26. Ibid., 1380.
27. Ibid., 1381.
28. Alexis Carrel and Montrose Burrows, "Human Sarcoma Cultivated Outside of the Body," *Journal of the American Medical Association* 55 (1910): 1732.
29. Alexis Carrel to Paluel Flagg, January 22, 1924, Correspondence F, Alexis Carrel Papers, Georgetown University: "We use dark wall and floor paint, dark gowns, and dark linen in our operating room in order not to have any reflected light. We have found that this is a great improvement for delicate work. The first gray operating room was built 15 years ago by Doctor R. W. Corwin of Pueblo, Colorado. His operating room was made entirely of lead, and it could be sterilized with steam."
30. Raymond Parker to John Paul, April 9, 1958, Tissue Culture Association Papers (hereafter TCA Papers), University of Maryland, Baltimore County (hereafter UMBC).
31. Raymond Parker to John Paul, April 9, 1958, TCA Papers, UMBC.
32. "Permanent Life of Tissue Outside Its Organism," *Scientific American*, 18 May 1912.
33. Albert Fischer, in *Biology of Tissue Cells* (Copenhagen, 1946), 255.
34. Alexis Carrel, "Rejuvenation of Cultures of Tissues," *Journal of the American Medical Association* 57 (1911): 1611.
35. Ibid.
36. Alexis Carrel, "On the Permanent Life of Tissues Outside of the Organism," *Journal of Experimental Medicine* 15 (1912): 523.
37. Ibid., 15:525–26.
38. Ibid., 15:516.
39. Alexis Carrel, "Contributions to the Study of the Mechanism of the Growth of Connective Tissue," *Journal of Experimental Medicine* 18 (1913): 289.
40. Ibid., 18:300.
41. This presentation, the second of 1912 by Pozzi on Carrel's work, was also reprinted in *La Presse Médicale* the next day. Professor Pozzi, "Résultats Nouveaux du Dr. Alexis Carrel Relatif à la Vie Manifestée

Permanente des Tissus Séparés de L'Organisme," *La Presse Médicale*, 19 June 1912, 532.

42. Alexis Carrel, "Pure Cultures of Cells," *Journal of Experimental Medicine* 16 (1912): 165–168.
43. For a detailed account of some of these controversies, see Hannah Landecker, "Technologies of Living Substance: Tissue Culture and Cellular Life in Twentieth Century Biomedicine" (PhD diss., Massachusetts Institute of Technology, 1999).
44. Alexis Carrel, "Technic for Cultivating a Large Quantity of Tissue," *Journal of Experimental Medicine* 15 (1912): 393–6.
45. Ibid., 15:396.
46. Alexis Carrel and Ragnvald Ingebrigsten, "Production of Antibodies by Tissues Living Outside of the Organism," *Journal of the American Medical Association* 58 (1912): 477.
47. Paul Ehrlich, "Vorwort" in Albert Oppel, *Gewebekulturen und Gewebepflege im Explantat* (Braunschweig, 1914), volume iii. 48913.
48. C. Levatidi, "Symbiose Entre le Virus de la Poliomyélite et les Cellules des Ganglions Spinaux, à l'État de Vie Prolongée in vitro," *Comptes Rendus de la Société Biologie*. 74 (1913): 1179.
49. Alexis Carrel, "Concerning Visceral Organisms," *Journal of Experimental Medicine* 18 (1913): 155.
50. Alexis Carrel, "Visceral Organisms," *Journal of the American Medical Association* 59 (1912): 2105.
51. Ibid., 59:2106.
52. Alexis Carrel, (n. 49 above), 155–61.
53. Alexis Carrel, "Conférence du Docteur Carrel," *La Presse Médicale* 77 (1913).

Chapter 8

"The doctors are so sure that they only are right": The Rockefeller Institute and the Defeat of Vivisection Reform in New York, 1908–1914

Bernard Unti

Historian in Residence, American University, Washington, DC

From its inception, the Rockefeller Institute was a lightning rod for the controversy over vivisection. Its establishment and its initiation of research using animal subjects sparked the formation of several organizations that persistently campaigned on the question, and by 1909 the Institute stood at the heart of efforts by medical scientists to defeat legislation that proposed regulation of animal experimentation in New York. Their unyielding opposition frustrated the hopes of those humane organizations that attempted to stake out moderate positions concerning vivisection. Equable approaches to the subject dwindled, and a period of intense polarization set in. The legacy of the scientists' success—a lack of authentic oversight bearing on the use of animals in research, testing, and education—was to last until the 1960s and 1970s, when the Laboratory Animal Welfare Act and subsequent amendments received the approval of the United States Congress.

The historical reputation of vivisection's critics as dogmatic abolitionists notwithstanding, the record reveals that some key animal advocates were neither as extreme in their demands nor as misinformed as medical scientists claimed. Indeed, they sought the kind of regulatory framework that the federal Laboratory Animal Welfare Act, and ensuing revisions, later imposed. The sincerity of advocates of the reform position has been conspicuously neglected by scholarship in the history of science and medicine. Yet, it is the reformers' position, one based on external supervision, and not the self-regulation supported by the scientific community, which became the norm by the end of the twentieth century.[1]

The first of the new organizations inspired by the founding of the Institute was the Brooklyn-based Society for the Prevention of Abuse in Animal Experimentation (SPAAE), formed in 1907. SPAAE built its regulationist position around the ideology of Albert Leffingwell, MD (1845–1916), the most active medical critic of experimentation in the United States during the years 1885–1915. From 1880, when he first undertook the question and consistently throughout his life, Leffingwell advocated the regulation of vivisection, never its abolition. Indeed, until his death in 1916, Leffingwell's name was virtually synonymous with the reform position. Between 1897 and 1907, about a half dozen reform-oriented societies sprang up, and Leffingwell was involved with most of them. He also testified at almost every state or federal hearing concerning vivisection during the period of 1896–1910, and pro-experimentation advocates considered him their most formidable American adversary.[2]

During the period of 1908–1914, SPAAE led the attempt to bring vivisection in New York under legal control. Its director was an attorney, Frederick Bellamy, and its advisory group included Leffingwell, the naturalist John Burroughs, and the Social Gospel minister John Haynes Holmes. Antoinette Gazzam, a woman of independent wealth from Cornwall, New York, paid its operating expenses. The organization's object was to "secure legislation which shall restrict the growing practice of vivisection as to limit it to competent experimenters, place it under such control as shall prevent unnecessary cruelty to animals, and render abuse a misdemeanor, without hampering the legitimate advancement of science." To effect these purposes, Bellamy drafted what became the Davis-Lee Bill, referred to the judiciary committees of both chambers of the New York assembly in 1908.[3]

For several consecutive sessions, the Davis-Lee legislation sought to establish conditions concerning the use of animals in certain instances. It called for the use of anesthesia in experiments, although it provided exceptions for tests of food and drugs, inoculation research, studies concerning the communicability of disease, investigations of recovery from surgery, and several other procedures. It prohibited the performance of experiments for demonstrating facts when they were not performed "as part of the course of study in a regularly incorporated college, or laboratory." Finally, it called for two annual reports "stating in general the methods and anesthetics used, the number and species of animals used, and the nature and result of such experiments performed during the previous six months," to be filed with the State Commissioner of Health. Entry to laboratories, and the right to initiate prosecution, could only be gained from a justice of the New York Supreme Court, upon the presentation of affidavits.[4]

As Leffingwell's articles and testimony had done, SPAAE literature cited the value of the English Cruelty to Animals Act of 1876 and the support of such scientific luminaries as Darwin, Huxley, and Spencer for careful control and state supervision of experiments. SPAAE professed support for experimentation if conducted under reasonable terms, but highlighted, among other abuses, the improper use of human patients brought to light in recent years as evidence of the absence of sufficient regulation.[5] Its supporters generally made three points: "first, that abuse is possible; second, that the law is inadequate to prevent or to punish such abuse; and third, that the Davis-Lee Bill would not interfere with the advance of science but would prevent abuse and render unnecessary cruelty a misdemeanor." In each legislative session, SPAAE invited experimental scientists to suggest amendments to the bill that would satisfy their desire to fully protect scientific research.[6]

SPAAE's position was greatly strengthened by the American Society for the Prevention of Cruelty to Animals' (ASPCA) renewed engagement with the subject of vivisection. In a development that greatly alarmed experimenters in the New York area, the Davis-Lee Bill received the public support of the ASPCA board of managers, which had been very wary and largely inactive on the issue since the death of its antivivisectionist founder Henry Bergh in 1888. However, after 1908, with Bergh's nephew and namesake, Henry Bergh Jr., once again active in the Society, the organization expressed cautious support for the principle of regulation that would not interfere with "reasonable, proper, and necessary investigation."[7] During the period of 1908–1912, Bergh Jr. attempted to bring scientists and humane advocates together in an effort to agree on a course of reform. Moreover, as SPAAE's strategy shifted in 1909–1912 toward calls for a statewide commission to investigate the practice of vivisection in New York, the ASPCA continued its support.[8]

The other new organization to appear at this time was the New York Anti-Vivisection Society (NYAVS), incorporated in 1908 by Diana Belais (1858–1944), the most combative of the advocates to emerge in the wake of the Rockefeller Institute's founding. Although Belais grew less effective as the years passed, during her first years of activism she was a force with which to be reckoned. The NYAVS greatly benefited from the support of the *New York Herald*, which gave all critics of animal experimentation a chance to present their views, but especially favored Belais.[9] As the first SPAAE initiative began, Belais launched her own legislative campaign, providing for inspection of laboratories by a committee of persons appointed by the state's Board of Regents, half of whom were to be drawn from the roster of the NYAVS. Belais's active opposition to Davis-Lee would hurt her bill's chances in the years ahead, due to the confusion and ill-will created by two competing bills treating the same question.[10]

Pressure from scientists at other institutions spurred the involvement of the Rockefeller Institute in the public debate. In early 1908, Columbia University physiologist Frederic S. Lee urged Simon Flexner to become active in the defense of experimentation, "especially because the feeling seems to exist in various quarters that since the present agitation centers largely in the work of the Rockefeller Institute, and because of the prominence of the Institute in the medical world, its authorities ought to take a leading part in the fight." Later that year, Flexner responded by taking a prominent public stand in defense of vivisection. It was to become a familiar role. During the 1908 session, Flexner explicitly attacked Davis-Lee's provision for anesthetics, telling one journal that anesthesia usually was not necessary in animal experimentation and that in other cases it might interfere with the development of the condition under study.[11]

Nonetheless, the Davis-Lee Bill, endorsed by 700 doctors within the state, was favorably reported out of the New York Senate judiciary committee, the first time that such a bill had ever been released from committee anywhere. Leffingwell and Bellamy both testified, and the reporting of the bill occurred despite attempts by the Medical Society of the State of New York to promote withdrawal of the doctors' endorsements, and the discord created by Belais's NYAVS, whose inspection bill died in committee. Early adjournment of the legislature frustrated attempts to move Davis-Lee through a comparable committee in the state's second legislative chamber, the New York Assembly.[12]

In the aftermath of the 1908 agitation, the Rockefeller Institute sought and secured an amendment to its charter specifically granting statutory permission to conduct experiments on animals. It was a self-conscious move, by which it was presumed the Institute could avoid legal vulnerability under section 10, chapter 375 of the Laws of 1867. This provision of the anticruelty statute stated that any institutions or laboratories that did not "exist or perform vivisection under the authority of any medical college or university [were] clearly liable to prosecution under this section whenever they undertake the performance of vivisection." For the Institute, a new kind of research institution, the risk of prosecution was not worth taking.[13]

Throughout 1909, the controversies surrounding the Institute intensified, largely due to agitation by Belais and the NYAVS, which maintained an antivivisection display outside the Institute, and, along with New Jersey groups, attacked its plans for a "vivisection farm" in New Jersey. Belais also engineered the publicity campaign in which Mary Kennedy, a former employee at the Institute, swore in an affidavit accusing Flexner and his colleagues of cruelty and neglect, especially in the area of post-experimental care. Even as Kennedy told her story, William Blakeney, an animal caretaker, abandoned his job, calling the top floor of the Institute "a chamber of horrors." The scandal erupted in December 1909 and carried over into 1910, drawing Flexner into extended public debate over the Institute's work and its treatment of animals. Flexner and his associates addressed the ensuing publicity crisis with a series of interviews defending the treatment of animals at the Institute, and trumpeting the benefits of its research.[14]

SPAAE's Davis-Lee legislation surfaced again during the 1909 session, along with the Brough-Murray Bill (Belais's proposal), once more demanding a system of inspection. This time, Bellamy secured endorsements for Davis-Lee from 27 humane societies throughout the state. However, neither bill made it out of committee, as the New York Medical Society rounded up a strong panel of witnesses, including Flexner, to testify at the March 1909 hearings.[15]

The reenactment of section 10, chapter 375 of the Laws of 1867, into the Penal Code Statutes of New York State also altered the context of debate. Questions had arisen about whether this section had been rendered inoperative by subsequent revisions of the cruelty-to-animals statute. The reenacted section specified once more that nothing in the anticruelty statute "shall be construed to prohibit or interfere with any properly conducted scientific experiments or investigations, which experiments shall be performed only under the authority of the faculty of some regularly incorporated medical college or university of this State."[16]

In Bellamy's opinion, the legislators considering Davis-Lee were "misled into thinking that this reenacted section 10 provided adequate legislation, and [that] it was because of this belief on their part that the Davis-Lee Bill was not reported out of Committee." Bellamy argued that section 10, chapter 375 had been obsolete and inoperative for many years, owing to the fact that all of the other sections of chapter 375 had been repealed in previous legislative sessions. Bellamy believed the recent reenactment of section 10 as section 185, chapter 40, of the Consolidated Laws of New York State vindicated his position, although he did not think that the reenactment would make much difference. The section, he wrote, "now stands for the little it is worth." At the same time, Bellamy contended that the 1909 reenactment set in doubt the validity of the Rockefeller Institute exemption, secured the year before. "The later law in 1909," he insisted, "repeals the authority given by the amended charter in 1908 to perform vivisection, and thus defeats the very scientific work it is claimed to protect." Moreover, Bellamy asserted, and the ASPCA agreed, "It is perfectly obvious to anybody who will read this clause [section 10, chapter 375 of the Laws of 1867, now upon the statute books as section 185 of article 16 of the Penal Code] that instead of being a provision intended to regulate the practice of vivisection or prevent its abuse, it is simply and only a provision expressly authorizing the practice of vivisection 'under the authority of the faculty of some regularly incorporated medical college or university of this State.'"[17]

Ultimately, the scientists were less worried about such technical/legal challenges than the breaking of ranks. In particular, the 1908–1909 campaign elicited a notable statement of support from William James, himself an experimenter, who, after an exchange of views with Albert Leffingwell, expressed his strong approval of a regulatory framework and his deep skepticism about the ability of scientists to police themselves without oversight. "Against any regulation whatever I understand the various medical and scientific defenders of vivisection to protest," James wrote. "Their invariable contention, implied or expressed, is that it is no one's business what happens to an animal, so long as the individual who is handling it can plead that to increase science is his aim. This contention seems to me to flatly contradict the best conscience of our time...." Although his scientific colleagues were aware of James's long-standing sympathy for this position, his public endorsement of regulation was a severe blow.[18]

Reverend John Haynes Holmes, the influential minister of the Community Church of New York, also wrote a strong endorsement of regulation. Like James, Holmes supported vivisection but considered it "so easily open to indescribable abuse...that it must be surrounded by the most careful and rigid restrictions." In response to experimenters' claims for immunity based on "private character, public spirit, professional ethics, [and] scientific consecration," Holmes also alluded to the "conscience of our time":

> Today, society is paramount, and not the individual or the class of individuals. The business man can no longer say: 'This is *my* business, and I will do what I want with it.' The railroad man can no longer speak of *his* railroad, or the factory man of *his* factory, or the tenement owner of *his* tenement. Society is extending its protecting hand over the great mass of men, women and children, protecting them from exploitation, abuse and cruelty by the favored and privileged classes. And this movement for the restriction of vivisection, as I regard it, is nothing but the further extension of this movement of social protection over the lower animals.[19]

Responding to such arguments, the state medical society issued a series of pamphlets that stressed the adequacy of statutory provisions and institutional self-regulation, asserted the inadvisability of special restriction, and minimized the extent of painful experiments as well as the capacity of animals to experience pain. While not acknowledging the legitimacy of any specific allegations against the Rockefeller Institute, experimenters argued that reform was unnecessary in the absence of authentic evidence concerning cruelty to animals in the name of science.[20]

Although the argument that extant legal authority was sufficient to control cruelty may not have originated with Flexner, he was its strongest proponent. This claim rested on a specific construction of the law secured by Bergh in 1867 and renewed or revised on several subsequent occasions. Writing against the restriction bill, Columbia Law School Dean George Kirchwey asserted that the general cruelty statute "is aimed at the vivisector who conducts his experiments without a due regard for the sufferings of animals experimented upon, as well as at the brutal citizen who inflicts needless pain on the lower animals...." As for section 10, Kirchwey argued, the Legislature had

> ...indicated clearly its belief that the Act covered scientific experiments not properly conducted, as well as its fear that the sweeping provisions of the Act might, but the saving clause, be construed to forbid all scientific investigations involving animal suffering. The fact that the general law contains no reference to vivisection does not, in view of its sweeping, general provisions, justify the hasty assumption that cruelty practiced in that form is not equally condemned with that practiced in any other form.[21]

Scientists could even point to two successful prosecutions conducted under this theory, in a case in which two men were convicted of treating unanesthetized animals cruelly for the purpose of vivisection or dissection in a parlor room experiment. In this case, the ASPCA found that it could arrest the men for conducting vivisection outside of an established college or other facility.[22]

Nevertheless, animal advocates condemned the argument that the extant law was adequate as disingenuous. It might be possible to instigate a prosecution of a quack or amateur vivisector operating out of his home under the statute. However, as humane advocates interpreted the New York statute, it left no room for the prosecution of any experimenter attached to an institution, as Kirchwey's and the scientists' arguments implied. Even if this were legally feasible, getting evidence of a specific cruelty in an institutional laboratory was extremely difficult, if not impossible, because as a matter of professional ethics, medical men did not testify against one another or one another's employees. There were no other witnesses in a context where outsiders were barred. Outside of New York, too, there were several notable instances in which anticruelty statutes had proved insufficient for the purpose of prosecuting cruelties allegedly perpetrated in the course of experimentation.[23]

Although the ASPCA's participation in the campaign for vivisection reform deeply troubled the scientific community, the American Humane Association (AHA)—a national humane organization headquartered in Albany—was entirely absent from the field during the conflict over vivisection in New York. In the late nineteenth and early twentieth centuries, the AHA, at the urging of Leffingwell, had stood at the forefront of regulationist approaches to vivisection reform. After William O. Stillman (1856–1924) became its president in 1904, however, the organization ceased to campaign on the issue and all of its pamphlets on the subject went out of print. Stillman was anxious to avoid controversy and kept his dealings with vivisection reform advocates to a minimum. Although he never offered an unequivocal endorsement of vivisection, it seems clear that Stillman recognized some of its medical benefits.[24]

For various reasons, the AHA during Stillman's presidency acted more upon his own priorities and inclinations than on any coherent or democratically agreed-upon agenda. There was no real debate within the AHA about how to proceed in regard to experimentation. Instead, Stillman attempted to placate the scientists, reassuring them that the AHA would pose them no trouble. At the height of the controversy over vivisection regulation, he invited Flexner, Keen, and (apparently) other medical scientists to become members of the AHA, and acquiesced to the suppression of discussion of vivisection at the organization's annual conferences. Stillman's humane colleagues may not have known about his recruitment of experimental scientists to membership, but they were not deceived about the AHA's retreat from its historic role in the pursuit of vivisection reform.[25]

For scientists, driving a wedge between critics of vivisection and the broad alliance of animal protection societies represented by the AHA was an important priority. From about 1909 onward, Keen attempted to dissuade prominent citizens, including President Taft, from lending their names to the AHA as honorary vice presidents, so long as vivisection came under consideration at its conferences.[26] Although the vivisection issue did not cause much open conflict between the organizations that composed the AHA, it did generate undercurrents of tension that prevented the development of a coalition strong enough to promote successful moderate reform. Stillman's decision to withhold support for any measures concerning vivisection served the agenda of research advocates by removing the humane movement's principal umbrella organization from any active participation in the debate.

In 1910, the Davis-Lee legislation, now known as the Bayne-Goodspeed Bill, was introduced again; it appeared as Bayne-Hoey in 1911, and then again as Bayne-Barnes in 1912. By that time, it involved a call for a state investigative commission to determine what legislation "if any, is needed to prevent unnecessary suffering of animals through such practice or its abuse, without interfering with properly conducted scientific experiments by competent experts."[27] As usual, there was no provision for inspection of laboratories, and, for the first time, the bill proposed no restriction or limitation on experimentation. Senator Howard Bayne himself explained the shift toward a call for investigation, suggesting that without facts about the conduct of animal research in the state, all of the proposed bills were impractical. Because the governor was charged to appoint the commission, Bayne asserted, no antivivisectionists would be chosen. Although vivisectionists attacked the notion of an investigative committee as a partisan subterfuge, Bellamy countered that the governor was free to appoint "such men as Dr. Flexner and [Cornell's] Dr. Ewing to represent research, and as Henry Bergh and Dr. Leffingwell to represent humanitarianism."[28]

Belais's bill, in various incarnations between 1908 and 1912, called for an inspection system under the banner of the "Open Door." Under later versions of her proposal, the New York State Board of Regents of would appoint persons with the authority to inspect laboratory facilities at any time. SPAAE specifically shunned the inspection approach, assuming it would be completely unacceptable to the scientific community. Although supporters of the SPAAE and ASPCA certainly would have preferred to see their bills considered separately from those sponsored by the NYAVS, they could not manage it. The consideration of both bills jointly within legislative committees played into a key strategy of the state's vivisection forces, their complete refusal to acknowledge any differences between the regulationist SPAAE and other groups concerned with vivisection, especially the NYAVS. The assignment of both bills to the same hearing made it easier to lump together all proposals as equally unreasonable. Indeed, Flexner and other scientists did not hesitate to adopt this position in their direct communication with animal advocates.[29]

Whatever the aims of the animal organizations, or the suspicions of the scientists, the legislative sponsors of such legislation did not support abolition, and expressed their desire to place the right to conduct experiments into the hands of competent professional men operating in accredited institutions. In the same vein, key supporters of vivisection reform like Holmes consciously distinguished between the SPAAE approach and one rooted in dogmatic antivivisection in deciding whether or not to retain membership in the various societies.[30]

Ignoring or discounting such perspectives, the pro-experimentation community held nothing back in its attempt to quash all legislative initiatives. Without question, their principal argument was that all restrictive legislation should be opposed as "the entering wedge" for a full-blown campaign of abolition.[31] New York's scientific community also attacked proposed legislation by asserting that the English Cruelty to Animals Act of 1876 had severely inhibited medical progress in that country.[32] In addition, the scientists assailed the technicalities of schemes for registration, certification, and record keeping. Flexner pointed out that since he was not a registered physician he would not be eligible to experiment under one of the proposals being considered.[33] Another common tactic of opposition was simply to express outrage that members of an august profession were even being accused of cruelty and impropriety.[34]

From the perspective of the scientists, the ASPCA's active support for regulation was the most threatening dimension of the era's legislative campaigns. The ASPCA came to its position after serious internal debate. In February 1909, three board members—Henry Bergh, Gordon Bell, and Jefferson Seligman—met with Flexner and Columbia University's John G. Curtis to exchange views on the subject. The scientists took the position that "any restriction on vivisection, no matter how slight, would seriously hamper scientific research," and insisted that the 1867 statute was sufficient to prevent abuse. The ASPCA representatives countered with their view that although vivisection was very likely "free from unnecessary cruelty" in the hands of experimenters like Flexner and Curtis, the probability of abuse by others was very high, and certainly difficult if not impossible to stop under the present statute. With some gravity, the committee members reported, "The doctors are so sure that they only are right and that no one else knows or can know anything about it, that they impressed your committee as imbued with a dangerous enthusiasm."[35]

After this encounter, the ASPCA committee recommended a system of licensure and a supervisory board to determine the qualifications of applicants, inspect laboratories, and require and maintain detailed reports of laboratory procedure. The committee counseled against support for the limitation of experiments in classroom demonstration, believing that "vivisection is necessary also to demonstrate to students facts already known." In this particular, the ASPCA backed away from the long-standing position articulated by Leffingwell, which of course conformed to England's Cruelty to Animals Act of 1876.[36]

One year later, Seligman and two other board members served on a second committee, convened to guide the ASPCA's deliberations in the aftermath of the allegations of cruelty at the Rockefeller Institute. The committee endorsed the contention of SPAAE's Bellamy that the extant statute did not reach abuses of vivisection, and suggested that any course of reform expressly make such abuse a misdemeanor under law. At the same time, after consultation with Governor Charles Evans Hughes, the committee recommended that a thorough investigation by a competent authority empowered by law should precede any further legislative proposals in New York. This led to an expression of support for the SPAAE Bill (Bayne-Goodspeed) calling for the governor to appoint an investigative commission. Thus, the Board committed itself to an "attitude of inquiry."[37]

The ASPCA's support seemed especially important in 1911 as Democratic leaders in Albany, including Robert Wagner and Al Smith, signaled their support for regulation. Defenders of experiments worked energetically to neutralize the ASPCA's participation in the pro-regulation campaign. They got some help from the press, as some newspapers harshly denounced the organization for supporting the Bayne-Hoey Bills during 1911. The ASPCA fought back gamely, explaining its position, chiding editorialists for their "reactionary" appraisals, and insisting that it was "in the fight to stay."[38]

In Bergh's critical letter to the *New York Times* in January 1911, he underscored the fact that the ASPCA had arrived at its policy after a series of attempts to persuade medical scientists to support "such legislative measures as would do away with the abuses, but not interfere with the reasonable practice of vivisection." These efforts had failed because of the scientists' "oft expressed ironclad intolerance of any proposed restrictive legislation whatsoever." In the aftermath of the medical scientists' recent attack against a bill "merely asking for an impartial State inquiry into the practice of vivisection, as at present conducted in this State," the ASPCA's efforts "to effect any reforms through the cooperation of the medical fraternity ceased," in favor of "active measures to secure that protection to our dumb wards against the infliction of all needless suffering which had justly been denied to them at the hands of the medical fraternity."[39]

As it turned out, the SPAAE did not stay in the fight. After one more round of activity in 1912, recognizing the futility of trying to regulate an increasingly influential cadre of researchers who flatly refused to be regulated, the SPAAE left the fray. Neither the ASPCA nor any other organization took steps to perpetuate the campaign for vivisection reform once the SPAAE disbanded several years later. During the 1913–1914 legislative session, SPAAE attempted for the fifth time to secure legislation to form an investigative committee to explore the question of how best to regulate vivisection in the state, and gathered more than 10,000 signatures in support of the measure. As it happened, this was the last coordinated effort at regulation by SPAAE or any other group in New York. Only the NYAVS remained, and it grew more shrill and more dogmatic in its condemnation of vivisection and modern scientific medicine. Diana Belais shifted toward a new strategy, supporting bills that exempted dogs from research. The humane societies that had fallen behind the SPAAE proposals for reform now abstained from further participation, leaving the field to her.[40]

Flexner believed that the ASPCA's withdrawal from the issue after the 1910–1912 campaigns was a critical turning point. That retreat made it possible to maintain that there was a legitimate humane movement, which accepted the necessity of vivisection, that could be distinguished from the unreasonable antivivisectionists who rejected it. SPAAE's proposals, drawing support from the more staid and moderate animal organizations, had denied Flexner and his colleagues this important and strategically useful claim.[41]

In the Progressive era, clearly, humane advocates who challenged animal experimenters had to confront the rapidly expanding cultural authority of medical science, and the increased political power and influence guaranteed by such éclat. Medical researchers could proudly claim that science was delivering on its promises, and they did so within the aura of credibility conferred by the Progressive era reliance on experts. By then, too, the experimentation community had built a network of influence that made it a relatively simple matter to ward off all regulation and antivivisection initiatives. The New York scientists, backed by wealthy and established institutions, were well-known and well-connected men. As part of their response to the Davis-Lee legislation, experimenters lined up the support of Governor Charles Evans Hughes, whose son had undergone treatment with Flexner's serum therapy. Both Keen and Cannon wrote to Hughes to disparage proposals for external inspection and oversight, and Keen assured Cannon that "you need not worry about any anti-vivisection law as long as he presides at Albany."[42] During the 1913 New York legislative campaign, with two bills coming up in the legislature, animal advocate Jefferson Seligman told the press that he had received a commitment of assistance from the new governor, William Sulzer. At the same time, however, Frederic Lee informed Cannon that there was no reason to worry that Governor Sulzer would sign either bill—"we're in touch with his physician." When one of the bills was reported out, the Rockefeller Institute's Henry James visited the majority leader and secured assurances that the bill would make no further progress.[43]

> If it is difficult to fully gauge the strength of the campaign for vivisection reform, one can at least say that it was not popular enough to overcome the influence and favor that medical scientists enjoyed with federal and state officials at the time of the movement's greatest vitality. Researchers proved to be better-connected politically than animal advocates and usually managed to kill off threatening bills in committee before they reached the assembly floor where, presumably, constituents might have urged their elected representatives to back inspection, oversight, investigation, and other measures.[44]

Historians of science and medicine commonly argue that experimenters did seek to institute internal reforms, through the mechanism of the American Medical Association's (AMA) Council on the Defense of Medical Research, founded in 1908. One of Walter Cannon's first acts as head of the council was to promulgate a set of voluntary codes for circulation to laboratories around the country. In developing the code, Cannon was motivated by his desire to defuse antivivisectionist criticism as well as to convince legislators and the public that the medical community was earnest about self-regulation. However, beyond the initial endorsement of the institutions to which Cannon appealed, there is a lack of historical evidence of compliance with higher standards of animal care within these institutions. Without such documentation, there simply is no ground for the claims of the medical science community to a long tradition of successful self-regulation.[45]

In any case, Cannon's promotion of the code did not satisfy humane advocates. Just a few years after the standards appeared, Henry Bergh Jr. reminded legislators that there were many institutions and people to which these regulations did not extend. Animal advocates also found it telling that, in 1913, the Medical Society of New York opposed an amendment suggested by Frederick Bellamy that would have incorporated the AMA rules into the penal code of New York.[46]

Never confident of unequivocal public support for their work, animal experimenters acted defensively and even deceptively well into mid-century. According to one historian, for example, in the more than two decades of his tenure at the *Journal of Experimental Medicine* (beginning in 1921) the Rockefeller Institute's Francis Peyton Rous altered the details, numerical figures, illustrations, and descriptions of experiments likely to pique antivivisectionists and other parties concerned with the welfare of animals. On occasion, too, researchers quietly took measures to address some of the issues that their critics had identified, without publicly acknowledging the source or validity of such criticism.[47]

Historians of science and medicine, by and large, have not been kind to the critics of vivisection, perhaps because many humane advocates, especially those who became active in either antivivisection or vivisection reform, tended to be skeptical and dismissive of the actual and potential benefits of animal experimentation. Although they were not alone in expressing their doubts, this tendency has led some authors to cast them as antimodern, antiscience, and misguided. Sometimes, no doubt, this may have been the case.[48]

However, in making such judgments, contemporary scholars have overlooked, just as the scientists did, the important distinctions that such critics drew between their respective positions about the appropriate methods and extent of regulation or restriction. Historical scholarship consistently slights the more moderate factions, leaving them out of the story or misrepresenting their approach as part of an "entering wedge" strategy. This approach adopts the scientists' viewpoint without honest or thorough interrogation, and thus badly skews historical understanding of the controversy over animal experimentation. A more careful consideration of the reforms humane advocates proposed complicates such portrayals, showing that the people who wanted to place vivisection under legal control raised ethical issues that, in recent years, our society has taken up in earnest. In important respects, they were ahead of their time, neither antimodern nor dogmatic.

More balanced historical scholarship also will acknowledge that some of the researchers' claims and arguments in the battles over vivisection were deceptive or plainly wrong. They invented medical diagnoses to underwrite their condescending misogyny.[49] They mischaracterized the particular details of regulationist proposals in order to discredit them.[50] They overstated the nature, extent, and impact of British regulation of vivisection under the Cruelty to Animals Act of 1876. Finally, they would never publicly admit, as they sometimes conceded to one another, that not all of the antivivisectionist charges were ill-founded.[51] Worst of all, animal experimenters killed off reform measures without ever offering convincing explanations as to how a requirement to register their facilities, obtain licenses, or provide statistics concerning the species and the numbers of animals used, and those used in painful procedures would substantially impede their activity.[52]

In 1914, an aging Albert Leffingwell presented his final thoughts on the subject of animal experimentation in *An Ethical Problem*, intending the work to be his own valedictory. Unfortunately, the work proved to be something of a valediction for the reform position to which he had devoted almost four decades. Leffingwell's hopes that someone else would pick up the torch he had carried were disappointed, as half a century would pass before others not only took up the case for regulation that he had championed but also overcame the spirited opposition of the medical and scientific community. By that time, scientific claims for complete freedom and autonomy in the conduct of animal research could be tested against a longer record of allegations of poor conditions and neglect of animal welfare concerns in medical research. By then, too, the need for such oversight appeared urgent, and the argument that there were ethical norms that society itself, rather than the medical science community alone, must determine, impose, and enforce, fell on more receptive ears.[53]

Endnotes

1. Susan Lederer, almost uniquely among historians of medicine and science in the United States, has taken the regulationist approach seriously; Susan E. Lederer, *Subjected to Science: Human Experimentation in America before the Second World War* (Baltimore, 1995), 34–5.
2. W. W. Keen to Walter Cannon, 26 November 1910, W. W. Keen to Cannon, 12 June 1911, and W. W. Keen to Cannon, 11 September 1911, William Williams Keen Papers (Keen Papers), American Philosophical Society, Philadelphia, PA (hereafter APS). Leffingwell's output includes "Does Vivisection Pay?" *Scribner's Monthly* 20 (1880): 391–9; "An Ethical Basis for Humanity to Animals," *Arena* 10 (1894): 477–8; *Does Science Need Secrecy?* (Providence: 1896); "Opposed to Vivisection in the School Room," *Brooklyn Eagle*, 12 April 1900, 7; *The Rise of the Vivisection Controversy: A Chapter of History* (New York, 1903); "For Restriction and Limitation," *Outlook* 76 (9 April 1904): 877; *The Vivisection Question* (New Haven, 1901); and *An Ethical Problem, or Sidelights Upon Scientific Experimentation on Man and Animals* (New York, 1914).
3. Antoinette Gazzam, *The Problem of Vivisection: A Plea for Proper Regulation* (New York, 1908).
4. Society for the Prevention of Abuse in Animal Experimentation (hereafter SPAAE), *1907–1909 Report* (1910), 30–2.
5. Susan Lederer has assessed the charge of human vivisection in *Subjected to Science*; "'The Right and Wrong of Making Experiments on Human Beings': Udo J. Wile and Syphilis," *Bulletin of the History of Medicine* 58 (1984): 380–97; "Hideyo Noguchi's Luetin Experiment and the Antivivisectionists," *Isis* 76 (1985): 31–48; and "Orphans as Guinea Pigs: American Children and Medical Experimenters, 1890–1930," in *In the Name of the Child: Health and Social Policy, 1870–1940*, ed. Roger Cooter (London, 1992): 96–123.
6. SPAAE, 10, 13.
7. Relevant correspondence and other statements of the ASPCA's support are reprinted in SPAAE, *1909–1911 Report* (1912): 15–16, 20–21, 37–41. The quotation from the 1908 ASPCA resolution is taken from SPAAE's organ *Vivisection Reform* 1 (February 1910): 13.
8. "Henry Bergh Would Restrict Vivisection," *New York Herald*, 16 August 1908, in ASPCA Scrapbook 12: 66, ASPCA Archives, New York City (hereafter ASPCA Archives); "At Odds over Vivisection," *New York Sun*, 14 January 1910; "Inquiry into the Needless Cruelties of Vivisection is Started by the SPCA," *New York Herald*, 14 January 1910; "Vivisection Inquiry by Animal Society," *New York Times*, 14 January 1910; "Noted Men in Debate on Vivisection Urge State Supervision of Practice," *New York Herald*, 1 March 1910; "Humane Bodies in Call for Inquiry," *New York Herald*, 11 March 1910; "Vivisection Foes Urge Governor to Aid New Bill," *New York Herald*, 16 March 1910; and "Colonel Wagstaff Re-elected," *New York Tribune*, 12 January 1912, Lee Scrapbook 3, Frederic Schiller Lee Papers, Columbia University Medical Archive, Augustus C. Long Health Science Library, Columbia University, New York, New York (hereafter Lee Papers); ASPCA Board Minutes, 10 March 1910, 114–116; ASPCA Board Minutes, 14 July 1910, 119–20; ASPCA Board Minutes, 9 February 1911, 140; ASPCA Minute Book 6, ASPCA Archives.
9. "Mrs. C. R. Flint for 'Open Door,'" *New York Herald*, 12 January 1910, Lee Scrapbook 2, Lee Papers; "The 'Open Door' Policy," *Our Dumb Animals* 44 (January 1912): 124; "The Other A-V's," *New York Herald*, 5 February 1910, Lee Scrapbook 3, Lee Papers; Diana Belais, "A Bit of History," *Open Door* 21 (January 1932): 1–2; SPAAE, *1909–1911 Report*, 23–4; and "Mrs. D. Belais, Animal Defender," *New York Times*, 15 February 1944.
10. SPAAE, *Report* (n. 4 above), 9, 15–16. Belais seems to have either alienated or avoided cooperation with

other people working on behalf of animals. Sue Farrell's Vivisection Investigation League (1911) began as a splinter faction of the NYAVS. When a number of groups working on the vivisection issue formed the Interstate Conference for the Investigation of Vivisection in 1912, Belais's organization did not participate nor was she involved with the 1913 Washington conference that brought together most of the other active antivivisection and vivisection reform advocates.

11. Frederic S. Lee to Simon Flexner, 16 January 1908, Box 1, Folder 3, Davis-Lee Correspondence 1907–1909, Vivisection Correspondence, Lee Papers; "Vivisection Calls for Sacrifice at the Rockefeller Institute," *New York Herald*, 7 June 1908; "Vivisection Defended by Dr. Flexner," *New York Journal*, 8 June 1908; "Dr. Flexner Tells of His Meningitis Experiments," *New York American*, 8 June 1908; "Dr. Flexner Tells What the RI Has Done Toward Vanquishing TB, Meningitis, and Other Diseases," *New York Times*, 18 October 1909, Lee Scrapbook 1, Lee Papers.
12. The foregoing discussion is based on the SPAAE, *Report* (n. 4 above).
13. "Assails Vivisection Status of Rockefeller Institute," *New York Herald*, 4 February 1910, Lee Scrapbook 3, Lee Papers; "Legal Status of Vivisection," *Vivisection Reform* 1 (February 1910): 3.
14. "'Vivisection Farm' Complaint Filed," *Journal of Zoophily* 18 (September 1909): 93–4; "New Jersey Plans to Drive Rockefeller Institute from State," *New York Herald*, 1 January 1910, Lee Scrapbook 2, Lee Papers; "Torturing Animals Declared Unnecessary," *Philadelphia Telegraph*, 11 January 1910; T. Wood Clarke, MD, "Scientific Vivisection," *Utica Observer*, 11 January 1910; "Dr. Flexner Denies Cruel Vivisection," *New York Times*, 17 January 1910; "Leaves Institute, Fearing for Life," *New York Herald*, 18 January 1910; Lee Scrapbook 3, Lee Papers; "The Rockefeller Institute Affidavits," *Vivisection Reform* 1 (February 1910): 11–3; and Susan E. Lederer, "The Controversy Over Animal Experimentation in America, 1880–1914," *Vivisection in Historical Perspective*, ed. Nicolaas Rupke (London, 1987), 248–9. The controversy can also be followed in the *New York Herald*, 27, 28, 29, and 31 December 1909, and 8 and 14 January 1910.
15. SPAAE, *Report 1909–1911* (n. 7 above), 9.
16. SPAAE, *Report* (n. 4 above), 17–8, 24–7; and SPAAE, *Report 1909–1911* (n. 7 above), 9.
17. SPAAE, *Report* (n. 4 above), 17–8, 25; Vivisection Reform 1 (February 1910), 3; and Frederick P. Bellamy, "Present Legal Status of Vivisection," *ASPCA Bulletin* 2, 5 (May 1911), 67.
18. William James, Letter to the *New York Post*, 22 May 1909, reprinted in SPAAE, *1907–1909 Report*, 46–47. Leffingwell discussed the letter his meeting with James, and James's views in *An Ethical Problem*, 119–222. James expressed an early opinion on the subject in an unsigned editorial, "Vivisection," *Nation* 20 (1875): 128–9. Leffingwell and other critics of vivisection were aware of James's support for their position at least as early as 1901; see Leffingwell's comments to the annual meeting of the AAVS in *Journal of Zoophily* 10, 2 (February 1901), 5. On the disappointment of James's colleagues, see Saul Benison, A. Clifford Barger, and Elin L. Wolfe, *Walter B. Cannon: The Life and Times of a Young Scientist* (Cambridge, 1987), 198–201.
19. John Haynes Holmes to Frederick P. Bellamy, 5 February 1909, reprinted in SPAAE, *1907–1909 Report*, 33–4.
20. George W. Kirchwey, *The Legal Aspect of Animal Experimentation in the State of New York* (New York, 1909); John G. Curtis, *Why are Special Laws To Restrict Animal Experimentation Unwise?* (1909); John Dewey, *The Ethics of Animal Experimentation* (1909); Frederic S. Lee, *The Sense of Pain in Man and the Lower Animals* (1908); and *Shall Anti-Vivisection Legislation Be Enacted?* (1910).
21. Kirchwey, 3–4; Kirchwey's position is recapitulated in the Medical Society of the State of New York, Undated Statement on Barnes Bill, folder 6, box 1, RG 600–1, Rockefeller University Archives, Rockefeller Archive Center, Sleepy Hollow, NY, USA (hereafter RAC).
22. *Shall Anti-Vivisection Legislation Be Enacted?*, 1–2; and John G. Curtis, *Why are Special Laws to Restrict Animal Experimentation Unwise?*, 1. For information on the case and the two prosecutions (*People v. Warschmidt* and *People v. Harrison*), see "Two Students Held for Death of Two Cats," *New York Press*, 12 December 1908; and "Skin Three Cats and Got Cells," *New York Herald*, 12 December 1908, ASPCA Scrapbook 12: 105–6, ASPCA Archives.
23. Sydney R. Taber, *Reasonable Restriction vs. Absolute License in Vivisection* (Chicago, 1907), 7–8.
24. In 1901, Stillman declared himself in favor of strict regulation, although there is no evidence that he ever campaigned on the issue; see American Humane Association (hereafter AHA), *Twenty-Fifth Annual Report* (1901), 58–9. For his quote concerning antisera, see S. G. Brabrook, "Vivisection of Dogs,"

Boston Herald, 2 September 1908, Lee Scrapbook 1, Lee Papers. In late 1879 and early 1880, "W.O.S." defended vivisection in an exchange of letters published in a Saratoga newspaper; see Henry B. King, "Vivisection Again," undated letter, *Daily Saratogan*, in ASPCA Scrapbook 8: 213, ASPCA Archives.

25. Flexner joined; see Flexner to Keen, 9 November 1911, and Keen to Flexner, 2 December 1911, in Keen Folder 1, and Nathaniel J. Walker to Simon Flexner, 8 November 1911, AHA Folder, Simon Flexner Papers (Flexner Papers), APS; and W. W. Keen to Walter Cannon 16 December 1913, Walter Cannon to W. W. Keen, 18 December 1913, Keen Papers, APS. On Stillman's colleagues, see Mary F. Lovell, "An Anomalous Position," *Journal of Zoophily* 19, 11 (November 1910), 127–8; J. B. Y. Warner and Frederick Bellamy, "To the Members of the American Humane Association," 2 January 1914, folder 9, box 3, RG 600–1, Rockefeller University Archives, RAC; Bellamy, "Humane Societies vs. Cruelty," *Proceedings of the International Anti-Vivisection and Animal Protection Congress* (New York, 1914), 64–5.
26. W. W. Keen to Walter Cannon, 13 November 1909; W. W. Keen to Walter Cannon, 13 November 1909; W. W. Keen to Walter Cannon, 18 November 1909; Walter Cannon to W. W. Keen, 19 November 1909; W. W. Keen to Cannon, 10 December 1909; W. W. Keen to Walter Cannon, 28 June 1910; W. W. Keen to Walter Cannon, 29 June 1910; Walter Cannon to W. W. Keen, 30 June 1910; W. W. Keen to Walter Cannon, 3 November 1910, Keen Papers, APS; and W. W. Keen to Simon Flexner, 11 November 1911, AHA Folder, Flexner Papers, APS. Interestingly, Mrs. Taft signed a petition in support of the regulationist position during this same period; see "Mrs. Taft to Help Curb Vivisection," *Philadelphia Times*, 17 February 1910, and "Mrs. Taft Joins Ranks of Washington Fighters to Curb Vivisection," *New York Herald*, 17 February 1910, Lee Scrapbook 2, Lee Papers, Archives and Special Collection, A. C. Long Health Sciences Library, Columbia University, New York, New York (hereafter CU); and "Comments and Reflections," *Journal of Zoophily* 19 (April 1910): 37.
27. The several versions of the bill are reprinted in SPAAE, (n. 7 above), 32–5.
28. "Anti-Vivisection Laws are Demanded of Legislature," *New York Herald*, 9 March 1911; "Vivisection Investigation," *New York Sun*, 15 March 1911; "Bill to Investigate Cruelty in Vivisection," *Buffalo Times*, 15 March 1911; "Vivisection Bill Seeking 'Light' Ready for Hearing," *New York Herald*, 22 March 1911, Lee Scrapbook 3, Lee Papers, Archives and Special Collection, CU; "Animal Vivisection," *Brooklyn Eagle*, 22 January 1912, Lee Scrapbook 4, Lee Papers, Archives and Special Collection, CU; SPAAE, (n. 7 above), 51; "The Anti-Vivisectionists' Bill," *New York Times*, 19 April 1911, Lee Scrapbook 3, Lee Papers, Archives and Special Collection, CU.
29. Simon Flexner to Frederick Bellamy, 7 February 1913; and Richard M. Pearce to Frederick Bellamy, February 1914, folder 9, box 3, RG 600–1, Rockefeller University Archives, RAC.
30. "Hopes to Correct Vivisection Evil," *New York Herald*, 16 January 1913, Lee Scrapbook 4, Lee Papers, Archives and Special Collection, CU; and "Items of Interest," *Vivisection Reform* 1 (February 1910): 15.
31. T. Frank Schamberg, "As to Vivisection," *New York Herald*, 27 July 1909, ASPCA Scrapbook 12: 211, ASPCA Archives; *Shall Anti-Vivisection Legislation Be Enacted?*, 3; Curtis, *Why are Special Laws to Restrict Animal Experimentation Unwise?*, 1; and "The A-V Bill," *New York Times*, 8 February 1911, Lee Scrapbook 3, Lee Papers, Archives and Special Collection, CU.
32. Jerome D. Greene, "Vivisection Fight Gratifies Doctors," *New York Times*, 25 April 1911, in Lee Scrapbook 3, Lee Papers, Archives and Special Collection, CU; and Curtis, *Why are Special Laws to Restrict Animal Experimentation Unwise?*, 1.
33. "Regulation Means Prevention," *New York Times*, 25 February 1910, Lee Scrapbook 3, Lee Papers, Archives and Special Collection, CU.
34. "Vivisection Bill Protest," *New York Sun*, 22 March 1911, Lee Scrapbook 3, Lee Papers, Archives and Special Collection, CU.
35. ASPCA Board Minutes, 14 January 1909, 70–1; ASPCA Board Minutes, 11 February 1909, 75–6, ASPCA Minute Book 6, ASPCA Archives.
36. ASPCA Board Minutes, 11 February 1909, 76, ASPCA Minute Book 6, ASPCA Archives.
37. ASPCA Board Minutes, 10 March 1910, 114–6; ASPCA Board Minutes, 14 April 1910, 119–20; ASPCA Board Minutes, 8 December 1910, 134–5; ASPCA Board Minutes, 9 February 1911, 140, ASPCA Minute Book 6, ASPCA Archives; "Vivisection," *ASPCA Bulletin* 1, 6 (May 1910), 69–71; "Vivisection," *ASPCA Bulletin* 2 (January 1911), 8; and "Popularity Versus Principle," *ASPCA Bulletin* 2 (June 1911): 76–7.
38. "[ASPCA] Asks for State Inquiry Into Vivisection," *New York Times*, 2 January 1911; "Go to Albany for

Vivisection War," *New York Herald*, 6 January 1911; "Vivisection Foes to Visit Governor," *New York Herald*, 13 January 1911; "SPCA Denies It Is Against Vivisection," *New York Times*, 23 January 1911; Henry Bergh, "In Fight to Stay," *New York Times*, 25 January 1911; "Hope for Inquiry into Vivisection," *New York Times*, 7 February 1911; "The A-V Bill," *New York Times*, 8 February 1911; "Active Friends of Dumb Animals," *New York Herald*, 10 February 1911; "The Bayne Bill," *New York Sun*, 22 March 1911; "Vivisection and the SPCA," *New York Times*, 25 March 1911; and "SPCA Attacks 'Reactionary' Press," *New York Times*, 3 April 1911, Lee Scrapbook 3, Lee Papers, Archives and Special Collection, CU; "The Facts Demanded," *ASPCA Bulletin* 2 (March 1911): 28–9; and "A Reactionary Press," *ASPCA Bulletin* 2 (April 1911): 44–5.

39. Henry Bergh, "In Fight to Stay," *New York Times*, 25 January 1911, Lee Scrapbook 3, Lee Papers, Archives and Special Collection, CU.
40. ASPCA Board Minutes, 5 October 1911, 162–3; ASPCA Board Minutes, 9 November 1911, 164–5, ASPCA Minute Book 6, ASPCA Archives. "To Continue Fight on Vivisection," *New York Herald*, 13 January 1913, Lee Scrapbook 4, Lee Papers, Archives and Special Collection, CU; "Animals' Friends Appeal to Albany Against Abuses of Vivisection," Undated Clipping, *New York Herald*, 1913, folder 8, box 23, RG 600–1, Rockefeller Archive Center, RAC; and "Bellamy Finds Startling Case of Vivisection," *New York American*, 1 January 1914, Lee Scrapbook 6, Lee Papers, Archives and Special Collection, CU. The most likely explanation for the disappearance of the SPAAE is that its funding collapsed. In 1910, Antoinette Gazzam, who had supported the organization after her mother's death, was the subject of lurid headlines after being sued by another woman for alienation of her husband's affections, "Theft of Love by Miss Gazzam Costs $50,000," *New York World*, 17 January 1910; and "Miss Antoinette Gazzam's Own Story," *New York Herald*, 17 January 1910, Lee Scrapbook 2, Lee Papers, Archives and Special Collection, CU. In a 1914 *New York Times* article, Bellamy was listed as counsel to the Vivisection Investigation League, "Why Go to the Legislature?" *New York Times*, 25 February 1914, Lee Scrapbook 6, Lee Papers, Archives and Special Collection, CU.
41. Simon Flexner to Walter Cannon, 24 November 1924, Cannon Folder 6, Flexner Papers, APS.
42. W. W. Keen to Walter Cannon, 22 June 1909; Walter Cannon to Hughes, 19 March 1910; W. W. Keen to Hughes, 18 March 1910; W. W. Keen to Walter Cannon, 21 March 1910, Keen Papers, APS.
43. Frederic S. Lee to Walter Cannon, 20 February 1913, and Frederic S. Lee to Walter Cannon, 10 April 1913, folder 24, box 1, Lee Papers, Archives and Special Collection, CU; "The A-V's," *New York Times*, 24 May 1913, Lee Scrapbook 5, Lee Papers, Archives and Special Collection, CU.
44. Benison, (n. 18 above), 286–7.
45. Lederer, "Controversy in America," 250; Lederer, *Subjected to Science*, 73; and Benison et al, *Walter B. Cannon*, 190–1, adduce, without evidence, that the code was successfully implemented. Nicolaas Rupke disagrees: Rupke (n. 14 above), 9.
46. Bergh made his observation at a March 1911 hearing in support of the SPAAE's Bayne-Hoey Bill; "Hearing on Bayne-Hoey Bill," *ASPCA Bulletin* 2 (April 1911): 47–8. In 1913, the Medical Society of New York's opposition to an amendment making violation of the AMA rules for conduct a misdemeanor, see "Machines to Break Dogs' Backs Now Used in Vivisection," *Washington Post*, 22 June 1913, Lee Scrapbook 5, Lee Papers, Archives and Special Collection, CU.
47. Lederer, "Political Animals," 69–79.
48. There are others, but conspicuous examples include Thomas A. Woolsey, Robert E. Burke, and Susan Sauer, "The Playwright, the Practitioner, the Politician, the President, and the Pathologist: A Guide to the 1900 Senate Document Titled *Vivisection*," *Perspectives in Biological Medicine* 30 (1987): 235–58; Benison, (n. 18 above); and Michael Bliss, *The Discovery of Insulin* (Chicago, 1982). Actually, an individual's attitudes toward animal research more readily correlate with his/her attitudes toward animals than with his/her faith in science. In a series of studies conducted between 1979 and 1982, individuals who expressed concern about animals, regardless of their feelings about science and scientific progress, were more likely to be concerned about animal use in research, testing, and education; H. Takooshian, "Opinions on Animal Research: Scientist vs. the Public?" *PsyETA Bulletin* (Spring 1988): 5–9. Susan Lederer points out that, for a time at least, antivivisectionists' skepticism about the fruits of bacteriological science, especially inoculations, were shared by many other Americans, including physicians: Lederer, (n. 14 above), 242.

49. The diagnosis that emerged from this misogynist discourse was "zoophil-psychosis." See "Love Animals? Hate Animals? You Have a Disease!" *New York American*, 23 March 1913, Lee Scrapbook 5, Lee Papers, Archives and Special Collection, CU; Craig Buettinger, "Anti-Vivisection and the Charge of Zoophil-Psychosis in the Early Twentieth Century," *The Historian* 55 (Winter 1993): 277–88; and James Peter Warbasse, *The Conquest of Disease Through Animal Experimentation* (New York, 1910), 158–61.
50. Albert Leffingwell, "Curbing Vivisection: A Measure to Regulate, Not Prohibit, the Practice," *New York Tribune*, 28 December 1902; AHA, *Twenty-Second Annual Report* (1898), 64; and AHA, *Twenty-Third Annual Report* (1899), 47–8.
51. W. W. Keen to Cannon, 6 May 1910, Keen Papers, APS.
52. One prominent defender of experimentation charged that such reports "would probably have as their only practical result the facilitation of ignorant and frivolous prosecutions followed by acquittal." See Curtis, (n. 20 above), 4.
53. Leffingwell, (n. 2 above), xiv–xv.

Chapter 9

The Start of a Cancer Research Tradition: Peyton Rous, James Ewing, and Viruses as a Cause of Cancer

Ton van Helvoort

Department of History, University of Maastricht, Maastricht, Netherlands

In 1939, the director of the Rockefeller Institute, Herbert E. Gasser, wrote that, unlike a quarter of a century earlier, cancer research was attracting a great deal of interest and was "full of life." In Gasser's view, experimental cancer studies could be divided into three general types: (1) tumor transplants, (2) hereditary factors, and (3) experimental cancer induction. Tumor induction could be achieved by two different methods. The first involved the application of tar, a method discovered by Japanese researchers Katsusaburo Yamagiwa and Koichi Ichikawa, whereas the second used an ultrafilterable "agent." The latter technique had been discovered by two researchers working at the Rockefeller Institute, Peyton Rous and James B. Murphy.[1] These two scientists disagreed on the nature of the agent: Rous regarded it as a so-called filterable virus, (i.e., a microorganism), whereas Murphy interpreted the agent as a chemical entity, a so-called transmissible mutagen. But whether the agent was alive or dead, they agreed that it could be used to induce a tumor in the pectoral muscle of a chicken.

At the start of the twentieth century, expectations ran high about the opportunities that bacteriology could provide in the search for the cause of cancer. Finding cancer parasites had seemed to be a matter of months rather than years. The tumor transplantation experiments of the early 1900s, however, had shown that these hopes were unrealistic. Therefore, many felt that Rous and Murphy's discovery of a filterable tumor agent in chickens signaled a revival of the parasitic theory of cancer. Research into similar agents in mammals (such as mice and rats) remained fruitless, and Rous suspended his cancer research in 1915. The 1939 Gasser report stated that cancer research around 1915 had been characterized by a certain malaise. Although other research institutes continued to work on cancer, the Rockefeller Institute put the subject on the back burner.

All of this changed with a series of publications by the British researcher William E. Gye and his coworkers in 1925.[2] They had reexamined the filterable agents of chicken sarcoma and claimed to have isolated similar filterable agents in mice. Gye's results were found to be irreproducible in a number of major respects, but a report on the occasion of the twentieth anniversary of the Rockefeller Institute in 1926 stated that although Gye might have been "too hasty in arriving at and announcing results, and especially conclusions," his publications had certainly had a stimulating effect on experimental cancer research as a whole. Cancer research had received a boost and had been "lifted out of certain ruts in which it had been moving."[3]

Gye's work also induced Rous to resume his work on cancer in the middle of the 1920s, and he concentrated once more on a possible infectious cause of cancer. In the early 1930s, he started to work on two new experimental models, involving fibromas and papillomas in the rabbit. Virus tumors were to become the topic of his 1935 Harvey Lecture.[4] Rous' work was one of the reasons Gasser concluded in 1939 that cancer research was about to enter new and promising territory.

In 1966, more than half a century after the discovery of the filterable agent for chicken sarcoma, Peyton Rous received the Nobel Prize for Medicine or Physiology for his work on tumor viruses. That it took fifty years after the discovery of the Rous Sarcoma Virus (RSV) for it to be rewarded with the Nobel Prize reflects the resistance against the concept of cancer viruses in clinical circles. However, in the mid-1960s, expectations among many laboratory-based researchers about the possible identification of human tumor viruses were running high. Dozens of tumor viruses had already been discovered in animals, including mammals, and just like six decades before, a solution to the human cancer problem seemed imminent. Nevertheless, many clinicians remained highly skeptical, largely because there was a consensus view that cancer in humans was not infectious, a condition implied by the identification of cancer viruses.

Certainly Peyton Rous' Harvey Lecture in 1935, which claimed the existence of tumor viruses, had sparked fierce resistance. The protocol for the Harvey lectures demanded that the first comment after a lecture should be of a complimentary nature. But the first to respond to Rous' lecture was pathologist James Ewing, who immediately launched into an all-out confrontation by vehemently denying any relevance of tumor viruses to the human cancer problem.[5]

Ewing was the director of Cancer Research as well as director of the Medical Board of the Memorial Hospital for the Treatment of Cancer and Allied Diseases in New York City. Memorial Hospital had been founded in 1884 as a hospital specializing in female cancer patients. From the turn of the century, it had served as a general hospital for a while; but, owing partly to Ewing's efforts, it had once again become a specialized cancer hospital in 1916. Ewing held the opinion that the human cancer problem had to be solved through further rationalization of radiation therapy and through laboratory studies of cancer in humans. He saw little use for the results of studies using experimental models.[6] The role of experiments, experimental models, and laboratory research in science have become a key theme in the history of science over the last few decades.

The high hopes about the study of tumor viruses for the cancer problem—symbolized by the granting of the Nobel Prize to Rous—were not fulfilled. Nevertheless, the research tradition on tumor viruses has made major contributions to our current knowledge of the oncogene paradigm, which dominates current cancer research. Because virus tumor research began at the Rockefeller Institute, it is only fitting to evaluate what resistance this experimental tradition had to overcome before becoming accepted. In so doing, the inherent tension between laboratory research on model systems and clinical practice is revealed. Because of the level of institutionalization and the status of biomedical science, this tension is usually hidden, but the rift between clinic and laboratory is vividly revealed whenever therapeutic claims are made from the laboratory. In a narrower sense, this essay investigates how tumor virus research acquired legitimacy with regard to the human cancer problem.[7]

The Memorial Hospital and James Ewing

The Memorial Hospital was opened in 1887 as the New York Cancer Hospital, also known as 'The Bastille," and was located at 106th Street and Central Park West.[8] At first, it included only a women's pavilion, but a men's department was soon added. In 1899, the name was changed to the General Memorial Hospital for the Treatment of Cancer and Allied Diseases, although the word "General" was dropped after seventeen years. In 1912, James Douglas, the president of the Phelps Dodge Corporation, made an endowment that allowed beds for clinical examination, X-ray equipment, and a clinical laboratory to be acquired. Douglas was interested in the application of radiotherapy in cancer treatment, and presented the hospital with 3.5 grams of radium for scientific research and cancer patient treatment.[9] In 1913, Memorial Hospital joined forces with Cornell Medical School in New York City, and James Ewing was elected president of the Medical Board.

The early 1920s was a time of great pressure for the Memorial Hospital because of the large number of patients seeking treatment with radium and X-rays. Initially, the Commonwealth Fund offered to support the hospital with a grant for radiotherapy facilities, but because the philanthropist Ogden Mills offered to do the same, the Fund withdrew its offer, concluding that it "has succeeded in largely achieving the purpose of its grant without paying it."[10]

In 1936, the General Education Board presented a gift of $3,000,000 towards the construction and furnishing of a new hospital on a site at First and York Avenues and 68th Street, which was donated by John D. Rockefeller (JDR) Jr, who had already become involved in cancer research a decade earlier. Dissatisfied with the progress being made by cancer research in laboratories like the Rockefeller Institute, JDR Jr. asked James B. Murphy of the Institute in the mid-1920s what he could do to stimulate cancer research more directly. Murphy advised him to provide financial support to Ewing and the Memorial Hospital, a recommendation that was more than generously implemented by JDR Jr. and his philanthropic foundations.[11] The new Memorial Hospital was opened in 1939. At the same time, Ewing resigned his post as director and was succeeded by Cornelius P. Rhoads.

Research at Memorial Hospital was clearly characterized by Ewing's notions of good cancer research. To begin with, he felt that the use of surgery in the treatment of cancer was greatly overrated. He once said to a surgeon at Memorial, "Well, my idea of a good surgeon is one who doesn't operate."[12] No wonder radiotherapy held such a prominent position at Ewing's hospital.

A second characteristic was Ewing's dislike of experimental models in cancer research. Although, at one time, he led the Loomis laboratory at Cornell University Medical College (414 East 26th Street) where experiments took place with tumor transplantation and tumor extracts, he remained highly skeptical of such research. In fact, his lifetime bibliography includes only a handful of papers on his own animal experiments. In Ewing's view, the focus had to be on the human cancer problem.[13]

Ewing was one of the few major cancer researchers to reject animal experiments. Many of them had pinned their hopes for solving the cancer problem on animal experiments, and particularly on bacteriology. The early twentieth century saw great interest in the parasitic theory of cancer, which even provided the impulse to found new institutes for cancer research. An example was the New York State Cancer Laboratory (Buffalo, New York), founded in 1898 by Roswell Park. Similarly, two research institutes founded in Germany during the early years of the twentieth century were based on the promise afforded by the parasitic theory of cancer: Ernst von Leyden's Cancer Barracks at the Berlin Charité Hospital and Vinzenz Czerny's 'Institut für experimentelle Krebsforschung' at Heidelberg.[14]

At the end of the ninetieth century, researchers had succeeded in transplanting tumors from one experimental animal to another and in keeping them growing. But this technique did not become commonplace until the experiments by Leo Loeb in 1901 and Carl O. Jensen in 1903. The aim of these types of transplantation studies was to find out the conditions under which tumors grow and involved experimentation with mostly mice and rats. However, the findings of these transplantation studies, meant that a parasitical cause of cancer had to be excluded. It was found that tumors were only obtained if at least one living cancer cell was transplanted.

Ewing was not the only one to reject the infectious nature of cancer theory. Ernest F.

Bashford, superintendent of Research of the British Imperial Cancer Research Fund, held the same opinion. In his view, the fundamental problem of cancer lay in the process controlling limited growth in normal cells, a control mechanism that failed in cancer cells. According to him, the key to the origin of cancer lay in the "potentialities of the cell itself."[15]

Transplant research yielded another significant finding, in that it revealed the essential difference between spontaneous malignant tumors and transplanted tumors. The failure of August von Wassermann's chemotherapy for cancer confronted researchers with the artificial nature of transplanted tumors. Wassermann, the inventor of the syphilis blood test that to this day bears his name, managed in 1911 to obtain complete remission of transplanted tumors in test animals using selenium-based chemical compounds. The *New York Times* reported on these findings as follows:

> . . . after several hundred chemical complexes of selenium, tellurium and eosin had failed one has been evolved that in ten days after its first injection cleaves and sloughs off the masses of organic tissue that composed the tumors, and only healthy tissue remains.[16]

However, soon, it had to be concluded that this chemotherapy had no effect whatsoever on human tumors. Apparently, the transplanted tumors in mice and rats were totally different from spontaneous tumors in animals and humans. Arguments for this conclusion became obvious after the failure of Wassermann's chemotherapy, and included the following. Tumors transplanted into animals were able to grow to immense proportions, sometimes as large as the animal itself. However, the animal hardly showed any concurrent weight loss or cachexia, which was a characteristic symptom of cancer in humans. In addition, the transplanted tumors remained encapsulated, whereas human tumors showed invasive behavior. Furthermore, the transplanted tumors rarely caused metastases and would grow particularly vigorously in young animals, whereas spontaneous tumors metastasized easily and occurred mainly in older organisms.[17] It seemed obvious that transplanted tumors bore little resemblance to the real cancer problem in humans. Therefore, the Rockefeller Institute decided, after having worked with Flexner–Jobling transplantation tumors for a few years, to end its cancer research effort. In 1923, Simon Flexner wrote, "Cancer research was for a time suspended at the Institute because progress was not being made with the old methods. It was revived later by Rous. . . ."[18]

The Rous Sarcoma Agent: Biological or Chemical in Nature?

In 1908, Peyton Rous performed some physiological and pathological research at Arthur S. Warthin's laboratory in Ann Arbor (Michigan) with a grant from the Rockefeller Institute. The results of this work were published in the Rockefeller Institute's *Journal of Experimental Medicine*, and prompted Simon Flexner to invite Rous to come and work at the Institute.[19]

After Rous performed some transplantation research on mice, he received a chicken with an enormous lump from a poultry farmer; the farmer was worried that the growth might be infectious. Rous classified it as a tumor, a spindle cell sarcoma. Because tumors in birds had hardly been studied, Rous decided to investigate. He found that the tumor could be transplanted into animals with a close family relationship to the original chicken. Repeated transplantations made the tumor increasingly aggressive, as was evident from the increasing numbers of metastases. This observation stimulated Rous to determine whether a cell-free filtrate could also transfer the tumor. For this purpose, the tumor was ground up in a saline solution and passed through a Berkefeld filter. These filters were assumed to be impermeable to even the smallest bacteria and were used as a test for the category of filterable viruses.[20]

Injecting a small quantity of the filtrate into the pectoral muscle of another chicken induced a tumor in the new host with the same histological and biological characteristics as the original tumor. The growth of the tumor led to an increase in the quantity of filterable agent. It was this increase, and the fact that the agent was able to pass through an ultrafilter, which made Rous decide that he was probably dealing with a minuscule parasitic organism. However, he could not exclude the possibility that it might be a nonliving agent: "It is conceivable that a chemical stimulant, elaborated by the neoplastic cells, might cause the tumor in another host and bring about in consequence a further production of the same stimulant."[21]

Within a short time, Rous and his coworkers were able to isolate several transplantable chicken tumors, some of which could be transferred by means of ultrafiltrate. Each agent caused a specific tumor that could be distinguished from other tumors. Various materials from the Peyton Rous archive show that he felt that the filterable agent was a filterable virus; that is, a living organism.[22] However, in his publications, Rous nearly always referred to it as a filterable "agent" or a filterable "cause" or "incitant."[23]

As we have seen, Rous interpreted the increase in the quantity of the filterable agent as the multiplication of a virus. But the behavior of the tumor did not correspond with the characteristics of an infectious disease, neither in natural circumstances nor in the laboratory. In natural circumstances, the tumors did not show epidemic behavior: natural transfer was never observed and the poultry farmer could be reassured. In addition, the metastases seen in the laboratory were found to arise from migration of already transformed cells to, for instance, the lung.

Rous eventually concluded that although the filterable agent caused the tumor, it did not play a clear part in the actual disease phenomenon. Thus, although the disease was caused by an extrinsic agent, its behavior depended purely on the neoplastic cells themselves. This meant that the possibility that the filterable agent was a chemical entity, as James B. Murphy contended, had to be treated as a serious option: ". . . there is nothing to suggest the presence of a parasitic cause for the disease, but much that has been held to favor the view of an intrinsic cell-derangement."[24]

Rous and Murphy agreed that the only way to prove that the agent was a living entity would be its in vitro propagation. In 1913, Rous wrote, ". . . the agent may be cultivable in plasma previously modified by the growth of cells."[25] Propagation of the filterable agent was a recurrent topic in the period from 1912 to 1915, when Rous ended his research into chicken sarcoma.

For nearly fifteen years thereafter, Rous stayed away from the tumor problem. It seemed that the bird tumors that could be transferred via filtrates were not the ideal experimental model with which to address the human tumor problem. Experiments on mice and rats did not yield any similar filterable agents. Simon Flexner, also "thought the lead was played out and told me as much."[26] The importance for human cancer research of the filterable virus tumors Rous had discovered was characterized by E. E. Tyzzer, chairman of the Harvard University Cancer Commission as follows:

> Notwithstanding the interest which the work on fowl tumors aroused, in no instance has a similar infectious agent been demonstrated in tumors of mammals. We have at

present, then, no grounds for believing that there is any specific infection associated with human tumors.[27]

The Reverse Approach: The Tumor Properties of Infectious Diseases

Fortunately, experimental cancer research was revitalized by the work of William E. Gye of the National Institute for Medical Research, which was published in the mid-1920s.[28] In an article in the *Lancet*, entitled "The Etiology of Malignant New Growths,"[29] Gye claimed to have discovered two factors that could play a part in tumor formation: one an extrinsic, filter-passing infective agent; the other an unstable cell-specific chemical factor. The latter factor determined the type of tumor produced by the virus. More specifically, his idea was that a virus linked to some product of a fibroblast produced a spindle-celled sarcoma, whereas one that linked to some constituent of an endothelial cell gave rise to an endothelioma, and so on. He also claimed to have propagated fowl tumor viruses and even to have developed a protective vaccine. Because of the promise that Gye's results seemed to hold for the control of cancer, his work was widely publicized.[30]

Once again, infectious principles became the focus of research into the possible causes of cancer, and Peyton Rous also resumed his research on this subject. Because his earlier attempts to isolate tumor viruses in mice had been fruitless, he now tried to approach the problem from the other end; namely, by studying the natural history of tumors in a population of mice. He adopted the experimental epidemiological approach developed by Simon Flexner and Leslie Webster at the Rockefeller Institute.[31] Rous investigated whether mice treated with tar were more likely to develop tumors if they led a normal, dirty life or if they were kept in isolation and fed sterile water and muscle tissue. The latter turned out not to be the case.

Rigorous isolation of a mouse population from any source of infection had enabled Rous to exclude the possibility of cancer generation by external living entities, but he had not been able to decide whether healthy animals could be carriers of agents that caused cancer at a much later stage. He compared such hypothetical saprophytic cancer microorganisms with commensal bacteria like staphylococci and colonic bacilli.[32]

Peyton Rous' work on the tumor problem was to receive a decisive boost with the adoption of two new model systems he received from his friend Richard E. Shope, who worked at the Princeton (New Jersey) branch of the Rockefeller Institute. In 1932, Shope shot a wild cottontail rabbit near Princeton and found under its skin small nodules that proved to be fibromatous tumors; the tumor could be transmitted by inoculation of filtrates.[33] In 1933, Shope again came across new experimental material when he isolated a papilloma from wild cottontail rabbits. When a filtrate of this papilloma was rubbed on the scarified skin of a rabbit, papillomas resulted. His papilloma virus provoked tumors in wild as well as domestic rabbits.[34]

Rous showed that these papillomas were not far removed from malignity and could eventually become malignant and metastasize. Furthermore, together with other workers, Rous showed that when the papilloma virus was rubbed over skin pretreated with tar, numerous carcinomas and papillomas developed. Carcinomas were also found to develop when papillomas were treated with methylcholanthrene.[35]

Rous had now taken the opposite approach from the one he had used for the Rous sarcoma. In that research, he had isolated a tumor virus that was indifferent with respect to the behavior of the tumor, whereas the papillomas had provided him with a model that was definitely infectious and had been shown to develop carcinogenic features. Rous conjectured that tumor development was a very slow and delicate process in which viruses and various carcinogenic substances each played their own part. In the mid-1930s, Rous felt justified to expound his ideas on the role of viruses in the development of cancer in his Harvey Lecture.

Criticism of Rous' Ideas: Focus on the Cell

As stated before, the early twentieth century was a time when expectations were high about the opportunities for bacteriology to solve the cancer problem. In his 1907 Harvey Lecture, James Ewing presented a survey of the various agents that had been held responsible for causing cancer. All kinds of agents were claimed to be cancer parasites, including bacilli, cocci, schizomycetes, protozoa, and other lower animal organisms (such as coccidia and microsporidia).[36] Ewing himself, by contrast, felt that the origin of cancer lay within the cell itself, and involved the acquisition of cellular autonomy and the derailment of the mechanism of cell multiplication. He dismissed the parasitic theory of cancer with the cynical words, "It would be a pity if the comprehensive view of the etiology of tumors which is revealed in the phylogeny and ontogeny of the human body were destined to be replaced by the crude conception of an invading parasite." According to Ewing, a parasite could not be argued out of existence from the nature of the tumor process, but it was "unnecessary, unsupported by analogy, and inconsistent with the history of most tumors."[37]

The contrast between an external, invasive agent as the cause of cancer and the view that its cause was to be found within the cell itself was to be a recurrent theme in twentieth-century cancer research.[38] If the disease were caused by an external, living agent, this would obviously imply an association with contagiousness, and this had indeed been the initial reaction when Rous and his colleagues had discovered the filterable agent of chicken sarcoma virus in 1911. When Rous' findings reached the newspapers in early 1912, the headline in the *New York Times* read, "Clue to Parasite as Cause of Cancer."[39] Although Rous himself was always cautious in his statements on the true nature of the filterable agent of his chicken sarcoma, the newspaper asked the general rhetorical question "Is Cancer Infectious?" The director of the Rockefeller Institute, Simon Flexner, felt obliged to reassure the public in the same newspaper article by saying that "cancer is certainly not readily infectious; in fact, there is no clinical evidence that it can be transmitted between human individuals."

The clinical evidence showing that cancer was not infectious, largely determined the response of clinicians to the findings of the experimental cancer research. In the first quarter of the twentieth century, many new experimental models were added to this research effort. The American plant pathologist Erwin F. Smith, for instance, worked on so-called crown galls in plants. Such neoplasms were caused by *Bacillus tumefaciens* and Smith had shown that crown galls showed tumorlike characteristics. Smith defended the thesis that this experimental material was useful as a model for the study of cancer in humans.[40] In a defiant article in *Science*, Smith advocated dropping the morphological approach to cancer research and replacing it with more experimental research:

> I do not mean to condemn the study of sections, but only to suggest that there are also other ways of looking at this problem, which is one of growing things. There is too much reasoning in a circle on the part of many of these writers, too much argument

> basing one assumption on another assumption as if the latter were a well-established and solid fact, too little clear thinking of a biological sort, too little first-hand knowledge of living plants and animals, too much dogmatism, too much orthodoxy, and not enough experimentation. Hence the pessimism and the discouragement. . . . These strong men, chiefly morphologists, have dominated the situation for a generation, but they have not explained cancer and they can not explain it, and they must now give way.[41]

Shortly after Gye's work had led to renewed publicity about the role of filterable agents (i.e., viruses) in cancer, German pathologists and clinicians felt they had to speak out against these ideas. At a conference of German pathologists on "Infection and Tumor Formation," the prominent surgeon Victor Schmieden stated,

> It is alien to the clinician's mode of thinking not to rely on conclusive evidence from human materials, but time and again to be referred to mammals, thence to birds, thence to cold-blooded animals and even to plants . . . [W]e must warn against attaching too much value to comparative observations from the animal or plant kingdom.[42]

In the mid-1920s, the British researcher Christopher H. Andrewes had sought to collaborate with Gye. Andrewes was to become one of the most prominent British virus researchers, whose authority in this field was evident from the fact that the Royal College of Physicians invited him to give a lecture in 1934. The subject, "Viruses in Relation to the Aetiology of Tumours," however, led to great controversy because Andrewes discussed Gye's work on the Rous sarcoma and Peyton Rous' own work on the Shope papilloma.[43]

As we have seen, the relation between viruses and cancer was a taboo subject to many clinicians. The 1927 international cancer conference in New York, organized by the American Society for the Control of Cancer, went so far as to pass a formal resolution stating that cancer was not an infectious disease: "The causation of cancer is not completely understood, but it may be accepted that for all practical purposes cancer is not to be looked upon as contagious or infectious."[44]

Orthodox pathologists like James Ewing saw the virus theory of cancer proposed by Gye, Andrewes, and Rous as a phoenix rising from the ashes of the old parasitic theory of cancer. Rous jokingly wrote to Gye that the three of them were like the Three Musketeers defending the virus theory, and warned that they would have to come up with solid evidence: "We are the Three Musketeers, you know, and must carry something more than blunderbusses."[45]

Cancer Viruses: A Contradiction in Terms?

In 1916, Ewing spoke favorably about Rous and Murphy's work with bird tumors.[46] But the interest in tumor viruses in the mid-1930s, and particularly the attempts to extrapolate these findings to the human tumor problem, provoked a fierce response from Ewing. In his view, research on human cancer had to be done by physicians, surgeons, pathologists, and radiologists. In line with the ideas expressed by the German surgeon Schmieden, Ewing felt that the focus ought to be on human beings, not on experimental models, ". . . the greatly improved outlook for the cancer patient has come from the combined efforts of clinical medicine in many departments, all directed to the more intelligent and detailed study of cancer in the human subject."[47] In fact, he claimed that the progress achieved in the struggle against cancer had resulted from improvements in surgical techniques, the application of X-rays, and radium therapy and the first steps in chemotherapy.[48] Ewing also felt that there were indisputable arguments to refute the viral hypothesis on the origin of cancer.

An important problem of the virus theory of cancer was the finding that tumors could be induced with the aid of X-rays or with certain types of tar. It had been discovered in the first two decades of the twentieth century that irradiating mice with X-rays led to sores, which sometimes developed into tumors.[49] Moreover, in 1914, Japanese scientists Yamagiwa and Ichikawa had found that they could induce cancers on rabbit skin by rubbing it with coal tar over a longer period of time, a process known as pinseln.[50] Thus, it was possible to induce cancer experimentally, and the method was found to work regardless of the nature of the test animal and the type of skin treated. The conclusion seemed inevitable that any cell could potentially be induced to become cancerous.

These findings forced the proponents of the virus theory of cancer to assume that the supposed cancer viruses were omnipresent (that is, present in all parts and all cells of the organisms concerned), so that they could be induced to tumor formation. During a debate with Andrewes and Gye at the Royal Society of London, pathologist Arthur Boycott concluded that ". . . when it became necessary to postulate a normal virus occurring in normal cells, one had better call it something else than a virus."[51] Boycott's conclusion was approvingly quoted by James B. Murphy in his criticism of the living nature of the filterable agent of Rous sarcoma; if one assumed that such an agent was a lifeless, chemical entity, said Murphy, there would be no problem in assuming this agent to be omnipresent.[52]

Thus, the debate on the question whether cancer could be caused by viruses centered on the problem of the relationship between the virus and the cell. As a virus researcher, Andrewes did not find it hard to accept that viruses might be present in all cells in a latent form. He felt there were enough analogies for such a situation, including Rickettsia-like organisms in normal cells, asymptomatic viruses in normal potatoes, latent bacteriophages (bacterial viruses) in normal bacteria, and even the example of innocent streptococci in the throat of a healthy person. Andrewes devoted his own 1939 presidential lecture to the British Royal Society of Medicine to viral latency as a key problem in cancer research.[53] Demonstrating the presence of these latent viruses in normal cells would require indirect techniques, such as immunological methods, since these viruses, which were invisible under the microscope, did not reveal their presence in any way as long as they did not become virulent. Andrewes thought that such viruses could undergo mutations that would make them virulent, thus revealing their presence.[54]

Peyton Rous also regarded the concepts of latency and "masking" of viruses as keys to an understanding of tumor formation. The papillomas he had received from Shope were Rous' main model system for tumor virus research. The papilloma virus was found to behave differently in different hosts, for instance in wild and domesticated rabbits. It was easy to isolate virus abundantly from papillomas in wild cottontail rabbits, but papillomas in domestic rabbits rarely allowed the virus to be isolated, and then only in very small quantities. It was found to be impossible to isolate papilloma virus from carcinomas. Serological and immunological techniques were used to show that the virus was present in two carcinomas derived from virus-induced papillomas. When the cancer cells proliferated, the quantity of the virus increased, but because the virus could not be isolated as an infectious agent from these carcinomas, Rous presumed that the virus was masked. Whether this was a chemical or physical process was still to be elucidated.[55] In the early 1940s, the phenomenon of virus masking was the main topic of research for Rous. Minutes of meetings with Rous' colleagues at the Rockefeller

Institute show that Rous concluded that they also felt virus masking to be the crucial problem of virus tumors.[56]

As mentioned in my introduction, Ewing responded furiously to Rous' Harvey Lecture. Nevertheless, he did not reject all experimental findings of virus tumor research; he just interpreted them differently. In fact, the controversy was about the definition of the cause of cancer.[57] Ewing made a distinction between the *causal* genesis of cancer and the *formal* genesis. He claimed that the causal genesis "involves the various agents or influence that act upon the normal cells in such a way as to cause such cells to break from centralized control and to grow unrestrictedly," with viruses being one category of those agents. The formal genesis of cancer, he explained, was the other basic process in cancer formation and was "undoubtedly a certain type of cell metabolism which produces rapid cyclic repetition of a series of events resulting in cell division."[58]

The difference of opinion between Ewing on the one hand and Rous and Andrewes on the other hand was that Ewing was prepared to see a role for viruses as causal agents in the sense of causal genesis, whereas Rous and Andrewes felt that viruses played a part in the formal genesis of cancer. For Ewing, the fact that the virus frequently could not be demonstrated to be present in a virus tumor meant that it could not play a role in its formal genesis. In a letter to Richard Shope, Rous explained the latter view,

> Doctor Ewing is representative of a large body of conservative opinion about cancer and its causation. As you will see, he takes the ground that because your virus cannot be got back again from domestic rabbits *the cells have gone off on their own and are proliferating independently of it*. This will be the view of many authors until you publish your experiments showing that the virus not only can be recovered in active form but that the growth can be propagated in series in domestic rabbits. (emphasis added)[59]

Rous reconciled the view that tumor viruses had to be a proximal cause of cancer with the noninfectious nature of cancer by pointing out the many preconditions that had to be met before cancer could arise. According to Rous, tumorigenesis was a very rare process. In a letter to Clarence C. Little, director of the Roscoe B. Jackson Memorial Laboratory,[60] he expressed this as follows:

> Viruses are responsible for some tumors of chickens, frogs, and rabbits, and the growths they cause so entirely resemble human tumors as to give support too the view that such agents may be responsible for some cancers in man. Yet certainly cancer is never transferred from patient to well person, as every doctor knows. If viruses provide the innumerable potentialities for cancer which exist in every healthy human body, then these viruses must enter it early, and become permanent residents within it, as many kinds of bacteria do, and like them produce no harm unless worked upon by favoring conditions.[61]

So-called carcinogenic chemicals were regarded as the main alternative to cancer viruses as external causes of cancer. In a lecture to the Board of Directors of the Rockefeller Institute, Peyton Rous listed the differences between neoplastic viruses and carcinogenic chemicals as causes of cancer (Table I).[62]

Table I shows that in Rous' view, carcinogenic substances only played a role in the induction of the tumor, whereas tumor viruses were the real, proximal cause of cancer. Rous saw the interaction between a virus and its host cell as a dynamic relationship, in which every action

Table I. **Relationship between Tumors and Neoplastic Viruses and between Tumors and Chemical Carcinogens**

Neoplastic Viruses	"Carcinogenic" Agents
are of one general kind: procured only from tumors	are of many diverse kinds: extraneous in origin
are narrowly specific as concerns animals acted upon and tumors produced	are largely nonspecific as concerns animals acted upon and tumors evoked
furnish the potentialities for tumor formation	are effective only if tumor potentialities are already present
themselves determine the kinds of growth arising	evoke growths representative of the preexisting potentialities
act directly, making cells become tumor cells	act indirectly, by provoking chronic tissue disturbance
increase as the tumors grow, and are often recoverable	disappear as the tumors grow
They cause tumors	They bring tumors into being

was followed by a reaction. Even if a virus was present in the cell for a brief period of time, this triggered a reaction on the part of the infected cell; if a virus induced a cell to proliferate, a symbiotic relation might arise between virus and cell, a relation of a dynamic nature. In Rous' view, this constituted a working partnership between virus and cell. In 1943, Rous expressed this concisely by saying that "viruses are actual workmen in the cellular world."[63]

This multifactor combination of virus and cell also explained how tumor viruses could be present throughout the organism, without making cancer an infectious disease. Rous wrote about tumor viruses in humans that

> if human cancer viruses exist, they must be carried everywhere that man goes, perhaps in or upon his body, as are bacteria; yet plainly they cannot produce tumors unless *a multitude of conditions are favorable*—a happening so infrequent as to remove them from the infectious category. (emphasis added)[64]

Thus, the controversy between Rous and Ewing boiled down to different views of the nature of viruses, as Ewing acknowledged in his correspondence with Rous: "I presume it all settles down to the question, what is a virus?"[65] To Ewing, the cause of cancer was an internal feature of the cell, about which very little was known: "The secret of malignancy seems still to remain enshrouded in the obscurities of intracellular life, where it will probably long remain."[66] On the other hand, Rous felt that virus tumors might offer the key to unlocking the cancer mystery: ". . . since what one thinks determines what one does in cancer research, as in all else, it is well to think something. And it may prove worthwhile to think that one or more tumors of unknown cause are due to viruses."[67] However, for the next two decades, the three musketeers Rous, Andrewes, and Gye were to find precious little support for their views.

Human Cancer Viruses?

Before World War II, Memorial Hospital moved to the medical complex encompassing the New York Hospital, Cornell University Medical College, and the Rockefeller Institute. Work at Memorial Hospital was divided into four branches: (1) treatment, (2) prevention, (3) education and training, and (4) cancer research. In 1945, cancer research at Memorial received a huge boost when a $4,000,000 donation by the Alfred P. Sloan Foundation allowed it to start building the Sloan-Kettering Institute for Cancer Research.[68] Cornelius P. Rhoads, who had succeeded Ewing as its director, set up laboratories for biology, steroid chemistry, biophysics, clinical research (on metabolism), antibiotics, protein studies, and chemotherapy. Inspired by the industrial research methods developed by Charles F. Kettering, Rhoads favored a highly structured approach to the cancer problem. Clarence C. Little of the Jackson Memorial Laboratory was not very enthusiastic about this conveyor belt approach, and felt that ". . . the individual worker might be too restricted by the organization of the laboratory and, in fact, that the place might be pretty grim to work in."[69]

However, Rhoads thought that no time should be lost in waiting for *the* great medical breakthrough. In an interview with *Time Magazine*, Rhoads said,

> Some authorities . . . think that we cannot solve the cancer problem until we have made a great, basic, unexpected discovery, perhaps in some apparently unrelated field. I disagree. I think we know enough to go ahead now and make a frontal attack with all our forces. Anyway, that's what we are doing. We'll follow every promising lead, and we know a lot of them. If the ivory tower men solve the problem ahead of us, we won't feel we've wasted our time.[70]

This approach basically continued the line of research developed by Ewing, focusing on cancer in humans. The main research lines at the Sloan-Kettering Institute were chemical carcinogenesis and chemotherapy.

Rhoads died in 1959, and was succeeded by Frank L. Horsfall Jr., who had previously worked at the Rockefeller Institute Hospital. Horsfall was a child of his time in the sense that he expected a great deal from research into tumor viruses, which had entered its golden era at the end of the 1950s. Horsfall expressed the arguments for these high hopes as follows:

> First, it is beginning to appear that most tumors of animals will be found to be virus-induced. Second, there seems to be no valid reason to think that human tumors are in any way unique or that they differ from tumors of other animals in any significant manner. Third, if viruses are associated with the inception of cancer in man, it seems possible that several beneficial advances might be developed. Through extension of principles that have evolved from studies of virus-induced cancer in animals it might be feasible to develop reliable procedures for early and specific laboratory diagnosis, so that effective treatment of early lesions could be instituted well before these lesions would ordinarily be detected on physical examination. Finally, it might be possible to develop specific preventive measures and, through appropriate immunization procedures, to prevent virus-induced cancerous changes at the cell level before they occur.[71]

Because the developments with regard to tumor viruses after 1960 are outside the scope of this study, which is concerned with the origins of tumor virus research, it seems best to leave the final evaluation of this school of cancer research to an expert in the field, George Klein:

> The current impression is that the oncogene-transducing, directly transforming class I retroviruses [e.g., Rous sarcoma virus and TvH] do not play any major causative role for naturally occurring cancers. Are the class I viruses freaks or perhaps even monsters generated by laboratory experimentations? Probably so. . . . All RNA tumour viruses

> that are known to contribute to the aetiology of naturally occurring animal or human tumours belong to the chronic or class II retroviruses that do not carry cell-derived oncogene sequences (feline and bovine leukemia viruses and HTLV-1). The DNA tumor viruses involved in the causation of naturally occurring tumours are highly diversified: from the small papilloma viruses to the large herpes viruses. The presently known viruses that cause tumors in nature represent a small but firmly established group. Some of them may eventually satisfy the original aspiration of the tumor virologist: immunological prevention.[72]

The comments on immunization in the aforementioned quotations by Horsfall and Klein signal a recurrent theme in debates about tumor viruses: if viruses should turn out to be the cause of cancer, this would create obvious opportunities for therapy, or even prevention through vaccination. According to Michael Bishop, who received the 1989 Nobel Prize for his discovery of oncogenes, Peyton Rous rejected the somatic mutation hypothesis and the possible hereditary nature of cancer, because these options led to fatalistic perspectives; they would make it very difficult to treat or prevent cancer.[73] As we have seen above, however, the real reason why Rous defended the virus hypothesis was that he felt that the somatic mutation hypothesis (involving mutations caused for instance by carcinogens and/or spontaneous mutations) provided insufficient explanation for the dynamic nature of the cancer process. In Rous' opinion, the natural history of tumors could be explained from a dynamic interaction between two organisms, the host cell and the tumor virus.

Conclusions: Clinic versus Laboratory

What does the confrontation between Peyton Rous and James Ewing tell us about the relation between experimental research in the laboratory and work done in the clinic? A classic example of the ideological confrontation between the approach focusing on the disease process in a patient on the one hand and laboratory science on the other was described by Russell Maulitz in his essay "'Physician versus Bacteriologist': The Ideology of Science in Clinical Medicine."[74]

It is hardly surprising that bacteriology was long regarded as the ideal example of medical laboratory science. Basically, this view stems from the fact that at the end of the nineteenth century, bacteriology managed to reduce infectious diseases to a one agent/one disease phenomenon. The ideology of experimental science thus became, "Find the cause, then you find the cure."[75] Nowhere was this more visible than in the history of cancer research. Memorial Director Cornelius P. Rhoads expressed this in the following succinct words:

> It is interesting to examine the reasons why so much thought is given to the study of the causes of cancer as a means to its cure. It seems to be a carry-over from the great days of bacteriology when the discovery of cause, in terms of a demonstrable microorganism, was equivalent to control by the procedures of public health: sanitation or the artificial induction of immunity by the use of vaccines. A popular area of study is the search for proof that cancer is due to a virus. Unfortunately, in much of the discussion of this topic, what is meant by a virus is not adequately specified. . . . Hence the search for a virus which might cause cancer was more than a simple investigation of cause; it carried with it the concept of transmission, of contagiousness, and the hope of the induction of artificial immunity.[76]

It was this ideology of monocausality that raised high hopes for bacteriology's ability to solve the cancer problem in the early 1900s. In the decades preceding World War I, this monocausal approach provoked a countermovement in the form of a holistic approach arguing that disease processes were not determined exclusively by causal agents but also by other factors, such as the host.[77]

The irony of the controversy between Rous and Ewing was that the clinically oriented Ewing stuck to a monocausal definition of viruses, whereas Rous used a conditional approach emphasizing the additional factors involved in cancer development. According to John G. Kidd, one of Rous' long-time collaborators in the papilloma virus research, Rous' motto was "Stay as Close to Nature as You Can." Rous stayed as close to nature as he could by opting for living experimental models like rabbits. He had serious doubts about the in vitro work that became popular from the 1950s onwards.[78]

Although in Peyton Rous we see a researcher using an experimental approach that believes in multiple causes and conditions, the ideology of science is largely dominated by a monocausal approach. Now that the oncogene paradigm has come to be embraced, there seems to be more interest in multifactorial causes, and researchers tend to speak largely in terms of risks and susceptibility factors.[79]

However, upon translation of the findings of the current genetic cancer research for the public at large, the multicausal approach loses many of its modalities. As the sociologist of science Dorothy Nelkin wrote,

> The gene in popular culture is an agent of destiny, an oracle, a blueprint, a medical crystal ball. . . . Deterministic language pervades mass media messages about the meaning of the genes. . . . In popular media reports, this statistically driven concept becomes reduced to cause—there are persons or families "at risk."[80]

This simplification of conditional factors into good genes and bad genes is so attractive to the public, because genetic explanations ". . . seem to offer compelling and simple explanations for complex and enduring human questions."[81]

This process of reification of risk and susceptibility genes as monocausal entities is not limited to situations in which scientific findings are being popularized. In view of the promises that the monocausal model holds for therapy and prevention, scientists themselves are not above invoking this ideology if they wish to raise support—financial or political—for gene therapy and for the companies trying to market such therapies. Bacteria, viruses, chemotherapy, and gene therapy are all concepts mobilized within the monocausal model of disease! The work of James Ewing and that of Peyton Rous are in fact powerful antidotes to excessive expectations deriving from a monocausal interpretation of disease processes.

Archival research for this essay was made possible by grants from the American Philosophical Society and the Rockefeller Archive Center.

Endnotes

1. "Gasser Report: Report on the Activities and Problems of the Rockefeller Institute," 3 October 1939, 45–6, volume 28, box 5, Record Group 439, Rockefeller University Archives, Rockefeller Archive Center, Sleepy Hollow, New York (hereafter RAC).
2. See, for instance, William E. Gye, "The Cancer Problem: Lloyd Roberts Memorial Lecture," *Lancet* 2

(1926): 989–95.

3. "The Developments of the First Twenty Years of the Rockefeller Institute and an Outlook for Further Growth," 17 April 1926, vol. 14, box 3, RG 439, Rockefeller University Archives, RAC.
4. Peyton Rous, "The Virus Tumors and the Tumor Problem," delivered 5 December 1935, *Harvey Lectures* 31 (1936): 74–115. With reference to his own work on Rous sarcoma from the 1910s and that of Gye in the 1920s, Rous was later to say that he "was saved by an Englishman." See Christopher Andrewes, "Rous, Francis Peyton (1879–1970)," *Biographical Memoirs of Fellows of the Royal Society* 17 (1971): 643–62, especially 646.
5. The historian Daniel Kevles once described tumor virus research as "pursuing the unpopular." See Daniel J. Kevles, "Pursuing the Unpopular: A History of Courage, Viruses, and Cancer," in *Hidden Histories of Science*, ed. Robert Silvers (New York, 1995), 69–112.
6. Andrew Cunningham and P. Williams, eds., *The Laboratory Revolution in Medicine* (Cambridge, 1992); Adele E. Clarke and Joan H. Fujimura, eds., *The Right Tools for the Job: At Work in Twentieth-Century Life Sciences* (Princeton, NJ, 1992); Muriel Lederman and Richard M. Burian, eds., "The Right Organism for the Job," *Journal of the History of Biology* 26 (1993): 235–367; Hans-Jörg Rheinberger and Michael Hagner, "Plädoyer für eine Wissenschaftsgeschichte des Experiments," *Theory in Biosciences* 116 (1997): 11–31.
7. For the history of cancer research see, for instance, Ilana Löwy, "The Century of the Transformed Cell," in *Science in the Twentieth Century*, eds. John Krige and Dominique Pestre (Amsterdam, 1997), 461–78; and Jean-Paul Gaudillière, "The Molecularization of Cancer Etiology in the Postwar United States: Instruments, Politics and Management," in *Molecularizing Biology and Medicine: New Practices and Alliances, 1910s–1970s*, eds. Soraya de Chadarevian and Harmke Kamminga (Amsterdam, 1998), 139–70.
8. *Milestones of Memorial Hospital*, 1938, 1944; folders 2069 and 2070, box 215, series 1.2, General Education Boards Archives, RAC. On the early years of the Memorial Hospital, see also Stephen S. Hall, *A Commotion in the Blood: Life, Death, and The Immune System* (New York, 1997).
9. For a history of radiotherapy in the United States, see Juan A. Del Regato, "The Unfolding of American Radiotherapy," *International Journal of Radiation Oncology, Biology, Physics* 35 (1996): 5–14. With regard to radiotherapy in Germany, where there was a severe shortage of radium, partly because of the lack of the sort of philanthropic tradition found in the United States, see Ton van Helvoort, "Scalpel or Rays? Radiotherapy and the Struggle for the Cancer Patient in Pre-World War II Germany," *Medical History* 45 (2001): 33–60.
10. Letter presented to the director of the Commonwealth Fund regarding Memorial Hospital, 5 June 1923, folder 1852, box 197, series 18.1 grants, Commonwealth Fund Archives, RAC.
11. Letter from Debevoise to Fred W. Stewart, 29 December 1947, folder 191, box 24, Office series, Medical Institutes subseries, RG 2 Office of the Messrs Rockefeller (OMR), Rockefeller Family Archives, RAC. See also Laurance Rockefeller's remarks, 1981, folder 264, box 27, series 3.2 Annual meetings papers at scientific sessions, RG 520, Memorial Sloan-Kettering Cancer Center (MSKCC) Archives, RAC.
12. Manuscript "My Most Unforgettable Character: Dr. James Ewing, Hayes Martin," p. 3, folder 371, box 38, series 7, RG520, MSKCC Archives, RAC.
13. See H. Martin, "Ewing's Professional Career," folder 66, box 4, series H. Martin, RG 500, MSKCC Archives, RAC. For biographical material on Ewing, see Fred W. Stewart, "James Ewing, M.D., 1866–1943," *Archives of Pathology* 36 (1943): 325–30; James B. Murphy, "James Ewing, 1866–1943," *Biographical Memoirs of the National Academy of Sciences* 26 (1951): 45–60; Cornelius P. Rhoads, "Ewing: The Experimental Method and the Cancer Problem," *Bulletin of the New York Academy of Medicine* 27 (1951): 606–22; Juan A. Del Regato, "James Ewing: 'Oncology . . . the Most Complex and Fascinating Field of Pathology,'" *International Journal of Radiation Oncology, Biology, Physics* 2 (1977): 185–98; LaSalle D. Leffall Jr., "James Ewing, M.D.: Contemporary Oncologist Exemplar," *Archives of Surgery* 122 (1987): 1240–3; Arty R. Zantinga and Max J. Coppes, "James Ewing (1866–1943): 'The Chief,'" *Medical and Pediatric Oncology* 21 (1993): 505–10.
14. See William Bainbridge, *The Cancer Problem* (New York, 1914), 5–6.
15. Ernest F. Bashford, "Introduction," in *Scientific Reports on the Investigations of the Imperial Cancer Research Fund No. 2. Part II, The Growth of Cancer Under Natural and Experimental Conditions*

(London, 1905), 1–12.

16. "A Chemical Surgeon Has Been Evolved," *New York Times*, 8 January 1912, folder 40, box 2, series H. Martin, RG 500, MSKCC Archives, RAC.
17. Jacob Wolff, *Die Lehre von der Krebskrankheit von den ältesten Zeiten bis zur Gegenwart. Band III: Erste Abteilung: Statistik. Tier- und sogenannter Pflanzenkrebs* (Jena, 1913).
18. Report by Simon Flexner, 19 October 1923, vol. 11, box 2, RG 439, MSKCC Archives, RAC.
19. For biographical material on Rous, see for example Christopher H. Andrewes, "Rous, Francis Peyton (1879–1970)," *Biographical Memoirs of Fellows of the Royal Society* 17 (1971): 643–62; Renato Dulbecco, "Francis Peyton Rous, 5 October 1879–February 16, 1970," *Biographical Memoirs of the National Academy of Sciences* 48 (1976): 275–306.
20. On viruses, see for instance Ton van Helvoort, "History of Virus Research in the Twentieth Century: The Problem of Conceptual Continuity," *History of Science* 32 (1994): 185–235.
21. Peyton Rous, "A Sarcoma of the Fowl Transmissible by an Agent Separable from the Tumor Cells," in *Selected Papers in Tumour Virology*, eds. John Tooze and Joseph Sambrook (Cold Spring Harbor, NY, 1974), 5–25; Michael B. Shimkin, *Some Classics of Experimental Oncology: 50 Selections, 1775–1965* (Washington, DC, 1980), 361–81.
22. For instance, see folder "Rous, FP: Work of the Laboratory for Cancer Research 1909–1912," RG 450.R762 Rous Papers, Rockefeller University Archives, RAC, in which it was stated that "More recently we have found a typical malignant tumor caused by an ultramicroscopic agent which behaves like a living organism, and without doubt is one." See also Peyton Rous to Stephen L. Baker, 4 October 1930, folder "Chicken Tumor #1," RG 450.R762 Rous Papers, Rockefeller University Archives, RAC: "My own belief has always been that the agents causing these tumors are viruses. . . ."
23. Rous would later write to a historian of science, "An older and wiser man prevented me from calling the chicken sarcoma a virus, as I wished to do first off, and suggested the word 'agent' instead. . . . He did me a good turn, since the virus proved in some ways so peculiar that not until the time of my Harvey Lecture in 1934 [*sic*], when the traits of viruses generally were better realized, could it safely be called such." See Peyton Rous to Greer Williams, 4 November 1958, folder "Williams, Greer," RG 450.R762 Rous Papers, Rockefeller University Archives, RAC.
24. Peyton Rous, "An Avian Tumor in Relation to the Tumor Problem," *Proceedings of the American Philosophical Society* 51 (1912): 201–5, especially 204; see also Peyton Rous, James B. Murphy and W. H. Tytler, "The Relation between a Chicken Sarcoma's Behavior and the Growth's Filterable Cause," *Journal of the American Medical Association* 58 (1912): 1840–1. The possibility of an intrinsic cell derangement would be defended intensely by Murphy as the most probable explanation. He spoke of a "transmissible mutagen." See James B. Murphy, "Experimental Approach to the Cancer Problem. I. Four Important Phases of Cancer Research. II. Avian Tumors in Relation to the General Problem of Malignancy," *Bulletin of the Johns Hopkins Hospital* 56 (1935): 1–31.
25. Report, 9 April, 1913, p. 2, folder "Rous, FP: Report 9 April 1913," RG 450.R762 Rous Papers, Rockefeller University Archives, RAC. It seems likely that Rous thought that viruses might be propagated in the absence of cells, unlike what was later to become the consensus opinion, and that he was supported in this view by Simon Flexner.
26. Rous to Jones, 12 May 1926, folder "Jones, Frederick Snowden," RG 450.R762 Rous Papers, Rockefeller University Archives, RAC. Elsewhere, Rous would say that Flexner, in a different context, once said, "The next best thing to knowing what problem to work on is knowing when to drop it." See "Will Gye and the Cancer Problem," folder Gye, Will E. #1, January 1953, RG 450.R762 Rous Papers, Rockefeller University Archives, RAC.
27. E. E. Tyzzer, "Report of the Director," in *Cancer Commission of Harvard University, Second Annual Report of the Collis P. Huntington Memorial Hospital for Cancer Research and of the Laboratories of the Cancer Commission of Harvard University, 1913–1914* (Boston, 1914), 14.
28. William E. Gye became director of the Imperial Cancer Research Fund in 1935. See Christopher H. Andrewes, "William Ewart Gye, 1884–1952," *Obituary Notices of Fellows of the Royal Society* 8 (1952): 418–30. On Gye, see also Joan Austoker, *A History of the Imperial Cancer Research Fund 1902–1986* (Oxford, 1988).
29. *Lancet* 2 (1925): 109–17.

30. Rous always adopted an attitude of aloofness in the discussion over Gye's results, viz. receptive but not convinced. Rous commented, "Gye must have realized this, for I was in England repeatedly within the next few years and he never asked for my allegiance—behaving admirably in this respect as in all others throughout our long friendship." See Peyton Rous to Alexander Haddow, 16 September 1957, folder "Cancer Research [Journal]," RG 450.R762 Rous Papers, Rockefeller University Archives, RAC.
31. Simon Flexner, "Experimental Epidemiology: Introductory," *Journal of Experimental Medicine* 36 (1922): 9–14; Simon Flexner and Leslie T. Webster, "Further Report on Experiments in Epidemiology," *Science* 59 (1924): 445–6. See also Olga Amsterdamska, "Standardizing Epidemics: Infection, Inheritance, and Environment in Interwar Experimental Epidemiology," in *Transmission: Human Pathologies between Heredity and Infection*, eds. Jean-Paul Gaudillière and Ilana Löwy (Amsterdam, 2001), 135–79.
32. Peyton Rous and Elizabeth Botsford, "The Incidence of Cancer in Tarred and Sheltered Mice," *Journal of Experimental Medicine* 55 (1932): 247–66.
33. Richard E. Shope, "A Transmissible Tumor-Like Condition in Rabbits," *Journal of Experimental Medicine* 56 (1932): 793–802; Richard E. Shope, "A Filterable Virus Causing Tumor-Like Condition in Rabbits and its Relationship to Virus Myxomatosum," *Journal of Experimental Medicine* 56 (1932): 803–22.
34. Richard E. Shope, "Infectious Papillomatosis of Rabbits," *Journal of Experimental Medicine* 58 (1933): 607–24.
35. Peyton Rous and Joseph W. Beard, "A Virus Induced Mammalian Growth with the Characters of a Tumor (the Shope Rabbit Papilloma). III. Further Characters of the Growth: General Discussion," *Journal of Experimental Medicine* 60 (1934): 741–66.
36. James Ewing, "Cancer Problems," *Harvey Lectures* 3 (1909): 34–88. See also Jacob Wolff, *Die Lehre von der Krebskrankheit von den ältesten Zeiten bis zur Gegenwart: Band I* (Jena, 1907), translated as *The Science of Cancerous Disease from Earliest Times to the Present* (Canton, MA, 1989), 431–590.
37. Ewing, "Cancer Problems," 34–88.
38. Ton van Helvoort, "A Century of Research into the Cause of Cancer: Is the New Oncogene Paradigm Revolutionary?," *History and Philosophy of the Life Sciences* 21 (1999): 293–330.
39. "Clue to Parasite as Cause of Cancer" and "Dr. Rous Finds Evidence That Disease Is Not Organic, as Has Been Believed: Is Cancer Infectious?," *New York Times*, 14 February 1912, folder Chicken Tumor #6, RG 450.R762 Rous Papers, Rockefeller University Archives, RAC.
40. Erwin F. Smith, "Studies on the Crown Gall of Plants: Its Relation to Human Cancer," *Journal of Cancer Research* 1 (1916): 231–309.
41. Erwin F. Smith, "Further Evidence that Crown Gall of Plants is Cancer," *Science* 43 (1916): 871–89.
42. Victor Schmieden, "Infektion, Parasitismus und Gewächsbildung," in *Verhandlungen der Deutschen Pathologischen Gesellschaft: Zweiundzwanzigste Tagung, gehalten in Danzig am 8.-10. Juni 1927*, ed. G. Schmorl (Jena, 1927), 21–36.
43. Christopher H. Andrewes, "Viruses in Relation to the Aetiology of Tumours," *Lancet* 2 (1934): 63–9, 117–24.
44. American Society for the Control of Cancer, *Cancer Control* (Chicago, 1927), 327.
45. Rous to William E. Gye, 28 December 1935, folder Gye, Will E. #3, RG 450.R762 Rous Papers, Rockefeller University Archives, RAC.
46. James Ewing, "Pathological Aspects of Some Problems of Experimental Cancer Research," *Journal of Cancer Research* 1 (1916): 71–86.
47. James Ewing, "Some Results of Modern Clinical Cancer Research," *Bulletin of the American Society for the Control of Cancer* 17 (August 1935): 1–6.
48. James Ewing, "The Public and the Cancer Problem," *Science* 87 (1938): 399–407. See also James Ewing, *Causation, Diagnosis and Treatment of Cancer* (Baltimore, 1931); and Lewis S. Pilcher and Frank E. Adair, eds., "International Contributions to the Study of Cancer in Honor of James Ewing," *Annals of Surgery* 93 (1931): 1–480.
49. This was discovered by Jean Clunet in 1908. See Michael B. Shimkin, *Contrary to Nature: Being an Illustrated Commentary on Some Persons and Events of Historical Importance in the Development of Knowledge Concerning Cancer* (Bethesda, MD, 1977), 247–8.

50. Katsusaburo Yamagiwa and Koichi Ichikawa, "Über die künstliche Epithelwucherung," *Gann* 8 (1914): 11–5; see Shimkin, *Contrary to Nature* (n. 49 above), 225–6.
51. Arthur E. Boycott, in James A. Murray, J. W. Cook, William Cramer, Christopher H. Andrewes, P. R. Peacock, James McIntosh, William E. Gye and Arthur E. Boycott, "Discussion on Experimental Production of Malignant Tumours," *Proceedings of the Royal Society of London, Ser. B* 113 (1933): 268–92.
52. James B. Murphy, "Experimental Approach to the Cancer Problem. I. Four Important Phases of Cancer Research. II. Avian Tumors in Relation to the General Problem of Malignancy." *Bulletin of the Johns Hopkins Hospital* 56 (1935): 1–31; see also Albert Claude and James B. Murphy, "Transmissible Tumors of the Fowl," *Physiological Reviews* 13 (1933): 246–75.
53. Christopher H. Andrewes, "President's Address: Latent Virus Infections and Their Possible Relevance to the Cancer Problem," *Proceedings of the Royal Society of Medicine* 33 (1939): 75–86.
54. Christopher H. Andrewes to Peyton Rous, 6 December 1935, folder Andrewes, Chr. #1, RG 450.R762 Rous Papers, Rockefeller University Archives, RAC; see also Christopher H. Andrewes and Richard E. Shope, "Changes in Rabbit Fibroma Virus Suggesting Mutation. III. Interpretation of Findings," *Journal of Experimental Medicine* 63 (1936): 179–84.
55. John G. Kidd and Peyton Rous, "A Transplantable Rabbit Carcinoma Originating in a Virus-Induced Papilloma and Containing the Virus in Masked or Altered Form," *Journal of Experimental Medicine* 71 (1940): 813–38; John G. Kidd, "The Detection of a 'Masked' Virus (The Shope Papilloma Virus) by Means of Immunization," *Journal of Experimental Medicine* 74 (1942): 321–44.
56. See "Virus Demonstration: Masking," "Rous, FP: Virus demonstration: Talk with Northrop," and "Rous, FP: What we know about the masked virus," folder Rous, FP: Virus Demonstration: Masking, RG 450.R762 Rous Papers, Rockefeller University Archives, RAC; "Talk with Dr. Northrop regarding masking virus," folder Northrop, John H. #3, RG 450.R762 Rous Papers, Rockefeller University Archives, RAC.
57. The debates on the causes of cancer have also been analyzed in Ton van Helvoort, "A Dispute over Scientific Credibility: The Struggle for an Independent Institute for Cancer Research in Pre-World War II Berlin," *Studies in History and Philosophy of Biological and Biomedical Sciences* 31 (2000): 315–54.
58. Anonymous, "Cancer and Viruses," *Bulletin of the American Society for the Control of Cancer* 20 (1938), 6–8, especially 7, which was most probably written by Ewing. See also James Ewing, "The Causal and Formal Genesis of Cancer," in British Empire Cancer Campaign, *Report of the International Conference on Cancer, London, 17th–20th July, 1928* (Bristol, 1928), 1–13. The Surgeon General Committee on Cancer Research adhered to the same dichotomy in the cause of cancer; see Stanhope Bayne-Jones, Ross G. Harrison, Clarence C. Little, John H. Northrop and James B. Murphy, "Fundamental Cancer Research: Report of a Committee Appointed by the Surgeon General," *Journal of the National Cancer Institute* 19 (1957): 317–25. Reprinted in *Journal of the National Cancer Institute 19* (1957): 317–25
59. Rous to Shope, 19 February 1935, folder Shope, R.E. #9, RG 450.R762 Rous Papers, Rockefeller University Archives, RAC; see also Richard E. Shope, "Serial Transmission of Virus of Infectious Papillomatosis in Domestic Rabbits," *Proceedings of the Society for Experimental Biology and Medicine* 32 (1935): 830–2.
60. In regard to Little and the Jackson Memorial, see for example, Karen A. Rader, "Of Mice, Medicine, and Genetics: C. C. Little's Creation of the Inbred Laboratory Mouse, 1909–1918," *Studies in History and Philosophy of Biological and Biomedical Sciences* 30 (1999): 319–43; and Jean Holstein, *The First Fifty Years at the Jackson Laboratory* (Bar Harbor, ME, 1979).
61. Rous to Clarence C. Little, 21 February 1940, folder Jackson Memorial Laboratory #5, RG 450.R762 Rous Papers, Rockefeller University Archives, RAC.
62. "Talk given to Board of Directors," 17 January 1942, folder Talk Board of Directors, RG 450.R762 Rous Papers, Rockefeller University Archives, RAC.
63. Peyton Rous, "Viruses and Tumors," in *Virus Diseases: By Members of the Rockefeller Institute for Medical Research* (Ithaca, NY, 1943), 147–70.
64. "Report on Experiments on the Cause of Some Cancers," October 1937, p. 26 folder Experiments on the Cause of Some Cancers, Report October 1937, RG 450.R762 Rous Papers, Rockefeller University Archives, RAC.

65. Ewing to Rous, 7 October 1935, folder Ewing, James, RG 450.R762 Rous Papers, Rockefeller University Archives, RAC.
66. James Ewing, "The General Pathological Conception of Cancer," *Canadian Medical Association Journal* 33 (1935): 125–35.
67. Rous (n. 4 above), 114.
68. Newspaper clipping, *New York Sun*, 19 October 1945, folder 1857, box 198, series 18.1 grants, Commonwealth Fund Archives, RAC.
69. Interview with Little by Heffron, 14 February 1946, folder 1854, box 198, series 18.1 grants, Commonwealth Fund Archives, RAC.
70. *Time*, 27 June 1949, folder 191, box 24, Office series, Medical Interests subseries, RG 2 OMR, Rockefeller Family Archives, RAC.
71. Frank L. Horsfall Jr., "Heritance of Acquired Characters: A Unifying Concept is Developed in Relation to the Genesis of Cancer," *Science* 136 (1962): 472–6.
72. George Klein, "Viruses and Cancer," in *Viruses and Cancer: Fifty-First Symposium of the Society for General Microbiology*, eds. A. Minson, J. Neil, and M. McCrae (Cambridge, 1994), 1–13.
73. J. Michael Bishop, "Cancer: The Rise of the Genetic Paradigm," *Genes and Development* 9 (1995): 1309–15.
74. Morris J. Vogel and Charles E. Rosenberg, eds., *The Therapeutic Revolution: Essays in the Social History of American Medicine* (Philadelphia, 1979), 91–107. See also Michael Hau, "The Holistic Gaze in German Medicine, 1890–1930," *Bulletin of the History of Medicine* 74 (2000): 495–524.
75. See also the essays in Christoph Gradmann and Thomas Schlich, eds., *Strategien der Kausalität: Konzepte der Krankheitsverursachung im 19. und 20. Jahrhundert* (Pfaffenweiler, 1999).
76. Cornelius P. Rhoads, "Perspectives in Cancer Research [1948]," in *Great Adventures in Medicine*, eds. Samuel Rapport and Helen Wright (New York, 1952), 743–57.
77. For instance, see J. Andrew Mendelsohn, "Medicine and the Making of Bodily Inequality in Twentieth-Century Europe," in *Heredity and Infection: The History of Disease Transmission,* eds. Jean-Paul Gaudillière and Ilana Löwy (New York, 2001), 21–79; see also Ton van Helvoort (n. 57 above).
78. John G. Kidd, "Stay as Close to Nature as You Can," in *A Notable Career in Finding Out: Peyton Rous (1879–1970)*, James S. Henderson, Phillip D. McMaster, John G. Kidd, and Charles Huggins (New York, 1971), 21–39.
79. For instance, see William D. Foulkes and Shirley V. Hodgson, eds., *Inherited Susceptibility to Cancer: Clinical, Predictive and Ethical Perspectives* (Cambridge, 1998).
80. Dorothy Nelkin, "Cancer Genetics and Public Expectations," in *Inherited Susceptibility to Cancer: Clinical, Predictive and Ethical Perspectives*, eds. William D. Foulkes and Shirley V. Hodgson (Cambridge, 1998), 46–59.
81. Dorothy Nelkin and M. Susan Lindee, "Good Genes and Bad Genes: DNA in Popular Culture," in *The Practices of Human Genetics*, eds. Michael Furton and Everett Mendelsohn (Dordrecht, 1999), 155–67.

Chapter 10

Women Scientists at the Rockefeller Institute, 1901–1940

Elizabeth Hanson

Director of Special Projects, The Rockefeller University, New York, NY

In 1929, Dixie Pelluet was appointed to the scientific staff of the Rockefeller Institute for Medical Research, displaying the following credentials:

> Miss Pelluet is a Ph.D. from Bryn Mawr, a student of [Professor] D. H. Tennant. She is now teaching at Murray State Teachers College, Murray, Kentucky. Her position is that of head of the Department of Biology. Her home is in Alberta, Canada; her father having been a professor in the University of Edmonton. She is 31 years of age.[1]

In the first decades of the twentieth century, opportunities for graduate education in the sciences had begun to open to women in the United States, and increasingly those women sought to enter the work force. Dixie Pelluet, with a doctorate from an elite woman's college, was one of the few dozen women scientists who, during its first four decades, worked at the Rockefeller Institute.

Over the past twenty years, historians studying women in science have asked increasingly sophisticated questions of their subject, moving from works of recovery—simply documenting the existence of women scientists over the last four centuries, few of whom were well-known—to investigating, for example, features of women's scientific careers that have helped or hindered their advancement, and the relationships between their private lives (e.g., marriages, families, and social networks) and their intellectual lives.[2]

Women's participation in American science over the last century is well documented, as are many of the social and institutional factors that conspired to limit their professional advancement and to render their contributions nearly invisible to later generations. This study of women scientists at the Rockefeller Institute begins as a work of recovery, and then explores the formal and informal institutional practices that shaped the experiences of a few of its women scientists.

The organization of the Rockefeller Institute was important to the careers of all Rockefeller researchers. Simon Flexner, the first director, structured the staff so as to create numerous short-term appointments that were essentially postdoctoral fellowships, with the intention that from these positions young scientists would find faculty positions at other universities and medical schools. These appointments were effective in launching the careers of many women as well as men.

Several factors point to the year 1940 as an appropriate cutoff date for the first era of women at the Rockefeller Institute. World War II disrupted the usual operations of the Rockefeller Institute; and in terms of education and other opportunities, the careers of the women who came in the 1940s as recent PhD's belong more to the second half of the century than the first. Also, in the mid-1940s, the Rockefeller Institute began to reevaluate its mission, a process that eventually resulted in a significant broadening of its areas of study to include physics and mathematics, and the addition of a formal, PhD-granting, graduate program. Finally, there was consistency of leadership and philosophy in the period considered here.

Simon Flexner was director of the Institute from 1902 to 1935, and his leadership was important to the experience of women scientists.

Women among the Scientific Staff

In its first decades, the Rockefeller Institute remained relatively small. In 1910, there were five laboratories with a total scientific staff of about 35; at its peak in 1935, the number of laboratories had grown to thirteen with a staff of 134. Because of rapid turnover in lower-level appointments, the number of scientists who worked on the Rockefeller Institute's staff between 1901 and 1940 was 543, according to one authoritative list. Of these, forty-three were women; archival records document at least nine more women scientific staff members, for a total of fifty-two women scientists. For the most part, these women worked in entry-level positions, with the title of fellow or assistant. These positions were distinguished by title and salary scale from appointments at the level of technician. In addition, several women worked at the Rockefeller Institute as visiting scientists or received grants from the Institute. They are not considered here, as so little information is available about them.[3]

At first glance, the proportion of women at the Rockefeller Institute (about 9 percent) seems relatively high compared with that for women working in science overall for the period. Margaret Rossiter has found that women made up 5.3 percent of medical scientists and 3.4 percent of chemists in 1938 based on entries in *American Men of Science*. But it also is important to account for the disciplines in which these women worked. Rossiter indicates that women tended to be clustered in subfields, accounting for higher percentages of bacteriologists and biochemists, for example. These were the main fields of study at the Rockefeller Institute; as a result, the generally higher representation in bacteriology and biochemistry of women seems likely to be the primary reason for the seemingly high proportion of women scientists at Rockefeller Institute. In addition, because most women worked at the Institute for only a year or two, they may never have made up 9 percent of the scientific staff at any one time, nor did they necessarily work together.[4]

Among the thirty-four women whose undergraduate institutions are known, half were educated at women's colleges founded in the late nineteenth century, with the largest contingent (six) from Wellesley. These women were the beneficiaries of science curricula developed at the new women's colleges. Data on graduate education are available for an overlapping set of thirty-four women: several of them earned their graduate degrees while being employed at the Rockefeller Institute or went on to earn a second degree after leaving the Institute. The largest number of PhD's was awarded by Columbia University. In fact, Columbia awarded more doctorates in chemistry and biochemistry to women than any other institution in the United States before 1938. Although very little information is available to break down this group by field of PhD, at least fifteen did research in bacteriology at the Rockefeller Institute, and thirteen worked in some area of chemistry.[5]

A few women earned second graduate degrees after leaving the Rockefeller Institute. Florence Frankel and Ann Kuttner added MD's to their credentials. Maude Menton worked at the Institute for a year between completing her master's degree and going on to both the MD and PhD. Such exceptional qualifications reflect the "Marie Curie strategy," described by Rossiter, by which women scientists in the 1920s and 1930s attempted to overcome employment discrimination with academic training that exceeded what was typical for male scientists. Indeed, at the Rockefeller Institute, some women were encouraged to seek additional degrees. "It was not too difficult for ladies to work at the Institute, but they always had trouble getting ahead—particularly the PhD ladies," remembered Tom Rivers, former head of the Rockefeller Hospital, in an oral history taken in the early 1960s. "Whenever I found one that had promise, I always advised her to get out and get an M.D., because as long as she had just a Ph.D. no one was going to pay any attention to her. One of the people I so advised was Ann Kuttner."[6]

At least nineteen women came to their appointments at the Rockefeller Institute immediately after completing their graduate degrees. Many of them had additional relevant work experience that preceded their advanced degree. Alice Armstrong, a physicist, had worked in Washington, D.C., in the Radium Section of the Bureau of Standards and taught physics at Wellesley before earning her PhD at Radcliffe. Clara Lynch, a mouse geneticist, taught at her undergraduate alma mater Smith College for seven years before completing a PhD at Columbia and coming to the Rockefeller Institute. Others had taught in high schools or small colleges, or worked in the bacteriology laboratories of urban public health departments.

Some of the women who came to the Rockefeller Institute had started out teaching—a more secure career than research, and one that did not require a graduate degree. They were older than the recent college graduates who filled many technician-level appointments. The Rockefeller Institute offered them the rare opportunity to switch from teaching to research. Letters of reference note dedication to their work, perhaps implying that these women would not soon leave their jobs to marry, and needed to support themselves. For example, a letter written for Angelia Courtney reads, "Miss Courtney would need rather a higher salary than a younger person (she is about thirty-three, I should say) for she is not working just for experience. She has gone into laboratory work after having become tired of teaching."[7] Similarly, Bertha Barker spent almost a decade in high school teaching, and then did graduate work at the Massachusetts Institute of Technology (MIT) with the well-known chemist, and founder of home economics, Ellen Swallow Richards. Although she did not complete an advanced degree, this experience paid off. A biologist at MIT recommended her to the Rockefeller Institute with these words: "Miss Barker would be quite a 'find' for you. She is not very young, but she had the wit and pluck to give up her teaching and start afresh in biology, and she has done exceedingly well."

The Rockefeller Institute was organized for the majority of research positions to be short term; this practice implemented the Institute's mission to spread the ideals of laboratory and clinical research by training young scientists who stayed a year or two and then carried their skills to other institutions. Given that women generally worked in temporary positions, and that they could not expect to achieve tenure positions, it is not surprising that most stayed only a short time: about half left the Institute after two years or less. For male researchers below the rank of member, the numbers were similar, about 40 percent.[8]

Postdoctoral work at the Rockefeller Institute boosted the careers of women scientists, just as it did their male counterparts. Two years as a fellow in bacteriology and pathology for Linda Lange, for example, were followed by a career teaching in medical schools, culminating in an associate professorship at the Johns Hopkins School of Hygiene and Public Health. Margaret Pittman, who stayed five years at the Institute, became known later for standardizing the pertussis vaccine for whooping cough. Seven others found positions teaching in medical schools, an additional seven continued careers elsewhere in academia, and four worked for local, state, or federal government agencies. Three went into industry, including Clara Nigg, who had worked under Nobel laureate Karl Landsteiner and went on to head the department of bacteriology and virology at E. R. Squibb.[9]

The Career Ladder and the Lunch Table

Simon Flexner set up a hierarchy of staffing that was a compromise between the practices of the European research institutes upon which he modeled the Rockefeller Institute and of American universities. Because the Institute did not grant degrees, he found the title of professor inappropriate for what was essentially a faculty position. Instead, scientists at the highest rank were known as "members of the Institute." Each member oversaw his own laboratory, and only full members of the Rockefeller Institute could head a laboratory. Of the scientific staff, only members of the Rockefeller Institute had permanent, or tenured, positions.

The next level of appointment was associate member, a position that was eligible for renewal every three years. Flexner intended that, after a second term at the level of associate member, scientists would "either rise to membership or resign from the Institute to accept professorships in the universities." Beneath the associate members were associates, who had two-year appointments, and assistants and fellows, with one-year appointments. All such positions could be renewed; but again, researchers with these titles were expected to "rise to the higher grades, or, as is common after periods of [ranging] from three to five years at the Institute, they leave to enter university work." The title of research scholar also was occasionally awarded; although never defined, it seems to have been a short-term or probationary appointment similar to fellow. It also was possible for a scientist to work at the Rockefeller Institute as an unpaid volunteer. These positions composed the scientific staff of the Rockefeller Institute. The scientific staff were assisted in the laboratories by technical staff, whose jobs also were defined hierarchically, and sometimes described as technicians, skilled helpers, and helpers.[10]

The majority of the women on the scientific staff were appointed at the level of fellow or assistant, and a few worked as unpaid volunteers. Two were appointed at the level of associate. In contradiction to his own rule, Flexner allowed one woman who worked her way up to associate member and three who stayed more than two terms as associates to stay at those levels without forcing them out or promoting them. As one member of the Rockefeller Institute later observed, "Simon Flexner just wasn't giving memberships to ladies." Before 1940, only one woman, Florence Sabin, achieved the status of member of the Institute, and she was hired at that level in 1924. Sabin was exceptional in other ways as well. She had been the first woman to become a full professor at the Johns Hopkins Medical School; and in 1925, she became the first female member of the U. S. National Academy of Sciences.[11]

Flexner's reasons for hiring Sabin remain to be discovered; however, it was not a decision that was meant to set a precedent. In 1929, the Board of Scientific Directors considered, but decided against, promoting Louise Pearce from associate member to member. Nearly thirty years passed before a second woman was appointed member.[12]

At the other end of the scale, the boundary between technician and assistant was occasionally violated, allowing technicians to move up to join the scientific staff. For the history of women in science, this boundary is significant. Early in the twentieth century, women scientists often were channeled into work classed at the technician level, and certain kinds of work were deemed appropriate for women and consequently assigned the low status of technical labor. In either situation, it was difficult for a woman technician to achieve a change in title and

M. Carey Thomas (left) and Florence Sabin at a Bryn Mawr graduation. Courtesy of the Rockefeller Archive Center.

raise in pay even when her work entailed independent research and her male colleagues doing similar work enjoyed scientific status.[13]

Promotions from technician to scientific staff were not made lightly at the Rockefeller Institute, perhaps particularly in the case of women staff. In 1924, Simon Flexner wrote to Rufus Cole, the head of the hospital,

> . . . it is not our intention to convert technical workers into staff members. As you know, I regard Miss Hiller's promotion to be a mistake, and I do not think it should be repeated. As far as I can make out, Mrs. Lancefield does Swift's work in a purely routine fashion. I do not see that she is more skillful than other technicians in the laboratories. She should, therefore be treated just as they are. I believe she has either a B. A. or a B. S. degree–something which other of our technical workers have.[14]

In fact, Alma Hiller and Rebecca Lancefield were both well on their way to completing their doctorates, and Lancefield had coauthored an important paper with Oswald Avery in 1919, the first to demonstrate distinct types among streptococcus bacteria, an important step toward understanding which types cause epidemics. Their educational backgrounds indicate that their career paths should have been to the scientific staff. Perhaps Flexner invoked the boundary between technical and scientific staff as a cost-saving measure. He added, in his letter to Cole, "As a technician her [Lancefield's] salary is also fixed." As it happened, both were promoted. Lancefield remained at the Rockefeller Institute for her entire career, and Hiller worked for thirty years under clinical chemist Donald D. Van Slyke.

The case of Marion Orcutt offers another view of the workings of the Institute—the tensions between the director and laboratory heads, and Flexner's efforts to enforce his "up and out" policy. Orcutt began as a technician in the Institute's Princeton, New Jersey, laboratories in 1918. Over the next five years, her name appeared on eight published papers; and by 1931, she had earned a master's degree and had been promoted to assistant. Flexner's decision to dismiss her in 1933 seems to have been balanced between her salary, the quality of her work, and his general employment policy. Flexner wrote to Orcutt's supervisor,

> A difficulty in passing her on to a hospital or commercial laboratory is her abnormal salary. She is merely a technician and nothing more. My suggestion is that you . . . tell her promptly but kindly that she is out of place on our scientific staffs and according to the Rules of the Institute a scientific staff appointee who is not promoted is always asked to find another place. Say that she has one more year in which to get located elsewhere . . . I believe this principle should be enforced at the Princeton Department as at the New York Departments. Those who do not rise must go.[15]

Rules of hierarchy were enforced to varying degrees both in the professional realm of job titles and promotions and informally in daily life at the Rockefeller Institute. Gradations in education and expertise among Institute employees were marked by dress codes. For example, hospital scientists and MD's wore white laboratory coats; scientists in other laboratories wore brown lab coats; male technicians wore short coats; and women technicians wore white dresses issued by the Institute.

The staff were also divided by where they ate lunch. Members, associate members, and other scientific staff had access to a faculty lunchroom. This was a dining room, with table service, where junior and senior scientists had the daily opportunity to mingle and talk shop.

Those who participated recalled it as a sort of ongoing seminar, and many of them attributed their later research success to conversations started in the lunch room. For women technicians and administrative staff a "ladies lunch room" was set up. They were required to work a certain number of hours per week in order to use the ladies lunch room, although this rule was flexible when put to the test. In the meantime, male nonscientific staff were forced to eat off campus at local pubs (the Rockefeller Institute had been built in a neighborhood of tenements and breweries); they protested against the undue expense of eating out and eventually were allotted a room in which to eat food that they carried in. The privilege of eating on campus was a contentious issue in the Institute's early history.[16]

The social codes surrounding lunch and other aspects of daily life at the Rockefeller Institute seem likely to have influenced women's effectiveness in doing science and getting promoted. It is not clear, for example, whether women scientific staff participated in the lunch room culture of the faculty. As late as the 1960s, at least some women felt discouraged from eating there, and thus were excluded from reaping the benefits of daily conversation with the senior staff. There also was sometimes confusion over whether women with PhD's were required to wear the same white uniforms as women technicians. At a time when "woman scientist" was almost a contradiction in terms, to dress like a technician would seem likely to have cemented a woman assistant's low status.[17]

No doubt, outright sexism also limited women's professional advancement, or prevented them from being hired in the first place. In 1927, when women rarely worked at the Rockefeller

Nellie Goldthwaite (third from right) was head of the chemistry department at Mount Holyoke College before joining the laboratory group of P. A. T. Levene (third from left), pictured here in 1908. Courtesy of the Rockefeller Archive Center.

Institute longer than a few years, a recent graduate of Bryn Mawr College was not hired as a technician because she was "too good looking to remain unmarried longer than two or three years." Another young woman got the job, one who would "cause no difficulties here in relation to young men." A quotation from Tom Rivers about Louise Pearce illustrates, at the very least, confusion about the place of women in the production of scientific knowledge. According to Rivers, ". . . when I got to know her at the Institute, [Pearce] was a rather good-looking person, and in her earlier days she must have been still better looking. I must say that by her actions at the Hopkins or at the Institute you wouldn't pick Dr. Pearce as a woman or a man. She was a research person. . . . She was that good."[18]

Windows of Opportunity

During World War I, many women found temporary employment related to war work or filled in for men who were fighting abroad. The war created opportunities for women scientists at the Rockefeller Institute as well. Simon Flexner wrote in 1918, "We are losing many of our staff to war duty. We are putting women in to carry temporarily such parts of their work as it is possible for them to do." Indeed, nearly one third of the women scientists at the Rockefeller Institute before 1940 were hired between 1916 and 1919.[19]

Members of the Rockefeller Institute's Board of Directors used their professional networks to bring scientists to the Institute, and two of them were affiliated with institutions in New York City that employed an exceptional number of women scientists. Through these connections, the Rockefeller Institute supported the research of several women. Board member L. Emmett Holt was a prominent pediatrician and head of Babies Hospital. In 1910, he initiated a chemistry laboratory there—staffed by physicians Angelia Courtney and Helen Fales, and a third worker named Grace Bill—and funded by the Rockefeller Institute. The Babies Hospital Laboratory of the Rockefeller Institute studied infant nutrition, collaborating with Rockefeller chemists P. A. T. Levene and Donald Van Slyke, and was active for about ten years.[20]

Hermann Biggs, another Rockefeller Institute board member, headed the bacteriology laboratory of the New York City Department of Health. The Department of Health as a whole provided extraordinary employment opportunities for women early in the twentieth century—including, for example, S. Josephine Baker, who directed its Division (later Bureau) of Child Hygiene. In Biggs' laboratory, women performed the routine bacteriological work, and several of them moved on to positions at the Rockefeller Institute. For instance, Marian S. Taylor brought a letter of recommendation from William Park, the head of the department. In addition, one of the department's most prominent bacteriologists (Park's "first assistant"), Anna Williams, received a research grant from the Rockefeller Institute.[21]

The Scientific Career for Women

Beyond providing young scientists with postdoctoral training and intensive research experience, the Rockefeller Institute helped investigators, including women, to progress in their careers by subsidizing tuition for graduate courses and sabbatical time to visit laboratories in Europe. Such support came directly from Simon Flexner. Flexner had a well-deserved reputation as a talent scout, and he was devoted to nurturing the development of laboratory scientists who would focus on medical questions. The Institute was only one vehicle for accomplishing this. Flexner also helped establish research fellowships administered by the National Research Council that were vital in supplying opportunities for postdoctoral training.[22]

Simon Flexner, while not actively an advocate for women in science, was both well versed in the debates surrounding the women's movement and cognizant of some of the obstacles to women's participation in science. In 1902, the year he became director, Flexner married Helen Thomas, younger sister of M. Carey Thomas, president of Bryn Mawr College. Flexner's sister-in-law was a staunch advocate of graduate education for women and had been instrumental in gaining women's admission to the first class of students at the Johns Hopkins Medical School. Flexner corresponded regularly with Carey Thomas and served as a spokesman for women's scientific education at Bryn Mawr fundraising dinners. Helen Thomas was educated at Bryn Mawr; after she and Flexner were married, she directed a publicity campaign for women's suffrage in New York City. Flexner marched with her in the first women's suffrage parade in the city.[23]

In June of 1921, Flexner delivered the commencement address at Bryn Mawr, on the subject of "The Scientific Career for Women." The speech was timely: Madame Curie's much publicized visit to the United States had taken place the month before, and women's potential for careers in science was a subject for debate in newspapers and magazines. In his talk, Flexner pointed to the differences in the ways boys and girls are raised as factors steering women away from scientific careers—their toys, and a tendency of fathers interested in science to communicate this to sons rather than daughters. "The examples might be multiplied in which because of custom the boy, but not the girl, has been subjected to influences extending over many years calculated to prepare or to lead him, if only insensibly, into the paths of science," Flexner wrote. He further acknowledged some of the hardships faced by women pursuing science:

> . . . the boy has other advantages to guide and spur him on: once launched on a scientific priority, he looks forward to a life's career and indulges the hope, if not the expectation, of being attended by some good woman. Now women have not yet been offered anything approaching a like opportunity to that put before men. The scientific career means too often for them, if consistently pursued, the denial of domestic companionships and compensations which men easily win and enjoy.

Later, in 1934, referring to the difficulties women faced finding employment in academia, Flexner wrote that "it is most regrettable that the opportunities for women in colleges are still so few."[24]

Flexner himself had firsthand experience not with sexism, but with antisemitism in the academy. His appointment as professor of pathology at the University of Pennsylvania in 1899 had been vehemently opposed, and was achieved only after the issue of whether he would be elected to the Medical Faculty Club had been sidelined. The prejudice astonished him; he claimed to have experienced nothing like it in his earlier career at Johns Hopkins. This episode, and the Quaker tolerance of his wife's family, seem likely to have informed his outlook when it came to seeking the most able researchers to staff the Rockefeller Institute.[25]

When it came to hiring women scientists, Flexner seems to have been fairly open-minded about assigning them to lower-level positions. In 1922, for example, he wrote to a colleague at Columbia University to ask about recent graduates in organic chemistry, and he specified "A man is preferred." But when his colleague responded with the names of one man and two women, Flexner interviewed both women and hired one of them, Lillian Baker, who then worked in the laboratory of Alexis Carrel for twenty-five years. Flexner also seems to have posted job openings with the Wellesley College placement office. This was how Alice Armstrong learned of an opening for "a young woman trained in physics, mathematics, and chemistry," and came to the Rockefeller Institute in 1927.[26]

A disproportionate percentage of the women at the Rockefeller Institute worked in the Department of Pathology and Bacteriology, which included Flexner's laboratory as well as others such as Eugene Opie and Hideyo Noguchi. It is not clear whether this reflects openness on Flexner's part to employ women or merely the fact that women were better represented in bacteriology than in other areas of science. At the Rockefeller Institute, women also tended to cluster in the Department of Animal Pathology in Princeton, another unit where the work centered on bacteriology.

Flexner supported individual women's careers in several cases by providing them tuition for graduate school. Evelyn Tilden, for example, began working in the laboratory of Hideyo Noguchi in 1916. By 1923, the Rockefeller Institute was paying for her PhD work at Columbia. Tilden's scientific education up to that point was unconventional: she had obtained it completely at Rockefeller and during summer courses at Woods Hole. She had been an English major as an undergraduate, and Flexner first hired her through an agency to help with editing Noguchi's papers (Noguchi was Japanese and he was not very fluent in English). Noguchi was so pleased with Tilden's work that he made her his assistant, because, as she later recalled, "he had trouble making his three laboratory workers understand what he wanted them to do."[27]

Tilden's letter suggests that she quickly became involved with the scientific work of the laboratory. As her expertise grew, her scientific talent must have been evident to Flexner. He believed it was worthy of investment. Their friendly correspondence indicates Tilden's pleasure in her work and her accomplishments, and that Flexner acted as her mentor. In 1923, she wrote Flexner about her courses: "If I carried the maximum work, winter and summer, I suppose I could finish in two years, but it is more entertaining to take it slowly. I set out chiefly for entertainment, but I have now embarked on a serious undertaking!" And near the end of her life, Tilden recalled, "When Dr. Flexner found that I wanted to do graduate work, he did everything he could to help me."[28]

After Noguchi died in 1928, the Rockefeller Institute continued to support Tilden until she finished her degree the next year. At this time also, she was promoted to assistant. In 1931, the Institute helped place her as assistant professor of bacteriology at Colorado Agricultural College. Despite her ability, Tilden clearly did not have a future at the Rockefeller Institute after Noguchi's death. When she accepted the position in Colorado, Flexner wrote, "It is a relief to have this matter settled." Tilden later became a full professor at Northwestern University.[29]

Flexner's support of Tilden was intended to help her in the next stage of her career rather than increase her value as an Institute employee. In other instances too, Flexner gave women who were not going to be promoted at the Institute the opportunity for sabbatical or further education that would help them find their next job. Ida Rolf, a chemist in P. A. T. Levene's laboratory, went to Europe in 1926 at Levene's suggestion, and with financial aid from Flexner. Flexner made it clear to her that, "as soon as practicable after your return it will be necessary for you to find another position." This leave time was a turning point in the career of Rolf, who later developed "Rolfing," a form of physical therapy.[30]

Another case suggests that Flexner's successor as director of the Rockefeller Institute, Herbert Gasser, continued his policy. After Alexis Carrel returned to France in the late 1930s, the Institute paid for the medical education of Irene McFaul. McFaul had been the head surgical

Evelyn Tilden at her microscope in the laboratory of Hideyo Noguchi in 1922. Courtesy of the Rockefeller Archive Center.

nurse in Carrel's laboratory and an employee of the Institute since 1912, but was not a member of the scientific staff. In 1943, at the age of fifty-four, McFaul received her MD from New York Medical College.[31]

Private and Public Lives

Historians studying women in science have found the relationships between women's private and professional lives to be revealing of how women's careers in science have developed, and what strategies women have adopted to succeed in science. Women's work in science has often intertwined with domestic responsibilities, and family networks have been important in gaining access to education and instrumentation. Daughters, wives, and nieces of scientists have often found family support for their research interests. Such relationships can bear directly on intellectual achievement.[32]

Family relationships come to light in the records of the Rockefeller Institute, although details are sparse. There were two father–daughter pairs of researchers. Clara Meltzer, an MD, and Samuel Meltzer, one of the first members of the Institute, worked together between 1901 and 1903, and coauthored the first paper published by Rockefeller Institute scientists. Clara Meltzer seems to have dropped out of science when she married another researcher in her father's laboratory, John Auer, who went on to become director of the Pharmacology Department at St. Louis University. Another faculty daughter, Dorothea Smith, who received her PhD from Radcliffe, worked in the laboratory of her father Theobald Smith from 1916 to

1919, and again in 1931. She continued a scientific career, teaching at Bryn Mawr College and the Medical School of the University of Pennsylvania.[33]

About a third of the women scientists working at the Rockefeller Institute were married, and at least a few had spouses who were scientists. A brief look at the lives and careers of two of these scientific couples—Rebecca Craighill Lancefield and Donald Lancefield, and Marian Irwin Osterhout and Winthrop J. V. Osterhout—suggests that further investigation would shed light on questions about relationships between private lives and scientific achievements.

Rebecca Craighill, born in 1895, was educated at Wellesley College, where her roommate's interest in zoology prompted her to switch her own major from english to biology. A scholarship enabled her to enroll at Columbia University and study bacteriology. In 1918, she received her master's degree, married a fellow graduate student—Donald Lancefield, who was in Thomas Hunt Morgan's famous genetics department—and was hired as a technical assistant to Oswald T. Avery and Alphonse R. Dochez at the Rockefeller Institute Hospital. The work with Avery and Dochez opened a set of scientific problems to Lancefield that she would pursue for the rest of her career: systematically classifying the streptococcal bacteria. In 1921–22 both of the Lancefields taught at the University of Oregon. Upon their return to New York, Rebecca Lancefield was re-hired at the Rockefeller Institute, this time in the laboratory of Homer Swift. Donald Lancefield joined the faculty of Columbia University in 1922; in 1938, he went to Queen's College.

Under Swift, Rebecca Lancefield continued her work on streptococci, becoming an acknowledged expert, and achieving somewhat belated recognition for her work. She earned her PhD in 1925 from Columbia, based on work done at the Rockefeller Institute. In 1943, she was elected president of the Society of American Bacteriologists, and in 1961 she served as president of the American Association of Immunologists. She was elected to the U.S. National Academy of Sciences in 1970. Professional advancement came slowly for Lancefield at the Rockefeller Institute. She served at the level of associate from 1929 to 1942, when she was promoted to associate member. In 1958, shortly before her retirement, she was made a full professor (the title of member had been converted to professor), but she never was head of her own laboratory.

Lancefield's slow climb up the ladder of title and salary at the Rockefeller Institute was typical of the experience of women scientists of her generation. More interesting are her scientific achievements, and the intellectual and emotional support she must have received from her husband, and from overlapping professional and personal relationships. Donald Lancefield's scientific colleagues, for example, were important in the Lancefield's social circle—they were close friends of geneticist A. H. Sturtevant and his wife, with whom they spent summers at Woods Hole.[34]

The career of Marian Irwin both blossomed and was curtailed through her professional association with and subsequent marriage to Harvard physiologist W. J. V. Osterhout. Irwin was born in Tokyo in 1889, the daughter of an American diplomat married to a member of the Japanese nobility. She was educated at Bryn Mawr College and in 1919 received her PhD from Radcliffe. She performed her graduate work under W. J. V. Osterhout and continued to work for him afterward. Irwin was a National Research Council fellow from 1923 to 1925—the first woman to receive this fellowship.[35] In 1925, when Osterhout came to the Rockefeller Institute, Irwin accompanied the move of his laboratory and was appointed as an associate at the Institute. In 1926, she became a member of the Corporation of the Marine Biological

Laboratory at Woods Hole. Between 1918 and 1932, she produced fifty scientific publications.

Nonetheless, by 1929, Simon Flexner had decided that Irwin's career at the Rockefeller Institute was near its end, and he informed Osterhout to "warn her that she is to expect no promotion and has reached (about) her maximum salary, and is not expected to remain here indefinitely." Despite this warning Irwin was reappointed, and then, in 1933, an unforeseen turn of events allowed her to stay at the Rockefeller Institute for the rest of her career. Osterhout suffered a heart attack that year, and his health was bad enough for him to contemplate retirement—at least his lab was broken up. At this time Irwin resigned her position at Rockefeller and married the recently divorced Osterhout. However, Osterhout recovered from his heart trouble, and Irwin continued to work in his laboratory for the next two decades. Because it was against Rockefeller Institute policy "to have husband and wife on the scientific staff," she worked without an official appointment. Irwin continued her association with the Marine Biological Laboratory, but she published no scientific work after her marriage.[36]

Conclusion

The last twenty years of work of historians writing about women scientists provide frameworks for interpreting newly "recovered" lives and careers of women in science. The education and careers of women appointed to the scientific staff of the Rockefeller Institute fall into patterns that have been described before. For the most part, their experiences seem to be typical of women pursuing scientific careers during the early twentieth century. At the Rockefeller Institute, women scientists encountered familiar barriers, but some of them also found mentors. Simon Flexner, in particular, supported women's pursuit of scientific careers, and his policy of advancing careers through what was essentially postdoctoral training benefited many women as well as men. At a time when academic appointments were rare for women scientists, the Rockefeller Institute supported the research careers of dozens of women pursuing scientific careers.

Endnotes

1. John Gowan to Dr. Ten Broeck, December 1929, folder 2, box 24, Record Group 450.1 Scientific Staff, biographical, Rockefeller University Archives, Rockefeller Archive Center, Sleepy Hollow, New York (hereafter RAC).
2. The approach taken here is indebted to the pioneering work of Margaret Rossiter, in particular, Margaret Rossiter, *Women Scientists in America: Struggles and Strategies to 1940* (Baltimore, 1982); see also, for example, Pnina G. Abir-Am and Dorinda Outram, eds., *Uneasy Careers and Intimate Lives: Women in Science, 1789–1979* (New Brunswick, NJ, 1987); Helena M. Pycior, Nancy G. Slack, and Pnina G. Abir-Am, eds., *Creative Couples in the Sciences* (New Brunswick, NJ, 1996).
3. Women scientists at the Rockefeller Institute first came to my attention during research for a book about the university's history, published on the occasion of its centennial: Elizabeth Hanson, *Achievements: A Century of Science for the Benefit of Humankind* (New York, 2000); on staff numbers, see George W. Corner, *A History of The Rockefeller Institute, 1901–1953: Origins and Growth* (New York, 1964), 331 and the graph, "Growth of the Rockefeller Institute for Medical Research," prepared by Merrill W. Chase in 1955, located in the office of the campus archivist at the Rockefeller University. A list of scientific staff is published as Appendix III in Corner, 588–95. Additional names of women scientists are found in the Rockefeller University Archives, RAC, mainly in RG 450.1 Scientific Staff, biographical.
4. A rough estimate of women at the Institute is 9 percent; women composed 8.6 percent of the scientific staff before 1940 on Corner's list; Rossiter, *Women Scientists* (n. 2 above), 136; Margaret Rossiter, "Which Science? Which Women?" *Osiris* 12 (1997): 169–85.

5. On chemistry PhDs awarded by Columbia University, see Rossiter, *Women Scientists* (n. 2 above), 150.
6. In 1912, Maude Menten joined physical chemist Leonor Michaelis in Berlin. Their work resulted in the Michaelis–Menten equation, which describes enzyme-catalyzed biological reactions. Michaelis came to the Rockefeller Institute late in his career, in 1929. On Menten, see Marelene and Geoffrey Rayner-Canham, *Women in Chemistry: Their Changing Roles from Alchemical Times to the Mid-Twentieth Century* (Philadelphia, 2001), 157–9; on the work of Michaelis at the Rockefeller Institute see Corner, *History of Rockefeller* (n. 3 above), 176, 201; and Tom Rivers, *Reflections on a Life in Medicine and Science: An Oral History Memoir prepared by Saul Benison* (Cambridge, MA, 1967), 83.
7. For A. Courtney, see Otto Folin to Simon Flexner, April 29, 1909, folder 22, box 7, RG 450.1 Scientific Staff, biographical, Rockefeller University Archives, RAC; for B. Barker, see W. T. Sedgwick to L. Emmett Holt, February 12, 1906, folder 25, box 2, RG 450.1 Scientific Staff, biographical, Rockefeller University Archives, RAC.
8. The estimate of length of service of male scientists is based on data in Appendix III of Corner, *History of Rockefeller* (n. 3 above), 588–95.
9. On Pittman, see Rossiter, *Women Scientists* (n. 2 above), 230; information about women's post-Rockefeller careers is culled from RG 450.1 Scientific Staff, biographical, Rockefeller University Archives, RAC, and from entries in J. McKeen Cattell and Jaques Cattell, eds., *American Men of Science*, 5th ed. (New York, 1933); Jaques Cattell, ed., *American Men of Science*, 8th ed. (Lancaster, PA, 1949).
10. On the organization of the Institute, see Simon Flexner, "Sketch of the First Twenty-Five Years of The Rockefeller Institute for Medical Research," box 1, RG 534U, Rockefeller University Archives, RAC; on ranks of technicians, see for example, the list of Alexis Carrel's staff in folder 2, box 2, RG 450.C232, Rockefeller University Archives, RAC.
11. The women whose appointments contradicted Flexner's rules during his term as director were Louise Pearce, Rebecca Lancefield, Alma Hiller, and Lillian Baker. The quotation is from Rivers, *Life in Medicine* (n. 6 above), 83.
12. Rivers suggests that William Henry Welch influenced Flexner to hire Sabin, (n. 6 above), 83; the minutes of the Board of Scientific Directors show that Pearce's promotion was on the agenda; see volume for 1929, RG 110.2, Rockefeller University Archives, RAC.
13. A well-known example of the segregation of women into technical work is the employment of women "computers," at the Harvard College Observatory in the 1890s, to perform the calculations necessary for classifying stellar spectra; see Rossiter, *Women Scientists* (n. 2 above), 53–5; on the question of scientist vs. technician, see also Naomi Oreskes, "Objectivity or Heroism? On the Invisibility of Women in Science," *Osiris* 11 (1996): 87–113.
14. Flexner correspondence, folder 19, Rufus Cole Papers, American Philosophical Society (hereafter APS), Philadelphia, Pennsylvania.
15. Simon Flexner to Carl Ten Broeck, February 18, 1933, folder "personnel," box 24, RG 210.3, Rockefeller University Archives, RAC.
16. The story of how René Dubos' career was launched in the Institute's lunch room is told in Carol L. Moberg, "Friend of the Good Earth," *Research Profiles No. 34* (summer 1989), The Rockefeller University Public Information Office. Material on the politics of lunch is located in folder 2, box 4, RG 210.3, Rockefeller University Archives, RAC.
17. Lunchroom etiquette in the 1960s, personal communication with Mary Jeanne Kreek; on uniforms, see Lillian E. Baker to Mr. Flinn, February 14, 1947, also personal communication with Mary Jeanne Kreek.
18. Women as well as men could be guilty of discrimination. Marian Irwin made the comments about the women technicians: "too good looking," Marian Irwin to Edric Smith, May 27, 1927, folder "Marian Irwin Osterhout correspondence," box 1, RG 450 Os 7, Rockefeller University Archives, RAC; "cause no difficulties," Marian Irwin to Edric Smith, May 31, 1927, folder "Marian Irwin Osterhout correspondence," box 1, RG 450 Os 7, Rockefeller University Archives, RAC; quotation from Tom Rivers, in Rivers, *Life in Medicine* (n. 6 above), 82.
19. Simon Flexner to Miss Marguerite Thomas, February 25, 1918, correspondence, Simon Flexner Papers, APS, microfilm copy at RAC.
20. See R. L. Duffus and L. Emmett Holt Jr., *L. Emmett Holt: Pioneer of a Children's Century*, (New York, 1940), 203, 209.

21. On Baker, see for example, S. Josephine Baker, *Fighting for Life* (New York, 1939); and Marian S. Taylor, folder 31, box 30, RG 450.1 Scientific Staff, biographical, Rockefeller University Archives, RAC; on Anna Williams, see "Anna W. Williams, Scientist, is Dead," *New York Times*, 21 November 1954; the Rockefeller Institute awarded research grants from its establishment in 1901 until 1917.
22. On Flexner, see for example, George W. Corner, "Simon Flexner," in *Dictionary of Scientific Biography*, ed. Charles Coulston Gillispie (New York, 1972), 5: 39–41.
23. Flexner's correspondence with M. Carey Thomas is in the Simon Flexner Papers, APS, microfilm copy at RAC; James Thomas Flexner, *An American Saga: The Story of Helen Thomas and Simon Flexner* (Boston, 1984).
24. Simon Flexner, "The Scientific Career for Women," *Scientific Monthly* 13 (August 1921): 97–105; Simon Flexner to M. Carey Thomas, July 24, 1934, Simon Flexner Papers, APS, microfilm copy at RAC.
25. James T. Flexner, *American Saga* (n. 23 above), 241–3.
26. "A man is preferred," Simon Flexner to Professor Henry Sherman, April 27, 1922, folder 18, box 2, RG 450.1 Scientific Staff, biographical, Rockefeller University Archives, RAC; Alice H. Armstrong to Dr. Bernard Lupinek, February 24, 1927, folder 5, box 2, RG 450.1 Scientific Staff, biographical, Rockefeller University Archives, RAC.
27. Evelyn B. Tilden to Dr. Koide, July 17, 1983, Tilden folder, Rockefeller University Archives on-campus office.
28. For "If I carried. . . .," see Evelyn Tilden to Simon Flexner, n.d., folder 20, box 31, RG 450.1 Scientific Staff, biographical, Rockefeller University Archives, RAC; For "When Dr. Flexner. . . .," Evelyn B. Tilden to Dr. Koide, July 17, 1983, Tilden folder, Rockefeller University Archives on-campus office.
29. For "It is a relief. . . .," see n.d., folder 20, box 31, RG 450.1 Scientific Staff, biographical, Rockefeller University Archives, RAC; on Tilden, see also her obituary in *Albuquerque Tribune*, October 24, 1983.
30. Folder 10, box 26, RG 450.1 Scientific Staff, biographical, Rockefeller University Archives, RAC; Lisa Connolly, "Ida Rolf," *Human Behavior* 6 (May 1977): 17–23.
31. Folder Irene McFaul, box 18, RG 210.3, Rockefeller University Archives, RAC.
32. On the relationships of private lives to scientific careers, see Abir-Am and Outram, *Uneasy Careers* (n. 2 above); Helena M. Pycior, Nancy G. Slack, and Pnina G. Abir-Am, eds., *Creative Couples in the Sciences* (New Brunswick, NJ, 1996); Bert Hansen, "Public Careers and Private Sexuality: Gay and Lesbian Lives in the History of Medicine and Public Health," unpublished manuscript.
33. On Clara Meltzer, see Corner, *History of Rockefeller* (n. 3 above), 57, 59, 118; also John Auer's obituary, "Dr. John Auer, 73, Educator, Is Dead," *The New York Times*, 2 May 1948. On Dorothea Smith, see folder 27, box 28, RG 450.1 Scientific Staff, biographical, Rockefeller University Archives, RAC; also J. McKeen Cattell and Jaques Cattell, eds., *American Men of Science* (Easton, PA: 1933), 1033.
34. The most thorough biography of Rebecca Lancefield is Maclyn McCarty, "Rebecca Craighill Lancefield," *Biographical Memoirs* (Washington, DC, 1987), 57: 227–46.
35. The press release issued by the Rockefeller University on Marian Irwin's death states that she was the first woman National Research Council (NRC) fellow, Marian Irwin Osterhout Correspondence folder, box 1, RG 450 Os 7, Rockefeller University Archives, RAC; about 5 percent of NRC fellowships were awarded to women. Margaret Rossiter argues that, statistically, it was twice as difficult for women to receive these fellowships than men. See Rossiter, *Women Scientists* (n. 2 above), 269–72.
36. First quotation is from Simon Flexner, April 30, 1929, Marian Irwin Osterhout Correspondence folder, box 1, RG 450 Os7, Rockefeller University Archives, RAC; on Osterhout, including his illness, see L.R. Blinks, "W.J.V. Osterhout," *Biographical Memoirs* (Washington, DC, 1974), vol. 44, which also suggests that Irwin and Osterhout's affair had prompted his divorce, the stress of which in turn brought on his heart trouble; on Institute policy against employing scientific couples, see Simon Flexner to Mr. Debevoise, June 1, 1933, folder, box 1, RG 450 Os 7, Rockefeller University Archives, RAC; on anti-nepotism rules more generally, see Rossiter, *Women Scientists* (n. 2 above), 195–7.

Chapter 11

Hideyo Noguchi, the Pursuit of Immunity and the Persistence of Fame: A Reappraisal

Aya Takahashi

Associate Professor, International Student Center, Hokkaido University, Sapporo-shi, Hokkaido, Japan

> *... if he had to go, what a magnificent death he met, standing alone on the firing line, exposed to the attack of a million foes in the form of contagion, and yet calmly, quietly analyzing his enemies, that with his last breath he might, if possible, discover means of vanquishing them, for the sake of succeeding generations.*[1]

Dr. Hideyo Noguchi is one of the greatest and most beloved medical scientists in modern history, well-known both for his earnest pursuit of immunology and tragic death in Africa in 1928. His historical popularity is shown by the publication, all over the world, of numerous newspaper articles, academic essays, and monographs about his life and work in the seventy-two years since his death.[2] These publications lament his early death, extol his scientific achievements, and praise his unique, respectable personality. The number of memorials erected to him also suggests that Noguchi is seen as a public figure: the Hideyo Noguchi Memorial Museum in Fukushima recognizes 144 busts and statues of Noguchi in the world;[3] and many institutes and buildings are named in memory of Noguchi in North America, Africa, Latin America, and Japan.

This international medical celebrity was based at the Rockefeller Institute for Medical Research (RIMR) from 1904 until his death in 1928. As suggested by the presence of his bust among those of the founder and early RIMR contributors, such as John D. Rockefeller Sr. and Simon Flexner, now at the present Rockefeller University, he was one of the key players in RIMR, which was emerging as a world center for fundamental medical research in the early twentieth century.[4] After his death in 1928, the Rockefeller Foundation's annual report included his portrait and an obituary at its beginning with the notice: "[i]n the death of Dr. Noguchi . . . the Rockefeller Institute [has lost] one of its most eminent scientific workers and most charming and deeply respected members."[5]

Theoretically, the reputation of a scientist is based on the indisputable scientific value of his or her work and achievements. However, this does not seem to apply in the case of Hideyo Noguchi. In his memorial address, Theobald Smith of the RIMR stated, "[t]he most impressive thing in Noguchi's scientific career was his marvellous industry."[6] Noguchi is, indeed, remembered less often as the bacteriologist who made the landmark findings upon which our present knowledge of immunity developed than for his incredible diligence, never-ending efforts, and self-sacrifice for the eradication of deadly infectious diseases. In fact, unlike several of his colleagues at the RIMR he was not awarded a Nobel Prize, and his findings were often criticized by his fellow scientists, causing controversy in bacteriological circles. Moreover, historical assessments of his work do not credit many of his claims. On what is this image of Noguchi as a great scientist based?

All who have read a biography of Noguchi would agree that his tragic death was inseparable from the image of this historic figure. When he died suddenly of yellow fever on an expedition to Accra, Ghana, newspapers reported his death using dramatic phrases in their headlines, such as, "Martyr for Science" and "Builded [sic] on Heroism."[7] Indeed, drama is the most important literary feature of his biographies. Gustuv Eckstein's *Noguchi*, an early Noguchi biography, is exciting because it depicts numerous events and happenings in international settings. As the *New York Times Book Review* wrote in 1931, Eckstein's book combines "the drama of life and the drama of science in one."[8]

Undoubtedly, Noguchi's discoveries and accomplishments have historical importance in the development of immunology. However, it seems that the image of Noguchi, or his "historical representation," was created and developed by the time and space in which he lived and is separate—although not completely—from his scientific achievements. Akira Nagai, who has analyzed Japanese biographies of Noguchi, argues that Noguchi's popularity is not based on his discoveries: unlike Pasteur and Koch, Noguchi was not a maestro in science, but he just kept up with the times. Nagai believes that the secret of his popularity was less his academic excellence than his outstanding "craftsmanship," which apparently made him close to common folks.[9] Nagai's study of Japanese literature on Noguchi suggests that his popularity could be influenced by the public image of Noguchi that was disseminated by publications and other means. This essay attempts to dissect the Noguchi myth from international perspectives, examining his biographies, looking at what happened around his death, and showing how people's memories of Noguchi were created.

A Great Man's Life from Sociohistorical Perspectives

Social historians have been reexamining descriptive stories of great men and women for the last two decades in attempt to combine their sociohistorical analyses of these outstanding individuals with mainstream studies of history. In so doing, they can locate a genius or exceptional individual in his or her own society, recognizing the political, economic, and cultural environments surrounding them. When the social factors, which are often overshadowed by superhuman abilities and talents, are considered, we can find these individuals' real historical importance as shown by some studies. Shirley Roberts's *Sophia Jex-Blake* and Monica E. Baly's *Florence Nightingale and the Nursing Legacy* are examples of such analyses in the social history of medicine.[10]

A critical analysis of the life and work of famous people is also useful for exploring major historical issues. Susan E. Lederer's study of Noguchi's luetin experiment and the antivivisection movement in America vividly describes his difficulties with raging antivivisectionists and conflicts between them and the RIMR. In doing so, she discusses public uncertainty about nontherapeutic research necessary for scientific advance in early twentieth-century America. Using relatively abundant material on Noguchi and the RIMR, she succeeds in revealing awkward relations between the general public and scientists who in their opinion were contributing to the national development.[11] The presence of the great man Noguchi in this historical issue made possible an excellent academic analysis of the interaction between scientists and lay people possible.

Thanks to Noguchi's historical popularity, a number of letters and documents relating to him remain, and we know his life story relatively well. However, as stories of great men are often presented as their triumphant histories, Noguchi's personal histories also tend to praise his outstanding skills and respectable personality. This essay will focus not on his greatness, but on the meaning of his extraordinary life to society. If the representation of Noguchi is examined by referring to contemporary circumstances, we will be able to rediscover the sociohistorical significance of his work, and also, to contribute to the discussion on the expected role of scientists in the early twentieth century.

Early Life of Noguchi

In most biographies of Noguchi, his dramatic life begins in unfortunate settings, which usually make an effective prelude to his triumphs as a scientist later in life. Seisaku Noguchi (later Hideyo) was born to a poor family in the Aizu district of northeastern Japan in 1876, during the period when Japan was striving to catch up with the Western "Great Powers." His father, who was supposed to be the main provider for his farming family, was an unreliable man: he earned little, drank a lot, and failed to take his responsibility as the head of the house. In fact, he hardly provided enough income to support his family. Compared with the drunken father, the mother, Shika, was an extraordinary woman. She raised two sons (including Seisaku) and a daughter by farming in place of her unreliable husband and doing men's work in nearby villages for the family's subsistence. Her diligence was legendary. Neighbors appreciated her industriousness and offered to lend a hand from time to time. In the strained circumstances of a rural family and in the presence of a great mother, Seisaku Noguchi's saga begins.[12]

Noguchi's poor childhood was dealt an additional blow by a tragedy. When Seisaku was two years old, he fell into the fireplace and severally burnt his left hand. Having little means to buy medicine or to have her son's injured hand treated by a rural doctor, Shika devoted herself to nursing him day and night. However, the burnt hand, which now became like a wooden rod, was of no use and made it impossible for Seisaku to become a farmer. His only means of escape from poverty was to climb the social ladder and become a white-collar worker by studying. Thus, although it was unusual for the child of a poor farmer to seek his future by schooling, Shika expected it of him. Seisaku's strong will to strive for academic excellence was due to and nurtured by his physical handicap and the psychological burden caused by his deformed hand.[13]

Seisaku's supermother is always presented as a significant part of the Noguchi saga. In fact, Noguchi biographies written in English as well as Japanese usually devote many pages to his mother, with his father mentioned only as an aside. In the Hideyo Noguchi Memorial Museum, the international center for Noguchi memorials, one entire showcase is dedicated to letters, photographs, and other items related to Shika, whereas there is a tiny number of exhibits relating to his father.[14] Shika had to be spotlighted in Noguchi's life because her toughness and industriousness have been considered the secret behind Noguchi's extraordinary diligence shown later in his research. Moreover, the official biography by the Hideyo Noguchi Memorial Association describes Shika as a "pious, strong-willed, and grateful woman," and states, "Hideyo Noguchi's perseverance, diligence, strong will and the rest of his personality were probably inherited from his mother."[15]

Seisaku's life changed after he met a local educator, Mr. Sakae Kobayashi, who offered financial support to the Noguchi family for his studies and took the economic and spiritual role of foster father for Seisaku for the rest of his life. Kobayashi's support made Seisaku's secondary school education possible. Under Kobayashi's guidance, Seisaku's own academic efforts brought him first place at his graduation. By that time, the disfigured fingers of his left hand had been surgically, if not completely, reconstructed by Dr. Kanae Watanabe, who had returned from Germany with the latest medical knowledge. Having been impressed by Dr. Watanabe's work, Seisaku decided to become a medical doctor and began working as an apprentice in Dr. Watanabe's clinic in Aizu Wakamatsu.[16]

During Seisaku's apprenticeship, he worked seriously, slept little, and taught himself medical subjects as well as German and English in the time between his tasks during the day and under the moonlight. After three years of self-study, he went to Tokyo to take the licensing examinations to become a medical practitioner. Immediately after his arrival in Tokyo, he passed the first part of the licensing exam with flying colors. Under the care of Dr. Morinosuke Chiwaki, a lecturer at the Takayama Dental College in Tokyo, Seisaku studied at the Saisei Gakusha, then the only private and liberal medical school in Japan, to prepare for the second part of the exam. He passed it within six months—a feat considering that excellent medical students usually took three years to pass the exam.[17]

In 1898, Mr. Kobayashi gave Seisaku a new name, Hideyo, meaning "winning fame in the world." In the same year, Hideyo Noguchi accepted a position at the Kitasato Institute for the Research of Infectious Diseases, which was not only a Japanese center for medical research but also an internationally renowned center for bacteriology. He worked as an assistant among elite Japanese scientists, many of whom had graduated from the medical school of the Imperial University of Tokyo. It would have been natural that he developed his wish to study abroad for the chance to make remarkable achievements and fulfill his desire to be a distinguished scientist: in the Kitasato Institute, he hardly had enough animals to experiment on; and more importantly, he could not exceed his seniors with their Imperial University of Tokyo degrees, because of the Japanese social practice of respecting seniority and conservatism in academia.[18]

Young Noguchi was treading a thorny path. However, his early life was the important period in which he developed his discipline and mental toughness. Flexner mentions in his obituary for Noguchi in 1929, "Mr. Kobayashi is said to have told Noguchi that his three main assets in life arose from his physical deformity, his poverty, and his stubborn will."[19] Not only did the description of his struggles in early days make an effective contrast to his success later but it was the source of his industriousness, which was an important quality for him to become an eminent scientist.

Noguchi's encounters with those who had offered him financial, educational, and psychological support are also the significant features in his biographies. In fact, the rural boy from the impoverished peasant family could not have dreamt of becoming a doctor without their help. Isabel Plesset named her biography of Noguchi *Noguchi and His Patrons*, because Noguchi's relationships with various individuals form the core of his saga. In the United States, his encounters with a few reliable individuals, indeed, became vital to his survival in a foreign country, but "Noguchi's long struggle with adverse conditions in Japan" made his early days in the U.S. no great hardship.[20]

Noguchi's Life and Work in the United States: Light and Shade

As we have seen, Noguchi's strong personality and ability to make incredible efforts are core components of his scientific excellence. Without them his life would not have become a heroic saga. If the combination of the personal and scientific aspects of his life is important for the image of Noguchi, we now need to examine the latter. Focusing on his scientific achievements, on which his reputation as a distinguished bacteriologist was based, the next section will attempt to show the extent of his academic contributions to contemporary science by reviewing some studies of Noguchi's work.

Noguchi arrived in Philadelphia in December 1899 and presented himself to Flexner, for whom he had worked as an interpreter during the latter's visit to Japan the previous year. For Flexner, however, it was an unexpected re-encounter. Flexner soon learned that Noguchi was penniless and had no one to rely on in America except for him. Managing to find financial support for him, Flexner found Noguchi a research theme—snake venoms—and an excellent supervisor, Weir Mitchell. Noguchi did not waste this miraculous chance to demonstrate his abilities. Research on snake venom, which disintegrates human hemolysis, was considered significant in immunology as well as pathology. Beginning by reading and reviewing the massive amount of existing studies on the subject, Noguchi submitted a 250-page review of the studies to Flexner in only two months. Under Mitchell's sympathetic supervision, his research had been accomplished: he was able to present a paper with Mitchell at a conference of the National Academy of Science held in Washington later that year. This was followed by the publication of his first paper in the U. S., "Snake Venom in Relation to Haemolysis, Bacteriolysis, and Toxicity" in 1902.[21] His achievements were recognized by the University of Pennsylvania, which gave him a position of assistant in 1902 and awarded him a Master of Science in 1907. His pursuit of immunity in toxic snakes continued in Woods Hole and Denmark, and later at the RIMR. He wrote twenty papers and a chapter of a medical text on this subject, and in 1909, his first monograph *Snake Venoms*, was published by the Carnegie Institution of Washington.

In 1904, Noguchi joined the newly founded RIMR at the invitation of the Institute's director, Simon Flexner, and worked in his laboratory. With Flexner's guidance and support, and working in Flexner's laboratory, Noguchi displayed his talent. By 1913, his remarkable contributions to bacteriology had been recognized by distinguished medical scientists such as Friedrich von Müller and Paul Ehrlich. As a result, he was promoted to the highest rank, member of the Institute, in 1914. By the time of his death, he had conducted research in a variety of fields at RIMR, publishing more than 200 papers on such achievements as the pure cultivation of the syphilitic organism, *Treponema pallidum*; the cultivation of the globoid bodies in poliomyelitis, the introduction of a skin test for syphilis; and the isolation and cultivation of the causative agent of yellow fever, *Leptospira icteroides*.

However, Noguchi's career at the RIMR was not entirely triumphant progress. For example, although Noguchi's snake venom research resulted in a detailed monograph, his eventual contributions to the field on this subject were limited. Noguchi's colleague at RIMR, Paul Franklin Clark, states in his article on Noguchi in 1959 that the studies by Mitchell and E. T. Reichert were "probably more important than those of Flexner and Noguchi," although he admits the "detailed descriptions of hemolysis produced by venoms and of the specific damage to the endothelium of blood vessels resulting in edema and hemorrhage were . . . the more significant contributions of Flexner and Noguchi."[22] Clark also mentions that in 1908, A. Calmette gave credit to Henry Sewall of the University of Michigan for the first preventive inoculation against snake venom (1887), although Calmette "expressed appreciation of the well organized work of Flexner and Noguchi."[23] These statements suggest that Noguchi's method was certainly appreciated as credible, but his findings were not necessarily the most beneficial to the advancement of immunology.

Trachoma, on which Noguchi worked from 1905, was also one of his well-known subjects of study. Despite his allegedly successful investigation of the cause of the disease, Charles Snyder mentions the scientific limitations of Noguchi's findings on trachoma. In May 1927, Noguchi presented his work at the American Medical Association Section on Ophthalmology and announced that he had succeeded in isolating the microorganism causing trachoma and in producing lesions in monkeys with it. As his claim had already been accepted by the five most prominent ophthalmologists in the country, who had visited Noguchi's laboratory at the RIMR and reviewed his work, his presentation was accepted with enthusiasm. Noguchi's announcement was initially believed to be a great discovery, because other investigators confirmed his work, but, more importantly, because he had already been recognized as the world's greatest microbe hunter. However, there were increasing questions on *Bacterium granulosis* (now known as *Noguchia granulosis*), with which Noguchi had allegedly produced trachoma.[24] Eight years after Noguchi's announcement, the etiologic agent in trachoma was proved to be a virus, not *Bacterium granulosis*.

As for the cultivation of "globoid bodies," which was based on Noguchi's assumption that viruses could grow in bacteriological media containing no living cells, it was also one of the research problems that Noguchi could not solve. George W. Corner mentions that Noguchi was shown findings contradictory to his own on the nature of viruses—they were "obligatory parasites upon living cells"—by his colleague, Thomas M. Rivers, at the RIMR in 1926. Noguchi did not respond to Rivers, whereas Flexner is reported to have said, "[t]his is a free country, Rivers; you must publish what you think is right."[25] After Noguchi's death, Flexner defended Noguchi's research for a long time until his claim was finally and completely discredited. As for Noguchi's work on rabies, Plesset finds that even "Flexner and Smith had both been doubtful of his work."[26] Moreover, Noguchi's work from 1916 on the cultivation of the organism causing Rocky Mountain Spotted Fever is known to have accomplished little. He did not fare any better in his research on Oroya fever and *verruga peruana* in the 1920s.

It was also difficult for Noguchi to get confirmation from his fellow scientists regarding his findings on *Treponema pallidum*. He began his attempt to cultivate Schaudinn's spirochete in 1905, already attempted unsuccessfully by other scientists. Noguchi inoculated rabbits, setting up "hundreds of culture tubes filled with many kinds of nutritive media," and sampling "the cultures on thousands of microscope slides."[27] As a result of his mass work, he thought that he had succeeded in cultivating *Treponema pallidum*. However, no one could follow his procedure and confirm Noguchi's result.[28] Although we do not know whether his cultivation was the work of a genius that no other scientist could replicate, or merely a wrong result, his claim could not be accepted.

Having reviewed some critical studies of Noguchi's major scientific achievements, it is clear that the results of many of his scientific endeavors were not necessarily objects of indisputable appreciation. Even his final voyage to Accra was an attempt to prove his disputed findings on yellow fever. In these circumstances, it would not be a surprise that there were whispers of his having committed suicide when he became a victim of yellow fever.[29] The aim of my critical evaluation of Noguchi's research and accomplishments is not to criticize the dead, but to show that his substantial scientific reputation was limited by enormous pressures and significant criticisms. He was never comfortably settled on the throne of bacteriological science.

In the Pursuit of Immunity

In terms of the interests of nation–states, Noguchi easily earned a good reputation and was lauded by them. He worked for several countries investigating the causes of deadly diseases. It is well-known that he was awarded a number of decorations and medals by countries such as Ecuador, Mexico, and France for his contributions to their strategic interests. His expedition to Ecuador in 1918 as a member of the Rockefeller Foundation (RF) yellow fever commission under Dr. W. C. Gorgas was one of his representative international contributions. Having been appointed a commission member for the RF's major public health program, Noguchi was, as usual, able to produce a positive result almost immediately. About a month after his arrival, he announced having found a spirochete in Guayaquil yellow fever, calling it *Leptospira.* It was what Gorgas had predicted, and Noguchi successfully answered his expectations. He thought that Guyaquil yellow fever was the "local manifestation of Weil's disease," the organism of which he had allegedly identified. Thus, a vaccine made from the culture that allegedly contained the yellow fever organism was used to inoculate military recruits. However, it must be mentioned that Dr. Mario Lebredo, the Cuban yellow fever specialist on the commission, warned Noguchi against his easy judgment on "yellow-fever cases."[30]

Considering the deadly disease as having been conquered by Noguchi, the Ecuadorians, who had wished to keep him for their country, "showered him with compliments and honors; gave him a gold medal, and appointed him an honorary senior surgeon with the rank of colonel." [31] In fact, the excitement the Ecuadorians showed over Noguchi's alleged discovery is understandable. The work of the Rockefeller commission had attracted their attention since the eradication of the deadly disease was significant in countering their rapidly decreasing population of healthy soldiers.

The strong hope of the Ecuadorians was suggested by their reception of the Rockefeller commission. When its members arrived, they were greeted with courtesy and enthusiasm by the city of Guayaquil and the entire country of Ecuador. Although their trip was planned secretly, they were welcomed by the delegates of the government, city, and the university on their arrival at the station. The city provided good hotel rooms for them, while the board of health constantly rendered every effort to facilitate their work at the Yellow Fever Hospital. The members of the commission met the president of Ecuador, the ministers, and other authorities.[32] For the Ecuadorians, conquering the disease was not another step in scientific advance, but the national hope of a poor state.

In 1923, Noguchi went to Salvador, Brazil, to identify the cause of Brazilian yellow fever. He wanted to confirm his findings that the cause of yellow fever was *Leptospira icteroides*, intending to dispel all scepticism towards his announcement. He was stationed at the Oswaldo Cruz Institute at the Federal University of Bahia, where he was received with courtesy and welcomed by distinguished scientists in Brazil.[33] During his short, three-month stay, his usual, intensified research was apparently successful in identifying *Leptospira icterohemorrhagiae* in yellow fever patients. His demonstration before the entire medical school of the university convinced them of his claims. His "success" perhaps added some more prestige to his reputation and enhanced the Brazilians' admiration for him. As a result, the Faculty of Medicine of the University voted for Noguchi's "brilliant and valuable scientific findings" on the *Leptospira icteroides* responsible for yellow fever, and his laboratory at the institute was named Laboratorio Doctor Noguchi.[34] The news pleased not only his colleagues at the RIMR and his patron, Simon Flexner, but also Wickliffe Rose and Frederick Russell of the International Health Board, of the RF. The successful outcome of Noguchi's work was thought to end all controversy so far as his yellow fever findings were concerned.[35]

Noguchi has been treated as a hero in Brazil since his research visit to the country. A relief of Noguchi can be found next to that of Oswaldo Cruz, the founder of the Fundação Oswaldo Cruz, in the library of the Federal University of Bahia, and a portrait picture of Noguchi and a plate bearing the inscription "Laboratorio Prof. Noguchi" still hang in the laboratory where Noguchi conducted his research. Noguchi seems to have been a popular social figure as well.

Takumi Yoshimizu, who researched Noguchi's legacy in Brazil found a "Noguchi Street" in Rio de Janeiro among the Roosevelt, Churchill, and Kennedy streets. He also found Noguchi's biography in a series of Portuguese-language biographies of famous people, such as Mussolini, Hitler, and Roosevelt. Moreover, it must be mentioned that there is a park named after Noguchi in Saõ Paulo, which was opened in 1967.[36]

Noguchi's efforts to solve the riddles of science directly and indirectly provided a hope for several people suffering from health problems. If his efforts ended without complete success, those who had wished for the discovery of the causes of diseases tormenting or killing them believed that he was right, or wished to thank him for his endeavors. His trachoma work was, indeed, one of his most gratifying efforts for the blind. On the death of Noguchi, Lewis H. Carris, managing director of the National Society for the Prevention of Blindness, appraised his work on trachoma as "extremely valuable" in efforts for the prevention of blindness. In 1928, Carris must have known that Noguchi's claim was in question, but he argued that it was important that "his work be continued."[37] People knew that the riddles of science could not easily be solved. Therefore, it was important for them to have scientists work on them and be concerned with their sufferings. Noguchi's real achievements were more than just scientific achievements, they were humanitarian achievements because they drew public attention to several important diseases. The humanitarian side of Noguchi's achievements was supported by his industriousness and enhanced by his early and tragic departure from this life.

International Grief

As mentioned earlier, after the world heard of Noguchi's sudden death, several newspapers and journals printed various obituaries of him. From the Noguchi material kept at the Rockefeller Archive Center alone, it can be seen that his death was, at the very least, grieved by North Americans, Latin Americans, Africans, Russians, and Japanese.[38] He was an international medical celebrity, and his early departure was very much regretted by the world. After his death, portrait photos of him were requested from the RIMR by numerous institutions and publishers for educational uses.[39] However, the historical facts need to be further explored to isolate the key factor in his popularity.

The shocking news of Noguchi's premature death circled the world immediately, and a flood of condolences poured into the RIMR in the form of letters and cables from not only his friends and academic colleagues but also from foreign associations and embassies of the countries for which he had worked.[40] In the obituaries from national institutions, he was described not merely as a bacteriologist with distinguished achievements but also as a respected international citizen who had made remarkable scientific efforts for the improvement of human beings.

On the one hand, official and honorary condolences from the governmental and national organizations expressed their gratitude for the contributions of an outstanding scientist and regretted the loss of the man who had sacrificed himself for the sake of their problems. On the other hand, the moving obituaries written by his scientific colleagues praised not only his work but also his extraordinary efforts and his loving personality. J. E. McCartney noted in his comments on the previous issue's tribute to Noguchi in *The Lancet* that

> He did not seek the many honors he attained, but loved science for its own sake. A keen thinker, a hard worker, a great scientist, his loss will be mourned by those who

> knew him, not only as a scientist but as a friend. . . . [Noguchi] was a "mass" worker, and I think that was one of the secrets of his great successes.[41]

Clearly, Noguchi was beloved not because he was an academic genius, but because he had pushed himself beyond normal human endurance in his search for the causes of disease. Thus, his life became "an inspiration to every conscious physician," according to the *New York State Journal of Medicine*.[42] The human side of Noguchi's reputation was enhanced after his premature death and tended to "marginalize" or almost erase critical comments on his work that had been around before his death. This protected reputation of Noguchi was often combined with the official gratitude shown by the national institutions in the form of condolences and honors. It was the RIMR that supported and kept the conceptual side of Noguchi's fame alive after death through a material representation.

Hideyo Noguchi's Death and RIMR

RIMR had an enormous influence in enhancing Noguchi's fame after death. It carefully managed affairs related to the late Noguchi, such as the transfer of his body and personal effects from Africa, including his research findings and papers. It was Flexner's office that dealt with and organized most Noguchi-related matters by answering inquiries about and making necessary arrangements for Noguchi after his death. Mrs. Noguchi relied on her husband's associates on almost every occasion, including finding out how to deal with a writer who was interested in Noguchi. For his funeral, the RIMR carefully considered the selection of a funeral agent, the wording of the invitations to the funeral, and a list of individuals and organizations to be invited. The Institute even helped with the financial settlement for Mrs. Noguchi to support her in bereavement. Nothing proceeded without Flexner's knowledge.[43]

RIMR also dedicated and arranged for Noguchi's grave. It selected the burial site, the boulder used as a tombstone, and the design of the plate on the boulder to match the pioneering character of Noguchi and the remarkable scientific achievements that he made in a foreign country. The unusual, natural gravestone to the memory of a Japanese scientist, which was similar to that of Thomas Edison, was erected in Woodlawn Cemetery in New York City. This was carried out neither by Mrs. Noguchi nor his close friends in the U.S. or family in Japan, but by Flexner, who consulted specialists,[44] predicting that the grave would be visited by many people for the long time to come. He was "eager to do the right thing as nearly as possible."[45] Flexner's sympathetic involvement in the management of Noguchi's death was obviously beyond his usual responsibility as director, suggesting his profound friendship with Noguchi and the RIMR's appreciation of Noguchi's contributions to the Institute.

A memorial service for Hideyo Noguchi, held by the New York Academy of Medicine on December 20, 1928, was also handled by Flexner and RIMR. The service was apparently initiated by the academy, but the RIMR practically orchestrated it. The service was meant to provide an opportunity to mourn for those who were not invited to Noguchi's funeral. Thus, invitations were sent to RIMR's Board of Scientific Directors and Trustees, 125 scientific staff, 20 administrative officers, 46 former scientific staff, and 128 persons outside of the Institute, in addition to the members of the Academy of Medicine and of the Harvey Society. George Vincent of the RF, William H. Welch, chair of the Scientific Directors of the

RIMR, and Flexner were key speakers. They spoke eloquently of how much Noguchi had contributed to the Institute through his bacteriological research, and emphasized all the risks he had taken.[46]

Flexner's obituary, or "biographical sketch of Noguchi," was one of the significant pieces of writings that influenced other obituaries and short biographies of Noguchi. In his bereavement, Flexner assembled data on Noguchi's life in Japan, and afterwards, and wrote a brief biography that became the most-cited source for Noguchi biographies. The sketch began with Noguchi's poor childhood and encounter with his foster father and patron Mr. Kobayashi, and his education in medicine—suggesting that he almost taught himself—all of which were described in sentimental tones. Noguchi's outstanding industriousness in the laboratory and his eagerness in research were depicted as having led to his remarkable achievements.[47] Flexner sent a reprint of his article whenever he received an inquiry about Noguchi's life and work from those who either had a personal interest or intended to write about Noguchi. RIMR itself also significantly contributed to creating the popular image of Noguchi. Copies of his serious portrait with his arms crossed, which was favored by Flexner, were frequently enclosed in replies to inquiries about Noguchi.

The RIMR certainly wished to present Noguchi as one of the representative members of the RIMR and a distinguished bacteriologist. Although, keeping Noguchi's memory favorable was a significant task for the Institute, Flexner wished for more than that. He wanted others to remember Noguchi as he knew him. As Flexner's memorial speeches and sketch suggest, he wished Noguchi to be known as an extraordinary individual as well as a great scientist. Even in 1957, Corner in preparing a history of the RIMR found it difficult to make an objective assessment of Noguchi, because there were still people alive who could be offended if he questioned "Dr. Flexner's wisdom" regarding Noguchi's image.[48] Noguchi's life and death were understood by the people and organizations in the ways they wished, and RIMR and Flexner were the architects and propagators of the Noguchi myth.

The Real Triumph of Noguchi

Noguchi's final efforts did not end in triumph: his *Leptospira* was not the cause of yellow fever. However, as William Welch argued, although Noguchi did not find the cause of the disease, his work could still be regarded as an important contribution. Welch remarked,

> It is a contribution of the first importance if it demonstrated that cases of infectious jaundice are, according to the best clinical traditions, occurring in epidemics diagnosed as yellow fever. It is of the utmost importance also to know whether the *Leptospira* is a secondary invader in yellow fever. Nor were Noguchi's studies limited solely to the spirochete. I would simply like to emphasize on this occasion that, whatever the issue as to the relationship of the spirochete to yellow fever, Noguchi's work constitutes a very important contribution to the subject.[49]

Welch's statement implies the core feature of scientific advance: truth is at the summit of thousands of indirect contributions and false results. However, in the early twentieth century, when imperialist competition was intense, and tropical diseases were spreading in developed countries, great expectations were placed on science. Although Noguchi lived and died in the closing period of the early and often unproductive stages of bacteriology, his efforts were never wasted, as his work was scientifically recognized as representing necessary steps towards the discovery of truth.

However, this was not the only reason for Noguchi's historical reputation. At Noguchi's memorial service, Mr. Setsuzo Sawada, the counselor of the Japanese Embassy stated,

> The rapid expansion of knowledge in recent years, its marvellous application to human life, the emergence of new problems—economic and social, national and international—all these have combined to engage the serious consideration of thoughtful men throughout the world who bear the responsibility for the welfare of mankind. In the face of such a situation, science, one of the main supports of modern civilization, has to play a still more important role than in the past in meeting the growing needs of humanity, and its further progress is most earnestly desired. In such a time as this, the irreparable loss we have sustained in the death of Noguchi is much lamented.[50]

His address suggested the important interaction between society and scientific advance, at the center of which stood Noguchi. In Japan, his biography was, in fact, used to teach moral lessons in a national reader for elementary school children in the 1930s and 40s. For the imperialist state, it was important to propagandize that even overseas one could devote himself to the emperor by conveying the message to the Japanese that studying science and making efforts would lead to developing the country and displaying Japanese abilities to the world.

In the view of a global society that interestingly valued academic knowledge, the scientific martyr became identified as one, perhaps necessary stage in the progress of human beings toward the divine. In international grief, questions as to Noguchi's real scientific achievements became trivial since the modern world had seen failures and successes in science; instead, the circumstances of Noguchi's life and death seemed to confirm the importance of effort, as well as successful results, in research.

The research for this essay was supported by the Rockefeller Archive Center Residency in the History of Basic Medical Research Program.

Endnotes

1. John D. Rockefeller Jr. to Mrs. Noguchi, May 22, 1928, folder 458, box 46, Rockefeller Boards series, Record Group 2 Office of the Messrs Rockefeller (OMR), Rockefeller Family Archives, Rockefeller Archive Center, Sleepy Hollow, New York (hereafter RAC).
2. Noguchi also appears in American biographical encyclopedias see *Who's Who in America*, 1 (Chicago, 1943), 902; *Dictionary of American Biography*, (London, 1934), 13:542–3; *Who's Who in American Medicine* (New York, 1925), 1111–2.
3. There is a display listing the locations of Noguchi's busts and statues in the Hideyo Noguchi Memorial Museum, Fukushima, Japan.
4. As for the foundation and early days of the RIMR, see John Ensor Harr and Peter J. Johnson, *The Rockefeller Century* (New York, 1988), 66–70; and The Rockefeller University, *From Institute to University: A Brief History of the Rockefeller University* (New York, 1985), 1–8.
5. The Rockefeller Foundation, *The Rockefeller Foundation Annual Report* (New York, 1928), 3–4.
6. Theobald Smith and William H. Welch, *Hideyo Noguchi, 1876–1928*, The Bulletin of the New York Academy of Medicine, second series, vol. 5 (New York, 1929), 879.
7. I found more than 100 newspaper and magazine clippings from all over the world in the Administrative Correspondence, folder 3, box 3, RG301.2, newspaper material, 21–31 May 1928, and folder 4, newspaper material, 1 June 1928–31 December 1947, Rockefeller University Archives, RAC.

8. Administrative Correspondence, 17 May 1931, folder 4, box 3, newspaper material, Rockefeller University Archives, RAC.
9. Akira Nagai, "Noguchi Hideyo den wa naze yomare tsuzukete kitanoka," *Hon no hanashi*, 3/2 (1997), 16–7.
10. Shirley Roberts, *Sophia Jex-Blake: A Woman Pioneer in Nineteenth-Century Medical Reform* (London, 1993); Monica E. Baly, *Florence Nightingale and the Nursing Legacy* (London, 1986).
11. Susan Eyrich Lederer, "Hideyo Noguchi's Luetin Experiment and the Antivivisectionists," *Isis* 76 (1985): 31–48.
12. Noguchi biographies usually include the description of his poor family. See, for example, Tsurukichi Okumura, *Noguchi Hideyo* (Tokyo, 1933), 49–53; Gustav Eckstein, *Noguchi* (New York, 1931), 4–9; and Isabel R. Plesset, *Noguchi and His Patrons* (New Jersey, 1980), 25–7.
13. See Okumura, *Noguchi* (n. 12 above), 53–71. He details Seisaku's diligence, which brought him academic awards in primary schools.
14. There are also a number of items relating to Shika, but there is only one photo of Hideyo's father shown in a small exhibit room in the Hideyo Noguchi Memorial Hall (Tokyo).
15. The Hideyo Noguchi Memorial Association, *Hideyo Noguchi* (Tokyo, 1992; reprint).
16. As for Noguchi's childhood, see the biographies stated in endnote 12, and The Hideyo Noguchi Memorial Association, *Noguchi Hakushi to Sono Haha* (Tokyo, 1959).
17. Noguchi Memorial Association, *Noguchi* (n. 15 above), 12–6; Plesset, *Noguchi* (n. 12 above), 38–44, 45–8.
18. Okumura, *Noguchi* (n. 12 above), 186–7, 205.
19. Simon Flexner, "Hideyo Noguchi," reprint from *Science*, 69 (1929): 7. The same biography appears in *The Smithsonian Report for 1929* (Washington, 1930), 595–608.
20. Flexner, "Hideyo Noguchi," 8.
21. The Hideyo Noguchi Memorial Association, *Noguchi Hideyo to dokuja* (Tokyo, 1990), 9–11; Simon Flexner and Hideyo Noguchi, "Snake Venom in Relation to Haemolysis, Bacteriolysis, and Toxicity," *Journal of Experimental Medicine* 6 (1902): 277–301; Plesset, *Noguchi* (n. 12 above), 75.
22. Paul Franklin Clark, "Hideyo Noguchi, 1876–1928," *Bulletin of the History of Medicine* 33 (1959): 4.
23. Ibid, 4–5.
24. Charles Snyder, *Our Ophthalmic Heritage* (London, 1967).
25. George W. Corner, *A History of the Rockefeller Institute: 1901–1953 Origins and Growth* (New York, 1964).
26. Plesset, *Noguchi* (n. 12 above), 146.
27. Corner, *History of Rockefeller* (n. 25 above), 112.
28. Ibid, 113.
29. Noguchi's distress behind his African expedition is analyzed by Claude E. Dolman, "Hideyo Noguchi (1876–1928): His Final Effort," *Clio Medica* 12 (1977): 131–45.
30. Plesset, *Noguchi* (n. 12 above), 180–1.
31. Ibid, 190.
32. The Hideyo Noguchi Memorial Association, *Collection of Hideyo Noguchi's Letters Written in English and German* (Tokyo, 1989), H. Noguchi to S. Flexner, 18 September 1918, 146–9.
33. Plesset, *Noguchi* (n. 12 above), 233.
34. A. Vianna to H. Noguchi, 12 January 1924, folder 14, box 1, RG450 N689, Rockefeller University Archives, RAC.
35. W. Rose to S. Flexner, 17 March 1924, folder 14, box 1, RG450 N689; F. Russell to S. Flexner, 6 February 1924, Rockefeller University Archives, RAC.
36. The Hideyo Noguchi Memorial Association, *Brazil no Noguchi Hideyo* (Tokyo, 1986), 6–18.
37. "Eulogizes Dr. Noguchi," 23 May 1928, newspaper cuttings, folder 4, box 4, RG450 N689, Rockefeller University Archives, RAC.
38. Published biographical materials, RG450 N689, folder 7, box 5, Rockefeller University Archives, RAC.
39. For example, the University of Oklahoma requested Noguchi's photo for a volume, *Health Science and Health Education: For College Students and Teachers in Training*. W.A. Buice to the Rockefeller Institute, 26 May 1928, folder 1, box 4, RG450 N689, Rockefeller University Archives, RAC. The American Book Company needed his photo to complete their pictures of scientists: American Book Company to the Rockefeller Institute, 25 March 1932, folder 2, box 4, RG450 N689, Rockefeller University, RAC.

40. See condolences from individuals, association, and embassies in Rockefeller University Archives, folder 1, box 3, RG450 N689.
41. J. E. McCartney's article in *The Lancet*, 2 June 1928, 1144, filed in folder 7, box 5, RG450 N689, Rockefeller University Archives, RAC.
42. Obituary appeared in *The New York State Journal of Medicine* 28 (1928): 788, folder 7, box 5, RG450 N689, Rockefeller University Archives, RAC.
43. See various correspondence between S. Flexner, E. Smith, W. Flinn, M. Noguchi, J. D. Rockefeller Jr., and other individuals in folders 2–4, box 3, RG450 N689, Rockefeller University Archives, RAC.
44. Coolidge to S. Flexner, 15 May 1929; S. Flexner to Coolidge, 20 May 1929; Coolidge to S. Flexner, 5 June 1929, folder 5, box 3, RG450 N689, Rockefeller University Archives, RAC.
45. S. Flexner to Coolidge, 7 February 1930, folder 5, box 3, RG450 N689, Rockefeller University Archives, RAC.
46. Correspondence between S. Flexner, E. Smith, and M. Noguchi, and invitation cards for the memorial service from 27 November–20 December 1928, folder 3, box 3, RG450 N689, Rockefeller University Archives, RAC; typescript minutes of the "Memorial Services to Dr. Hideyo Noguchi," 20 December 1928.
47. Flexner, "Hideyo Noguchi."
48. G. Corner to P. Clark, 15 October 1957, folder 2, box 4, RG450 N689, Rockefeller University Archives, RAC.
49. Smith and Welch, "Hideyo Noguchi" (n. 6 above), 885–6.
50. Typescript minutes of the "Memorial Services to Dr. Hideyo Noguchi," folder 3, box 3, RG450 N689, Rockefeller University Archives, RAC.

Chapter 12

Gasser, Bronk, and the International Network of Physiologists

Abigail Tierney

IBM Consulting Services, North Harbour, UK

This essay is part of an ongoing project, comparing the methods of collaboration and the patterns of innovation within four highly successful English research schools. My central premise is that the scientific achievements of the Nobel Laureates leading these schools—Charles Scott Sherrington, Henry Hallett Dale, Archibald Vivian Hill, and Edgar Douglas Adrian—are best understood in terms of their relationships with other entities; i.e., collaborators, funding bodies, institutions, instruments, research programs, reward systems, students, and teachers. In particular, my research has shown that the scientific innovations produced in the four research schools were dependent on collaboration between young and enthusiastic scholars, who brought their unique skills and personalities to bear on the scientific achievements of the English laboratories. Fortunately, fruitful cooperation was not confined to England, but continued to flourish once these overseas workers returned home, obtained positions, and shared their English physiology experience with their colleagues and students. Therefore, everyday contact, face-to-face discussions, and shared spaces and facilities, are not always the appropriate categories by which to study collaboration. Instead, this international community was constituted through correspondence networks, exchanges of personnel, international campaigns, and shared hobbies. I examine these forms of collaboration, while also providing an account of the motivations that drove the collaboration and a description of the achievements that it produced.

The international network of physiologists functioning during the first half of the twentieth century was large and diverse, and it would therefore be impossible to cover each of the members in turn, as what would be gained in breadth would be lost in depth. I choose to focus on the American scientists Detlev Wulf Bronk (1897–1975) and Herbert Spencer Gasser (1888–1963), examining the significant positions they held within the network of physiologists. The rationale for focusing on these two scientists comes from studying the correspondence network cultivated by the community of physiologists. These collections of letters, which represent the chief form of communication within the network, portray Bronk and Gasser as dominant members of the international community, as well as highly visible participants among the American contingent of physiologists. Bronk and Gasser were able to wield such influence because they functioned within the national and international community of scientists on several different levels. First, their forays into this community began when they spent time as junior researchers in England during the 1920's, which gave them the opportunity to court powerful patrons and forge lifelong friendships. Second, on their return to America they both gained important positions within the American scientific community, which enabled them in time to reciprocate the patronage they had received in England. Third, as leading figures at the Rockefeller Institute for Medical Research, they were able to facilitate financial support and recruit personnel from English laboratories. Finally, as active members of the American scientific elite they were able to promote neurophysiology at an international level through the National Academy of Sciences, as foreign members of the Royal Society, and in Gasser's case as a Nobel Laureate.

Gasser and Bronk are also an obvious choice on international collaboration because their career paths and personal objectives overlapped on many occasions; from their early decisions to specialize in electrophysiology, through to the time that they both spent in Hill's laboratory in England, and finally as members of the Rockefeller Institute. Their common experience led to shared ideals, and provided several opportunities for combining their influence in the support of neurophysiology. Although Bronk and Gasser provide the backbone for this essay, the roles played by other members of the American community of physiologists provide the essential social and institutional framework that enabled Bronk and Gasser to act as facilitators in international collaboration. It is hoped, therefore, that focus on these two influential members of the network will reveal the more general nature of the dynamics at play in the international community.

The analysis will draw on the rich collection of primary sources housed at the Rockefeller Archive Center. These include the personal and scientific papers of Gasser and Bronk, which contain several hundred letters, written over a fifty-year period, from Gasser and Bronk to members of the international network, and it is this invaluable correspondence that provides the main framework for this research. The contents of these letters make apparent the unique personalities and strong friendships among the international network of physiologists. These core documents will be examined in combination with the personal correspondence of other physiologists, including Adrian, Dale, Hill, Ragnar Granit, and Alexander Forbes, and the official papers pertaining to the Rockefeller Foundation and the Rockefeller Institute. I hope that this blend of personal and institutional communications will provide complementary insights into the institutional factors that ran alongside Gasser and Bronk's personalities, in fostering an atmosphere of collaboration and cooperation in neurophysiology during the twentieth century.

Gasser and the Reciprocity of Patronage

Gasser in London

The regular visits and collaborations between physiologists during the first part of the twentieth century broke down the idea of laboratory-based communities and instead created a vision of a single community based on an international network of scientists. Although international exchanges of physiology personnel occurred in the nineteenth century, it was primarily between European laboratories, in particular Britain, Germany, and France. In science generally, there were several factors that facilitated a shift towards transatlantic collaboration—not the least of which was the improvement in transportation—along with the growth of wealthy foundations, which were increasingly willing to fund scientific research in foreign countries. In the case of physiology, the improvement in transatlantic transportation as a result of the steam ocean liners, and the influence of the Rockefeller Foundation, were the chief catalysts for encouraging a cooperative relationship between English and American physiologists.

Herbert Gasser began to develop his position within the international community in 1923, on the advice of Abraham Flexner, and traveled to Europe on a grant provided by the Rockefeller Foundation. While in Europe he spent two years in England, where he worked in London with Dale and Hill. Although Gasser was only twenty-five, he arrived in London with knowledge of cutting-edge experimental techniques and in possession of sought-after instrumentation techniques, which he had developed with Joseph Erlanger at Washington

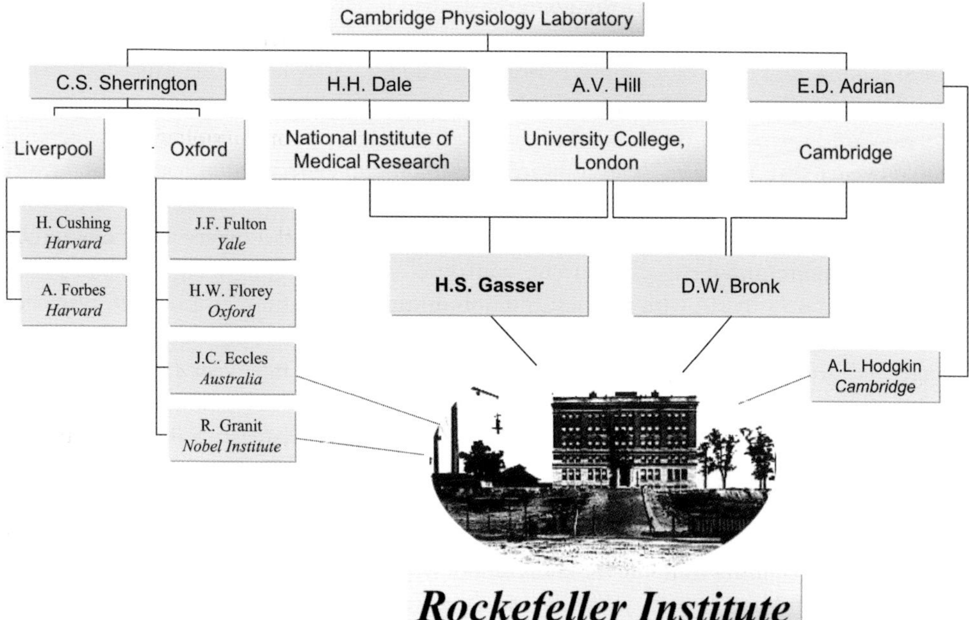

The exchanges of personnel between England and America that are specifically mentioned in this essay.

University in St. Louis. Specifically, Gasser brought his designs, along with the necessary technique, for constructing a triode valve amplifier and a cathode ray oscillograph, which could be used to analyze the exact form of the amplified action potential of nerve fibers. Although there are no contemporary letters recording Gasser's stay in London, the collaborative research with Dale and Hill are recorded in three papers, with Gasser as coauthor.[1] It is also clear from his later reminiscences that he found the experience inspirational, not least because his time with Dale and Hill perfectly combined his interests in pharmacology and electrophysiology. Almost twenty years after leaving London, Hill wrote to congratulate Gasser on his Nobel Prize and recalled the "faculty" and "quick energy" Gasser had demonstrated during their collaboration. In fact, Gasser was working at University College of London when the news of Hill's Nobel Prize broke and on comparing his feelings on these two occasions, Gasser told Hill, "I am sure I was much more thrilled and excited then than I was this year."[2] The good impression that Gasser made on Dale and Hill, in particular his willingness to share ideas and expertise was rewarded with lifelong patronage and friendship from these two influential physiologists. This three-way friendship and collaboration provided the foundation for one of the most productive and influential branches of the international community.

Gasser at the Rockefeller Institute

After leaving London, Gasser returned to Washington University, where he continued to work with Erlanger. However, in 1931 he accepted an appointment in New York as professor of pharmacology at the Cornell University Medical College, and five years later took over from

Simon Flexner as director of the Rockefeller Institute. These successive appointments reflect the growth of Gasser's reputation as a research scientist. As director of the Rockefeller Institute, Gasser was now able to reciprocate the patronage he had received from his London colleagues.

By 1936, Hill had recognized Gasser's increasing profile in American science, and wrote to ask him if he would support a young British physiologist, Alan Hodgkin. This story began when Hill decided to send Gasser a copy of Hodgkin's PhD thesis on the nature of the process of conduction in nerve. In this letter, Hill described Hodgkin as a "very remarkable person" and told Gasser that "It is almost an unheard-of thing for an experimental scientist at Trinity to get a fellowship in his fourth year, but this youngster has done it."[3] Gasser had "great fun" reading Hodgkin's dissertation, and told Hill that he was very pleased to see a first-class study of nerve mechanics to challenge the current "romantic" attitudes in physiology.[4] Gasser passed a copy of Hodgkin's thesis, with its "beautiful job of experimentation" to Erlanger, primarily because he felt that Hodgkin's interests were closer to the work being done in St. Louis.[5] Erlanger had already heard of Hodgkin's work a year earlier during a visit Hill had made to St. Louis. Therefore, Erlanger read the thesis "with the keenest of interest," and wrote a letter to Hodgkin expressing his admiration at how well he had executed an attack on a fundamental problem, although he questioned the conclusions Hodgkin had reached.[6] Such encouragement from the two leading American physiologists in his chosen area of nerve physiology, provided Hodgkin with a great confidence boost. In his autobiography, Hodgkin recalls having read the majority of the papers from the St. Louis school while reading for his Part II of the Natural Science Tripos, and here he was, just two years later, gaining Erlanger's encouragement.[7]

This initial contact between Hodgkin and the two distinguished American physiologists also served to open doors into the American scientific community for Hodgkin. The extended circle of patronage, as initiated by Hill, culminated in 1938 when Hodgkin spent a year with Gasser at the Rockefeller Institute. Hodgkin's autobiography provides an extremely vivid picture of his year spent at the Institute. It is clear from letters written at the time, and his own reminiscences, that he felt his own work benefited greatly from the new techniques he learned, the different scientific cultures he experienced, and the collaborative work he completed. For example, shortly before leaving for New York, Hodgkin had the good fortune of isolating a single nerve fiber in a crab, but was having difficulty adapting his electrical technique to ensure accurate recordings of this new preparation. However, he gratefully acknowledges the help he received almost immediately after arriving at Rockefeller Institute, when Dr. Toennies, the electronics expert in Gasser's group, pointed out that it was essential to use a cathode follower when attempting to record rapid changes in a high-resistance preparation, such as a single nerve fibers. Hodgkin also compared the informality of the Cambridge laboratory, in which "You might easily start in a bare room and have to build most of the equipment yourself"[8] for which you would be expected to pay the bill, with the facilities at the Rockefeller Institute:

> I have an "office" room to write in and a lab with superb equipment which looks much more professional than anything you see in Cambridge. I shall run to seed because so far I have had extremely little "gadgeteering" to do. Everything was put into order when I arrived and if anything goes wrong I ask the advice of Toennies. I think it is a pity that there aren't more highly trained assistants in Cambridge. Of course it is much easier to have them in a lab which is entirely devoted to research than in one which has a great deal of teaching to do. But still, there is room for a great deal of improvement in Cambridge.[9]

In this letter, Hodgkin touches on the different benefits provided by the cultures of the two institutes. In Cambridge, Hodgkin felt there was much to be said for the "do-it-yourself" mentality concerning scientific instruments, which enabled the scientist to stay in touch with the rapid developments in instrumentation, at a time when such developments were a crucial part of the ongoing progress in physiology. On the other hand, Hodgkin was grateful for the plentiful supply of instruments, along with the technical assistance he received during his year at the Rockefeller Institute. This allowed Hodgkin to concentrate on pure research than instrumentation; in another letter home he declared that "Work is much more peaceful here than in Cambridge; this is partly due to the excellent apparatus and partly the fact that most of the 'bottle-washing' is done by assistants."[10]

According to his own assessment of his year at the Rockefeller Institute, Hodgkin concluded that although he had missed the "easy casualness" of Cambridge, researching at the Rockefeller Institute had helped to turn him "from an amateur scientist into a big professional scientist."[11] Also commenting on the success of the year, Gasser told Hill, "We have enjoyed having Hodgkin here this year tremendously. You are to be congratulated on having him: he should make his mark in physiology on an all-time basis."[12] Hodgkin was to fulfil Gasser's expectations when he was awarded the Nobel Prize in 1963. Hodgkin's year at the Rockefeller Institute brought the collaboration between Hill and Gasser full circle; a circle which began in 1925 when Gasser collaborated with Hill at University College, and was completed in 1938 with Hodgkin's year of research at the Institute. This example of the exchange of personnel highlights the importance of informal connections in scientific patronage for determining the success of the international community.

A. V. Hill and the Rejuvenation of Biophysics at University College of London

Gasser was appointed to the Executive Committee of the Rockefeller Foundation on April 6 1938, and seven years later he had another opportunity, this time as a member of the Executive Committee of the Rockefeller Foundation to repay Hill for the faith he had shown in Gasser as a young researcher. At the end of World War II, Hill wrote to David Nachmansohn, another physiologist at the Rockefeller Institute, describing the "extremity of disrepair" that had befallen his laboratory and his lost faith in the scientific spirit.[13] The first step on the road to restoration was taken in 1945, when Hill applied to the Rockefeller Foundation for a grant to improve facilities and to fund a research school in biophysics. In October of the same year, the Executive Committee approved the application, and awarded the sum of $72,900 to University College for research in physiology under the direction of Hill.[14] It is difficult to assess the importance of Gasser's support in determining the success of this application, as Hill had two other supporters in the Foundation, Alan Gregg and D. P. O'Brien. However, this does not mean that Gasser's support was not instrumental, particularly because of the relative risk associated with the grant, given that Hill was fifty-nine and close to retirement. The fact that Gasser did play a part in the decision-making process is clear in a letter he wrote to Hill:

> Last month it was my privilege in the Executive Committee of the Foundation to join in helping to get going your laboratory at University College. What an all round pleasure![15]

Although the grant only offered a solution to the material problems facing post-war physiology at University College, there is evidence to suggest that it also restored Hill's crushed spirit. There can be no doubt that Hill owed some of this revival to Gasser, and the network within which the friendship functioned.[16] It is clear both from his own European travels and from the enthusiastic manner in which he encouraged Hodgkin, that Gasser believed international collaboration to be an important factor in scientific innovation. The same belief in international collaboration lay behind the stipulation in Gasser's will, that his Nobel Prize money should be used to fund an exchange of personnel in neurophysiology, between the Rockefeller Institute and the Karolinska Institute in Sweden.[17] This benefaction also helped to ensure that the Rockefeller Institute would continue as a center of collaboration within the international community of physiologists.

Bronk the Scientific Statesman

Bronk in England

Bronk's lifelong devotion to English physiology, and the beginning of his fascination with all things English, began in the 1928 when he traveled to England on a National Research Council Fellowship to work with Adrian and Hill.[18] Like Hill's acceptance of Gasser three years earlier, Adrian did not offer Bronk a place in the Cambridge laboratory for benevolent reasons, but because he recognized that Bronk's training in physics and physiology would be ideal for the electrophysiological research currently underway in the Cambridge school. It is also evident from their correspondence that Adrian hoped Bronk would bring some fresh blood into the laboratory at a time when Adrian found himself "devoid of ideas."[19] To provide context to this self-deprecation, it is important to recall that Bronk's application came during the period when Adrian was doubting his own ability, particular his attempts to prove that the all-or-none law applied to motor nerve fibers, as well as sensory fibers.[20] Although Gasser had officially been based with Hill and Dale during his research trip, he had nevertheless been able to provide Adrian with help during a crucial stage in the motor nerve research. In his memoir of Bronk, Adrian recalled how it was Gasser who had provided him in 1926 with the technical assistance to reassemble the Keith Lucas apparatus with the addition of Gasser's three-stage amplifier. The fact that Adrian refers to Gasser's inspirational assistance within his memoir of Bronk, further indicates his hope that Bronk would provide a similar catalyst for progress and he was not disappointed.[21]

One of the main obstacles preventing any progress in motor nerve experiments was the difficulty of restricting the number of fibers being tested. However, with Bronk's assistance, Adrian was able to develop dissecting techniques for isolating a small number of fibers adjacent to the muscle. As a direct result of this technique, Adrian successfully showed that nerve impulses in motor fibers had the same frequency as sensory fibers. Adrian was undoubtedly impressed with the work Bronk did during his stay in Cambridge, describing him as "a real collaborator and not just a learner."[22] In 1932, when Adrian was jointly awarded the Nobel Prize with Sherrington, he wrote to Bronk thanking him for the role he had played in the prize-winning research. In these few lines, it is clear that Bronk had enabled Adrian to rediscover his own confidence, along with his passion for physiology:

> I don't forget what a great deal I owe to your visit in 1928, not merely in the scientific way: you have the power of diffusing encouragement which has meant a great deal to me & to Hill as well in our work & in our life too.[23]

The researchers in Cambridge had been so successful that Bronk chose to put off his departure for London on several occasions. However, once he arrived in November 1928, he found that he could be just as happy working at University College. Once again, he brought the mathematical and technical skill of a physicist combined with his experience as a physiologist. Hill and Bronk were both among the first self-confessed biophysicists, and in this new and emerging discipline they turned to each other for help and inspiration. This mutual support and inspiration, which shaped Bronk and Hill's friendship was clearly reflected in Bronk's decision to model his laboratory at the newly established Johnson Foundation, on the intellectual framework he had experienced at University College.

Bronk had found his research with Adrian and Hill extremely rewarding; and like Gasser before him, this visit to England signaled the beginning of many long lasting friendships with the British physiologists and their families. However, before these friendships could flourish, Bronk would have to find his own place within the international network of physiologists and within the American scientific community. It will become clear, that as Bronk's reputation within the American and international scientific community grew in stature, the balance of power between himself and his English patrons leveled out. However, the correspondence between Adrian and Bronk always contained a tone of admiration and worship on Bronk's part. Bronk's admiration for Adrian seemed based on a feeling of disbelief that he was deserving of such friendships, and it is probably this disbelief that guarded against complacency, and provided the unwavering impetus for Bronk to continually foster and cultivate his position within the network throughout his life.

Bronk at the Rockefeller Institute

As far back as 1934, Hill had given Bronk the following warning: "If you are not careful, with all your love of organizing things for other people, you will be a College President before long."[24] In this prophetic statement, Hill foresaw that Bronk's personality destined him for jobs within the politics of science. When Bronk became president of the Rockefeller Institute in 1953, he was in the perfect position to promote and follow his love and skill for organizing and motivating scientists. Like Gasser before him, Bronk also utilized his position at the Rockefeller Institute, and his connections with the Rockefeller Foundation, to support international collaboration in science.

The Rockefeller Institute had been founded as a center for research in the biomedical sciences. In 1935, Gasser took over from Simon Flexner as director of the Institute, and he continued to promote the research ideals on which the Institute had been founded. The reasons Gasser maintained the status quo are twofold. First, Gasser was primarily a laboratory scientist rather than an administrator; and second, his tenure spanned the Great Depression and World War II, when funds for further development were tight and enthusiasm for development scarce.[25] In comparison, in 1946 when Bronk was invited by Gasser to become a member of the Institute's Board of Directors, he came on board with a vision. This vision centered on transforming the Rockefeller Institute into a university that would specialize in graduate teaching as well as research. In 1953, Gasser retired and Bronk accepted the position of president of the Institute, from which time he began in earnest to implement his proposed reforms, which became known amongst his friends as "Det's great educational experiment."[26]

While at the Rockefeller Institute, Bronk inaugurated an important program that provided visiting fellowships for eminent foreign scientists. This fellowship program was part of Bronk's larger vision for transforming the Rockefeller Institute into a center of excellence for graduate teaching. Bronk had always believed that he had greatly benefited from his year researching in England, where he had worked side-by-side with leading scientists from different countries, who had different techniques, attitudes, and traditions. Therefore, he resolved to establish fellowships that would bring foreign scientists to the Institute, where they would deliver a course of lectures to graduate students, and if they had sufficient time, they could use the Institute's facilities to continue research of their own. This program was based on the same ideals that had provided the rationale for the Johnson Foundation Lectures, which Bronk had inaugurated twenty years earlier. As with the Johnson Lectures, Adrian immediately became one of Bronk's primary candidates for a visiting fellowship.[27] Another member of the international network of physiologists who benefited was the Swedish scientist, Ragnar Granit, who was a visiting lecturer at the Rockefeller Institute on an annual basis for ten years. Such a scheme succeeded in raising the international profile of the Institute and also provided Bronk with the opportunity to spend time with his old friends, while returning the hospitality and kindness he had received during his visits to Europe.

Bronk's motivation for such a program was undoubtedly, as he told Adrian, to further "the unity of institutions of higher learning throughout the world."[28] By 1950, Bronk had all but given up laboratory research and had become a full-time scientific statesman, as evidenced by his election as president of the National Academy of Sciences in 1950. The fellowship program at the Rockefeller Institute gave Bronk an opportunity to put into practice his vision for the unity of science through international collaboration and cooperation. On a more personal level, such a fellowship program also provided Bronk with the prospect of interacting with his European colleagues on an annual basis, for holding dinner parties, organizing sailing holidays, and hosting weekends at the family home in Media. An indication that such a program promoted friendships as well as collaboration is clear in 1957, when Adrian lectured at the Institute and was strongly encouraged by Bronk to bring his wife Hester. When Adrian was elected a Trustee of the Rockefeller Institute in 1961, Bronk had found yet another vehicle for bringing Adrian to the Institute on an annual basis. In the way of persuasion, he told his mentor, "You started me in science; now help me build this unique graduate university."[29]

The importance Bronk gave to his role as a host to European scientists is reflected in the President's house that was built for him and his family at the Rockefeller Institute. As well as being a beautiful family home with a spectacular view of the East River, it also had an impressive reception area suitable for entertaining a hundred guests, and several independent guest suites where Bronk could accommodate visiting friends and colleagues.[30] The idea behind the President's house was probably the Masters' lodges that Bronk had visited in Cambridge and in a similar way its architecture highlights "a very particular set of relations."[31] In the case of Bronk, his active lobbying for this house to be built, along with his input into its design, highlights his changing relationship with science. At the heart of one of the leading scientific research institutions in the world, Bronk decides to build a house for entertaining guests, rather than a research laboratory. This signifies Bronk's career shift from a scientific researcher to a scientific statesman.

Nobel Network

The broader research project, out of which this essay grew, began as an attempt to explain why so many Nobel Prizes were awarded to British neurophysiologists and their students during the

Herbert Spencer Gasser, Director of the Rockefeller Institute for Medical Research, 1935–1953, in 1936

Detlev Wulf Bronk, President of the Rockefeller Institute/University, 1953–1969, in 1962

twentieth century. The answer, so far, draws on a complex interaction of the individual creativity of Nobel Laureates on the one hand, and social and institutional factors facilitating collaboration and innovation on the other hand. This essay, which focuses on the transatlantic network of patronage and collaboration provides a further insight into the reasons for the high number of Nobel Laureates among this community. Specifically, Gasser and Bronk's correspondence points to two possible reasons for the high percentage of Nobel Laureates. First, the correspondence network testifies that the Nobel population within the international community of physiologists became a self-perpetuating elite. This was possible because once a physiologist received a prize, he became a permanent nominator for future prizes. Moreover, many members of the physiological community occupied important academic positions and were also called upon to nominate potential prize winners. Second, Gasser and Bronk's letters show how an international network provided its members with a large pool of resources on which to draw, both materially and socially, in order to facilitate scientific innovation.

Nobel Prize nominations are understood to be confidential, but there is evidence on more than one occasion that within this community of physiologists possible winners were discussed and vigorous campaigning took place. Correspondence with John Fulton in the year leading up to the award of Gasser's prize shows that Fulton and David Lloyd wrote a proposal for the Nobel Prize in which they nominated Gasser. When Fulton and Lloyd informed Gasser of their intentions, he treated the information with characteristic modesty, claiming that fortune had placed him in a very favorable position.[32] On receiving the Nobel Prize, Gasser continued to take a modest yet beguiling stance, and in the following quotation he beautifully captures the mixed emotions that so many newly crowned Laureates face:

> Joe and Herbert, that's us. All the old faults and foibles, tempered we hope by some virtues; our affection for our old friends intensified; dazzled at the moment by standing in too much bright light, made a little humbler by our good fortune and the thought that our essays at pure research should be so rewarded, beset with mixed emotions. Thus, inadequately expressed is a picture of what it is like to get the Nobel Prize.[33]

Once Gasser became a Nobel Laureate, he gained permanent nominating rights, and in 1946, he used this privilege to nominate Ragnar Granit for a prize in Medicine and Physiology. Granit was the Swedish physiologist who had worked at the Johnson Foundation under Bronk, and had spent an extended period collaborating with Sherrington in Oxford. While in Oxford, Granit had the opportunity to forge friendships and connections with Fulton and John Carew Eccles in Oxford, and also with Detlev Bronk, who was working in Adrian's laboratory at the time. In other words, Granit was a central actor in the international network of physiologists that grew from the young researchers working in England during the 1920s. As well as nominating Granit, Gasser was also given the onerous task of producing a special report on the Swede's work for the Nobel Foundation. Gasser's admiration for Granit is clearly evident in this report, but it nevertheless took another twenty years before the campaign finally came to fruition, when Granit received the Nobel Prize in 1967.

Although not a Nobel Prize winner himself, as an important member of the American scientific establishment Bronk also joined this campaign. After meeting Granit in England, Bronk continued to foster their friendship, and in 1929, he brought Granit to work at the Johnson Foundation. It was here that Granit first collaborated with Keffer Hartline, with whom he was jointly awarded the Nobel Prize in 1967. Given the fact that Granit and Hartline had both worked at the Johnson Institute under Bronk's directorship, it is not surprising that Adrian wrote to Bronk in 1948 to ask if he would nominate Granit and Hartline for a Nobel Prize.[34]

Productive Debate

The fierce debate over the electrical versus chemical transmission of nerve impulses was led by Sherrington's student Eccles on the one side, and Dale on the other. During this debate, which spanned more than twenty years between 1921 and 1945, the chemical theory slowly displaced the previously accepted account that nerve impulses were transmitted at the synapse by electrical means. The discussions between the two opposing schools of thought were largely carried out in England, particularly within the meetings of the Physiological Society and in the pages of the *Journal of Physiology*. However, Gasser entered the fray and adopted the difficult and ambiguous role of arbiter, despite his tendency to side with the electrical theorists. The dispute is interesting in its own right, but it also provides a window through which to examine the role Gasser cultivated for himself within the international community of physiologists.

Gasser found himself drawn into the debate when Sir Charles Lovatt Evans approached Eccles in 1935, to ask if he would write an article for *Physiological Reviews* (1937) on the subject of "reflex action." Eccles felt this subject was unsuitable at present, and offered instead to produce a review on "synaptic and neuromuscular transmission." He also wrote to Gasser, who was a member of the editorial board for the journal, to inform him of his intention. In this letter, Eccles explained that "chemical mediator people have had it all their own way in the matter of reviews on this subject, e.g., Dale's various efforts, Cannon's and Loewi's articles etc. other conceptions having gone by default." Eccles believed that the time was therefore ripe for a more balanced review of the subject, demonstrating that "chemical mediators are not the whole story."[35] He obviously believed that in writing to Gasser he was writing to a fellow supporter of the electro-theory and concluded his letter with the following assertion: "There is no doubt that the position with regard to smooth muscle has to be reconsidered, and this will lead to a new outlook both on skeletal muscle and on synaptic transmission between nerve cells."[36]

This letter from Eccles put Gasser in an awkward situation because he had already commissioned two other physiologists to write a review for the same issue, but from the chemical rather than the electric point of view.[37] In the interest of fair play Gasser therefore decided that rather than having two overlapping reviews in one issue, he would bring together the various proposals in the form of a published symposium. Gasser wrote to Eccles informing him of this new plan and added that he felt a paper from Eccles "would be in a much better strategic position alongside the other two than in isolation."[38]As the chairman of this symposium, Gasser wanted to give each review a fair hearing and expressed his hope that it would be positive discussion of nerve transmission at the synapse, focusing on the synapse rather than controversial theories.[39] To achieve this, he told the various contributors that they should construct their accounts around positive rather than negative statements. More specifically, Gasser warned Lorente de Nó, a researcher from his own lab at the Rockefeller Institute and a staunch defender of the electrical theory, "not to introduce any controversial material." On the other side, Gasser insisted that Alexander Forbes, who had chemical leanings, be given the final and the longest position in the program "so that he could give a general evaluation of the situation."[40]

The proceedings of the symposium were published in 1940 as a special issue of *Journal of Neurophysiology*. Despite Gasser's attempts to foster an atmosphere of positive inquiry, he was disappointed to find out that several physiologists still felt the symposium was biased. In a letter he wrote to a colleague, Gasser berated the difficulty of discussing the subject outside the realm of controversy.[41] He also expressed his feelings of disappointment to Bronk, asking why he had been "pushed into the limelight for electrical transmission" and looking for reassurance that he "never concocted sentences in which I set myself down on one side or the other." The symposium and the published proceedings stirred up a lot of emotions and provided a catalyst for several scientists to vent their views in the public arena.

Back in London, Dale decided to write a note in *Science* clarifying several points from the chemical point of view. Gasser saw Dale's note and immediately took it as a veiled criticism of the symposium and therefore wrote an apology to his former collaborator in which he explained his original motivations for publishing the symposium. Gasser also maintained that Fulton had wrongly pigeon-holed him as one of the ringleaders of the electrical theory:

> Now the last thing that I want to be is the leader of a cult, and if I were I should want to be a "true believer." I can see a number of reasons for my reputation. One can be "the general assumption that if one is not for something, one must be against it.[42]

In his reply to Gasser, Dale assured his former collaborator that he had never suspected him of being the ringleader of the "electragonists."[43] He stated in fact, that he only ever saw Gasser as a "very cautious and judicial man of science, wishing to have all relevant facts properly put forward and considered." Gasser's willingness to listen to most arguments and take them on their relative merits provides an important part of the explanation of why he became such a crucial figure in the international community, which looked to him for guidance. For example, Gasser's support of Eccles meant a great deal to him during this period, when Eccles was feeling increasingly isolated in his own country. In November 1936, just a few weeks after Dale's Nobel Prize was awarded, and hence a particularly difficult time for Eccles and other supporters of the electrical hypothesis, Eccles wrote to Gasser, thanking him for his continued support: "Very many thanks for your letter. It cheered me up a great deal. My work falls very flat in England, and it is very encouraging to find interest in it elsewhere, especially from you, if I may say so."[44]

In the correspondence between Gasser and the participants of this debate, the vehemence with which each scientist defended their chosen theory is palpable, but so is the importance that each participant afforded to the stimulating and positive effects of such a debate between friends and colleagues. Perhaps Eccles and Fulton took some challenges to heart, but overall this debate is indicative of the mutual support the physiologists received from one another regardless of which stance they took. For example, in a letter that Eccles wrote to Dale in 1937, he told his scientific adversary that "this controversy has taught me a great deal, and I have greatly enjoyed it. In fact, I myself feel that I have grown up (physiologically speaking) under its stimulating influence."[45] It is obvious that Dale felt the same way, for when he heard in 1939, six years prematurely, that Eccles might be warming to the idea of the chemical transmission of nerve impulses, he expressed his concerns in the following letter to him:

> It will really be too bad if we are no longer able to discipline our enthusiasms, and sharpen our criticism of our own experiments, by the thought of what our friend Eccles may say, and the fear of leaving a weak link in our chain of mail, through which he may insert one of his barbs.[46]

Shared Hobbies

One important aspect of the international community of physiologists yet to be mentioned is the hobbies they shared and the pastimes they enjoyed, which helped to foster a sense of community over and above their common scientific purpose. In particular, the personal correspondence between Bronk, Hill, Adrian, Forbes, Granit, and Hartline contain hundreds of references to sailing and mountaineering. Within this international community, congresses and research trips seemed to necessitate a day sailing on the Norfolk coast in England or around Arcadia and Woods Hole in the United States. Alternatively, for those who enjoyed mountaineering, a trip would be arranged to the Swiss Alps. For example, when Bronk took a second trip to England in the summer of 1931, Adrian suggested that they spend July climbing in Europe, with the hope that they would arrive back in Cambridge with "renewed enthusiasm."[47] Although worried that he would prove "a terrible dud,"[48] Bronk succumbed to Adrian's persuasion; and as a result of this first climbing holiday, Bronk became passionate about this outdoor pursuit and the two families enjoyed many more climbing holidays together. In addition to climbing, many of the members of the international community of physiologists were avid sailors, in particular Adrian, Bronk, Granit, and Forbes. So when Granit was planning a trip to America, Bronk asked Granit if he would have time to "participate in our most important scientific activity which is, of course, the study of the sea from the deck of a small boat."[49]

What is interesting as far as this analysis is concerned, is the relative back seat Gasser occupied in these jamborees, particularly in comparison with the other members of the international community of physiologists. Adrian captured Gasser's attitude towards such active hobbies in Gasser's memoir that he wrote for the Royal Society:

> He was a charming host, sensitive and considerate and with many interests outside scientific matters. He had travelled widely and enjoyed the country and the sea, but he went there tidily dressed, with a faint air of the metropolis still about him and an entirely natural dignity enhanced by his striking figure.[50]

The hobbies and holidays shared by the members of the international community of physiologists are testaments to the personalities that were involved. This aspect of the network should therefore not be viewed separately from their scientific pursuits, but rather as an extension of the philosophy that many of these physiologists shared towards science in particular, and life in general, for throughout my primary research I have come across references to "friendship, fun and adventure."[51]

Conclusion

Through the restoration of the social and material factors facilitating scientific innovation in a transatlantic network of physiologists, I endeavored to show that the scientific achievements within this particular network of physiologists depended on the individual creativity of the "actor" combined with the social and institutional factors of the "network." Although such an analysis entails the deconstruction of Gasser and Bronk's scientific identities as promoted within the traditional context of scientific discoveries, the purpose is not to make the scientist disappear. Rather, it is hoped that by recovering the collective story of scientific achievement, a more vivid, dynamic, and multidimensional image of Gasser and Bronk has emerged. They should be remembered not only for their science but also for their managerial skills, their hospitality, their networking, and their political savvy. This essay has also demonstrated that the collaborative network was of an informal and ad hoc nature, grounded in strong personal friendships built on mutual respect and reciprocity. This informality was made possible by the relatively small size of the specialty of neurophysiology as it developed during the first half of the twentieth century. This meant that it was still possible for the scientists to know each other personally, and to visit and correspond with other on a regular basis.

One of the crucial factors allowing Gasser and Bronk to make inroads into the community of physiologists was their visits to Europe in the 1920s, where they worked with Dale, Hill, and Adrian. As young researchers, Gasser and Bronk gained the respect of these three physiologists, and the British physiology community in general, which provided them with a sound footing within the community, along with reliable and enthusiastic patrons. It was also clear that Gasser and Bronk brought very different skill sets to bear on the network. On the one hand, Gasser was accepted as a member on the basis of his scientific achievements; on the other hand, Bronk functioned as a central facilitator as a result of his administration and communication skills. However, neither scientist would have made such inroads into the community had he lacked a combination of these skills.

Early in his career Bronk had been a talented scientist, who had achieved some important scientific breakthroughs, in particular in his collaborations with Adrian and Hill. In comparison, towards the latter part of his career, Gasser became a reasonably successful administrator at the Rockefeller Institute. In other words, Bronk and Gasser were skilled scientists and adept networkers. Functioning over and above the various positions that Gasser and Bronk held in Europe and in America were their personalities. It would seem that Gasser was quiet and modest, whereas Bronk was more of an extrovert, though with a modest assessment of his own achievements.[52] As patrons and teachers within this network, their combined support and kindness to young researchers were essential in the cultivation of the community, and their modesty meant that they were never complacent, and that they consistently sought to bolster their own positions within the network. Together, these friends therefore brought the perfect combination of skills to bear on the international community; overall, their networking and collaborations go a long way towards explaining the strength of the transatlantic axis of the international network.

Endnotes

1. Archibald Vivian Hill (AVH) and Herbert Spencer Gasser (HSG), "The Dynamics of Muscular Contraction," *Proceedings of the Royal Society B* 96 (1924): 53; Henry H. Dale and Herbert S. Gasser, "The Pharmacology of Denervated Mammalian Muscle. I. The Nature of the Substances Producing Contracture," *Journal of Pharmacology and Experimental Therapeutics* 29 (1926): 53; H. H. Dale and H. S. Gasser, "The Pharmacology of Denervated Mammalian Muscle. II. Some Phenomena of Antagonism, and the Formation of Lactic Acid in Chemical Contracture," *Journal of Pharmacology and Experimental Therapeutics* 28 (1926): 287.
2. AVH to HSG, Dec 23, 1944, and HSG to AVH, Dec 22, 1944, folder 6, box 1, Record Group 302.6 Herbert Gasser Papers (HG Papers), Biographical, Rockefeller University Archives, Rockefeller Archive Center, Sleepy Hollow, New York (hereafter RAC).
3. AVH to HSG, Nov 30, 1936, folder 6, box 2, RG 302.2 HG Papers, Correspondence, Rockefeller University Archives, RAC.
4. HSG to AVH, Dec 22, 1936, folder 6, box 2, RG 302.2 HG Papers, Correspondence, Rockefeller University Archives, RAC.
5. HSG to J. Erlanger, Dec 23, 1936, folder 13, box 1, RG 302.2 HG Papers, Correspondence, Rockefeller University Archives, RAC.
6. J. Erlanger to A. Hodgkin, Jan 6, 1937, folder 13, box 1, RG 302.2 HG Papers, Correspondence, Rockefeller University Archives, RAC.
7. Alan L. Hodgkin, *Chance and Design: Reminiscences of Science in Peace and War* (Cambridge, 1992).
8. Ibid., 66–71.
9. A. L. Hodgkin to C. Fletcher, November 5, 1937, quoted in Hodgkin, *Chance* (n. 7), 91–2.
10. A. L. Hodgkin to Mrs. Hodgkin, Oct 30, 1939 [*sic* 1937?], quoted in Hodgkin, *Chance* (n. 7), 94.
11. Hodgkin, *Chance* (n. 7), 95.
12. HSG to AVH, June 14, 1938, folder 6, box 2, RG 302.2 HG Papers, Correspondence, Rockefeller University Archives, RAC.
13. AVH to David Nachmansohn, July 30, 1945, folder 130, box 15, series 401A, RG 1.2, Rockefeller Foundation Archives, RAC.
14. Oct 19, 1945, folder 130, box 15, series 401A, RG 1.2, Rockefeller Foundation Archives, RAC.
15. HSG to AVH, Nov 13, 1945, folder 6, box 2, RG 302.2 HG Papers, Correspondence, Rockefeller University Archives, RAC.
16. AVH to D. P. O'Brien, Nov 8, 1945, folder 130, box 15, series 401 A, RG 1.2, Rockefeller Foundation Archives, RAC.
17. HSG to the Rockefeller Institute for Medical Research, Nov 10, 1950, folder 7, box 2, RG 302.4 HG Papers, Subject File, Rockefeller University Archives, RAC.
18. Detlev Wulf Bronk (DWB) to AVH, May 21, 1927, folder 3, box 82, vol. 2, RG 303-U Detlev Bronk

Papers (DB Papers), Administration, Rockefeller University Archives, RAC.

19. Edgar Douglas Adrian (EDA) to DWB, Feb 6, 1927, folder 1, box 87, vol. 2, RG 303-U DB Papers, Administration, Rockefeller University Archives, RAC.
20. For further context, see R. G. Frank, "Instruments, Nerve Action, and the All-or-None Principle," *OSIRIS* 9 (1994): 208–35.
21. Edgar D. Adrian, "Detlev Wulf Bronk," *Biographical Memoirs of Fellows of the Royal Society* 22 (1976): 1–9.
22. EDA to DWB, Nov 1, 1928, folder 1, box 87, vol. 2, RG 303-U DB Papers, Administration, Rockefeller University Archives, RAC.
23. It is indicative of the pride Bronk felt in this letter that he had the original framed. EDA to DWB, Oct 30, 1932, folder 11, box 87, vol. 2, RG 303-U DB Papers, Administration, Rockefeller University Archives, RAC.
24. AVH to DWB, September 9, 1934, folder 16, box 87, RG 303-U DB Papers, Rockefeller University Archives, RAC
25. DWB to EDA, July 29, 1963, folder 2, box 87, vol. 2, RG 303-U DB Papers, Administration, Rockefeller University Archives, RAC.
26. Ragnar Granit to DWB, June 3, 1957, folder 17, box 7, RG 303.1 DB Papers, Administration, Rockefeller University Archives, RAC.
27. EDA to DWB, Dec 12, 1955, folder 1, box 87, vol. 2, RG 303-U DB Papers, Administration, Rockefeller University Archives, RAC.
28. DWB to EDA, March 3, 1956, folder 5, box 87, vol. 2, RG 303-U DB Papers, Administration, Rockefeller University Archives, RAC.
29. DWB to EDA, Nov 1961, folder 5, box 87, vol. 2, RG 303-U DB Papers, Administration, Rockefeller University Archives, RAC.
30. This description of the President's house at Rockefeller University is based on descriptions given by visiting scientists, as well as my own experience when I attended a reception at the house to celebrate the centennial of the Rockefeller University.
31. A. Dugale, "Materiality: Juggling Sameness and Difference," in *Actor Network Theory and After*, eds. J. Law and J. Hassard (Oxford, 1999), 113–135.
32. John Farquhar Fulton to HSG, Jan 4, 1944, folder 1, box 2, RG 302.2 HG Papers, Correspondence, Rockefeller University Archives, RAC.
33. HSG to W. J. Meek, Oct 31, 1944, folder 6, box 1, RG 302.6, HG Papers, Biographical, Rockefeller University Archives, RAC.
34. EDA to DWB, May 23, 1948, folder 2, box 87, vol. 2, RG 301-U DB Papers, Administration, Rockefeller University Archives, RAC.
35. John Carew Eccles (JCE) to HSG, Dec 1, 1935, folder 12, box 1, RU 302.2, HG Papers, Correspondence, Rockefeller University Archives, RAC.
36. Ibid.
37. Ibid.
38. HSG to JCE, Feb 2, 1936, folder 12, box 1, RG 302.2 HG Papers, Correspondence, Rockefeller University Archives, RAC.
39. HSG to Henry Hallett Dale (HHD), May 8, 1940, folder 9, box 1, RG 302.2 HG Papers, Correspondence, Rockefeller University Archives, RAC.
40. Ibid.
41. HSG to John Farquhar Fulton, Oct 18, 1939, folder 1, box 2, RG 302.2 HG Papers, Correspondence, Rockefeller University Archives, RAC.
42. HSG to HHD, May 28, 1940, folder 9, box 1, RG 302.2 HG Papers, Correspondence, Rockefeller University Archives, RAC.
43. HHD to HSG, June 20, 1940, folder 9, box 1, RG 302.2 HG Papers, Correspondence, Rockefeller University Archives, RAC.
44. JCE to HSG, Nov 14, 1936, folder 12, box 1, RG 302.2 HG Papers, Correspondence, Rockefeller University Archives, RAC.
45. CE to HHD, June 19, 1937, 35.25.8., 3–4, Henry Hallett Dale Papers (RS 93HD), Royal Society, London.

46. Dale to JCE, February 11, 1939, RS 93HD 35.25.13.
47. EDA to DWB, May 9, 1931, folder 2, box 87, vol. 2, RG 303-U DB Papers, Administration, Rockefeller University Archives, RAC.
48. DWB to EDA, June 18, 1931, folder 2, box 87, vol. 2, RG 303-U DB Papers, Administration, Rockefeller University Archives, RAC.
49. DWB to R. Granit, April 3, 1951, folder 13, box 7. RG 303.1, DB Papers, Correspondence, Rockefeller University Archives, RAC.
50. Edward D. Adrian, "Herbert Spencer Gasser," *Biographical Memoirs of Fellows of the Royal Society* 10 (1964): 78.
51. AVH to DWB, Aug 1961, folder 16, box 87, vol. 2, RG 303-U DB Papers, Administration, Rockefeller University Archives, RAC.
52. W. R. Amberson to HSG, April 4, 1956, and Gasser to Amberson, April 16, 1956, folder 1, box 1, RG 302.2 HG Papers, Correspondence, Rockefeller University Archives, RAC.

Selected Bibliography

Manuscript and Archival Sources

Edgar Douglas Adrian Papers, Trinity College Archives, The Wren Library, Trinity College, Cambridge.

Detlev Wulf Bronk Papers, The Rockefeller Archive Center, Sleepy Hollow, New York.

Henry Hallett Dale Papers (93 HD), Royal Society, London.

Alexander Forbes Papers, Harvard Medical School Archives, Francis Countway Medical Library, Harvard Medical School, Boston.

Herbert Spencer Gasser Papers, The Rockefeller Archive Center, Sleepy Hollow, New York.

Archibald Vivian Hill Papers (AVHL) Churchill College Archives, Churchill College, Cambridge.

Charles Scott Sherrington Papers, Physiology Library, Physiology Department, Oxford.

Primary Printed Sources

Dale, Henry Hallett. "Some Recent Extensions of the Chemical Transmission of the Effects of Nerve Impulses," in *Nobel Lectures, Physiology or Medicine: 1922–1941.* London, 1965.

Dale, Henry Hallett, and Herbert Spencer Gasser. "The Pharmacology of Denervated Mammalian Muscle. I. The Nature of the Substances Producing Contracture." *Journal of Pharmacology and Experimental Therapeutics* 27 (1926): 53.

Dale, Henry Hallett, and Herbert Spencer Gasser. 'The Pharmacology of Denervated Mammalian Muscle. II. Some Phenomena of Antagonism and the Formation of Lactic Acid in Chemical Contracture." *Journal of Pharmacology and Experimental Therapeutics* 28 (1926): 287.

Eccles, John C. "Developing Concepts of the Synapses." *Journal of Neuroscience* 10 (1990): 3769–81.

———. "The Inhibitory Pathways of the Central Nervous System." Chap. 9 in *Sherrington Lectures.* Liverpool, 1969.

Gasser, Herbert Spencer, and W. Hartree. "The Inseparability of the Mechanical and Thermal Responses in Muscles." *American Journal of Physiology* 58 (1924): 396.

Hill, Archibald Vivian. *Adventures in Biophysics.* The Eldridge Reeves Johnson Foundation for Medical Physics. Philadelphia and London, 1931.

———. *The Ethical Dilemma of Science and other Writings.* New York, 1960.

———. *Trails and Trials in Physiology: A Bibliography, 1909–1964; With Reviews of Certain Topics and Methods and a Reconnaissance for Further Research.* London, 1965.

Hill, Archibald Vivian, and Herbert Spencer Gasser, "The Dynamics of Muscular Contraction." *Proceedings of the Royal Society B* 96 (1924): 53.

Secondary Sources

Adrian, Edgar Douglas, "Herbert Spencer Gasser." *Biographical Memoirs of Fellows of the Royal Society* 10 (1964): 75–82.

———. "Detlev Wulf Bronk, 1897–1975." *Biographical Memoirs of Fellows of the Royal Society* 22 (1976): 1–9.

Bacq, Zenon M. *Chemical Transmission of Nerve Impulses: a Historical Sketch.* Oxford, 1975.

Brink, Frank, Jr. "Detlev Wulf Bronk, 1897–1975." *Biographical Memoirs of Members of the National Academy of Sciences* 50 (1979): 3–87.

Corner, George W. *History of the Rockefeller Institute: 1901–1953 Origins and Growth.* New York, 1964.

Dale, Henry H. "Autobiographical Sketch." *Perspectives in Biology and Medicine* 1 (1958): 125–37.

Davey, Lycurgus M. "John Farquhar Fulton." *Neurosurgery* 43 (1998): 185–7.

Feldberg, Wilhelm. "The Early History of the Synaptic and Neuromuscular Transmission by Acetylcholine: Reminiscences of an Eye Witness." Chap. 3 in *The Pursuit of Nature: Informal Essays on the History of Physiology.* Edited by Alan Lloyd Hodgkin. Cambridge, 1976.

———. "Henry Hallett Dale." *Biographical Memoirs of Fellows of the Royal Society* 16 (1970): 77–173.

Fenn, Wallace O. "Alexander Forbes." *Biographical Memoirs of Members of the National Academy of Sciences* 40 (1969): 113–41.

Frank, Robert J. "Instruments, Nerve Action, and the All-or-None Principle." *Osiris* 9 (1994): 208–35.

Fulton, John Farquhar. *Selected Readings in the History of Physiology.* Baltimore, 1930.

Gasser, Herbert Spencer. "Sir Henry Dale's Contribution to Physiology," *British Medical Journal* 1 (1955): 1355–6.

Grillner, Sten. "Ragnar Granit, 1900–1991," *Biographical Memoirs of Fellows of the Royal Society* 41 (1995): 184–97.

Harte, Negley B., and John North. *The World of UCL, 1828–1990.* Rev. ed. London, 1991.

Hodgkin, Alan Lloyd, "Beginning: Some Reminiscences of My Early Life (1914–1947)." *Annual Review of Physiology* 45 (1983): 1–16.

Hodgkin, Alan Lloyd. *Chance and Design: Reminiscences of Science in Peace and War.* Cambridge, 1992.

———. "Edgar Douglas Adrian." *Biographical Memoirs of Fellows of the Royal Society*, vol. 25 (1979), 1–73.

Hodgkin, Alan Lloyd, Andrew F. Huxley, Wilhelm Feldberg, William Albert Hugh Rushton, Richard A. Gregory, and Robert Alexander McCance. *The Pursuit of Nature: Informal Essays on the History of Physiology.* Cambridge, 1976.

Horwitz, Norman H. "John Farquhar Fulton." *Neurosurgery* 43 (1998): 178–84.

Hughes, Thomas Parke. *Networks of Power: Electrification in Western Society, 1880–1930.* Baltimore and London, 1983.

Huxley, Andrew F. "My First Visit to the MBA." *Physiological Society Magazine* 27, Summer (1997): 8–9.

Katz, Bernard. "Archibald Vivian Hill." *Biographical Memoirs of Fellows of the Royal Society* 24 (1978): 71–149.

Kohler, Robert E. *Partners in Science: Foundations and Natural Scientists 1900–1945.* Chicago and London, 1991.

Morell, Jack B. "Individualism and the Structure of British Science in 1830." *Historical Studies in the Physical Science* 3 (1971): 183–204.

Tansey, E. M. "It wasn't all work: Plymouth in the 1930s." *Physiological Society Magazine*, vol. 27, Summer (1997), 10–12.

———. *Sir Henry Dale and Autopharmacology: The Role of Acetylcholine in Neurotransmission*, Clio Medica, no. 33 (Amsterdam, 1995).

Thomson, Arthur Landsborough, and Medical Research Council. *Half a Century of Medical Research.* London, 1973.

Chapter 13

James B. Murphy, the Rous Sarcoma Agent, and Origins of Modern Cell Biology

Carol L. Moberg

Senior Research Associate, The Rockefeller University, New York, NY

The disease of cancer will be banished from life by calm, unhurrying, persistent men and women, working with every shiver of feeling controlled and suppressed, in hospitals and laboratories, and the motive that will conquer cancer will not be pity nor horror; it will be curiosity to know how and why.[1]

In 1995, the Rockefeller University celebrated the fiftieth anniversary of the founding of modern cell biology. The science began in 1945 with a remarkable picture, the first electron micrograph of a whole cell, and it provided convincing views of structures inside a cell that went beyond the realm of biological entities then known to exist (see Fig. 1 on p. 265). The micrograph appeared in a *Journal of Experimental Medicine* article by Albert Claude and Keith Porter, cancer researchers from the Rockefeller Institute for Medical Research, and Ernest Fullam, an electron microscopist at the Interchemical Corporation in Manhattan. Fifty years later, George Palade, a founding father of cell biology, referred to this historic micrograph as the "birth certificate" of the newborn science and called the nurturing Rockefeller environment its "cradle."[2]

If this image marked a revolution in biology, then one can argue that another micrograph taken about a year later by Claude and Porter actually changed history (see Fig. 2 on p. 266). In this micrograph of an intact cell, the conspicuous small, dark bodies that appear singly, in pairs, or in small rows are viruses. It is the first picture of a cell infected with Chicken Tumor I, known today as the Rous sarcoma agent or virus. The story of the forty-year search for the agent that causes this sarcoma rests on these microbodies; it is a story permeated with controversy and frustration. Many of these experiments took place in the laboratory of James B. Murphy at the Rockefeller Institute. Events during four formative years—1911, 1925, 1937, and 1945—show why this micrograph ended another phase of cancer research and gave modern cell biology a dramatic start.

1911, Cancer Research at Rockefeller Institute

The story began in 1911 during a brief collaboration of two pathologists, Peyton Rous and James Bumgardner Murphy. Both initially joined Simon Flexner's laboratory of Pathology and Bacteriology to study cancer. All three men were former students of the great pathologist at Johns Hopkins, William Welch, who was also president of the Rockefeller Institute's Board of Scientific Directors.

According to Welch, cells were classified as normal, tumor, neoplastic, and malignant. He also taught that the cause of cancer lay within the growth mechanisms of normal cells. Despite Welch's warning, "Whatever you do, don't commit yourself to the cancer problem," these young pathologists seemed undaunted by its challenges.[3]

Most Rockefeller Institute scientists were studying acute infectious diseases. At the time, research on chronic, degenerative diseases was considered unproductive. Cancer, in particular, was seen as too mysterious for profitable attack. Perhaps unknown and underappreciated by today's standards is that

> disgrace and a certain amount of social opprobrium were connected with cancer. It was concealed by patients and their families and by sympathetic doctors . . . there was grave doubt on the part of many—and perhaps most—doctors as to its curability.[4]

From the beginning of cancer research, tumors were studied by transplanting them into blood relatives of the species from which they came. Because this method of propagation and transmission of tumors was limited, and technically difficult, Murphy's initial task was to find other ways to keep tumors alive in the laboratory. Within a few months, he made two substantial contributions that eliminated the need to transplant tumors. He found a way to grow tumors on the embryonic membrane of fertilized eggs. In addition, he created freeze-dried or lyophilized cell-free extracts that allowed the successful transfer of the original tumor by injection.[5] Murphy's freeze-dried technique provided a second way to transmit cell-free tumors. A filtration technique was reported independently in 1892 by Dimitri Ivanovski in Russia and in 1899 by Martinus Beijerinck in Holland as a means of extracting the active agent, now known to be a virus, that causes the tobacco mosaic disease. By grinding up the malignant tissue and passing it through an earthenware filter, the cells and bacteria are held back while the ultramicrobes, or viruses, pass through.[6]

Rous used this filtration method to examine a chicken breast sarcoma and discovered a cell-free agent that seemed responsible for the tumor. Murphy's freeze-dried technique confirmed the filtration results, but Rous relegated this method to a four-line footnote in his 1911 report "A Sarcoma of the Fowl Transmissible by an Agent Separable from the Tumor Cells."[7] Three years later he and Murphy published full reports on three types of cell-free extracts—based on filtration, lyophilization, and glycerination methods—that were equally successful in inducing malignant sarcomas in fowl without losing the activity of the original tumor.[8] The lyophilized extracts of the tumor agent proved superior when sending samples to scientists around the world who wanted to study the chicken sarcoma.

In the 1911 report, Rous called the "self-perpetuating agent in this sarcoma of the fowl . . . a minute parasitic organism" without using the word virus. However, he did not rule out the possibility that an agent of another sort might be at work, namely, that "a chemical stimulant, elaborated by the neoplastic cells, might cause the tumor."

With these statements, Rous exposed the divisive opinion over cancer causation that would prevail for the next half century. Was the sarcoma agent a virus or was it a chemical? This controversy took place not only among scientists worldwide but, more remarkably, it also separated Rous and Murphy.

Tumor pathology in the early twentieth century was "utterly opposed to any theory of an infectious origin of cancer." When Welch examined the chicken growth, he admitted it was a tumor but, as Rous said, he "got around it" as a case peculiar to chickens. Rous reasoned that the "agent lives and that it belongs in the animal kingdom." In contrast, Murphy viewed malignancy as a universal cell potentiality that becomes activated after a break in internal mechanisms controlling cell growth. Consistent with Welch's teaching, Murphy maintained that cancer arose from endogenous chemical alterations inside the cell rather than from an exogenous living virus.[9]Within the Rockefeller Institute the controversy between Rous and

Murphy maintained a special intensity for forty years. Their relationship was politely circumspect, for as Rous once told Murphy, their difference of opinion "does not matter as the end will tell the true story."[10] In the end, of course, both men's views contributed to understanding cancer causation. Rous' sarcoma agent was ultimately found to be a retrovirus, and Murphy's chemical interpretation of the agent was not far from the idea of the oncogene that was proposed nearly four decades after he called it a "transmissible 'mutagen'."

However, within a few years, the collaboration of Murphy and Rous reached an impasse. They could neither culture the agent nor produce cell-free extracts from mammalian tumors. They went their own ways.

Rous abandoned work on the sarcoma agent forever. He returned to cancer research only two decades later when a mammalian tumor was discovered by a Rockefeller colleague, Richard Shope. Murphy considered leaving the Rockefeller Institute, but an unusual coincidence kept him and cancer research there. Henry Rutherford, a Vermont resident, bequeathed $200,000 to the Rockefeller Institute. This enormous sum, equal to the Institute's founding bequest from John D. Rockefeller Sr. in 1901, was given expressly to investigate "the causes and nature of cancer and methods of its prevention and treatment."[11]

From this point until mid-century, Murphy headed a Rockefeller Institute laboratory devoted to cancer that became a microcosm for testing the latest techniques, trying new instruments, and nurturing many young cancer scientists. A search for the nature of the chicken sarcoma, or Chicken Tumor I as it was called in the laboratory, was one part of his research program that included clinical, immunological, genetic, and environmental (radiation and chemical) approaches to malignancy. But it was the search for the cause of the sarcoma that led to a discipline devoted to the biology of cells.

1925, Keeping Cancer Research Alive

In 1925, the lead offered by Rous' 1911 discovery was taken up by William F. Gye in England.[12] He was the scientist credited with reviving the Rous sarcoma as worthy experimental material. Nevertheless, both Rous and Murphy were apprehensive of Gye's ability to cultivate a microbe from a chicken tumor.

Murphy was among the first to subject Gye's work to severe tests that quickly discredited these controversial studies.[13] To perform the experiments, Murphy brought several scientists to his laboratory to begin a new search for the sarcoma agent. One was Albert Claude from Belgium, a new MD who was well informed about the Rous sarcoma and had clear ambitions to study its cancerous properties. Before leaving Europe, Claude acquainted himself with tumor histology and pathology, the possible microbial cause of cancer, tissue culture of the S-37 sarcoma, and metabolism of cancerous tissues. Therefore, he was quite disappointed to learn on his arrival that Murphy had already tried and eliminated these latest techniques to study the sarcoma.

Among other projects, Murphy assigned Claude the task of isolating and purifying the tumor agent. Within a short time, they hypothesized that the agent was a transmissible mutagen, in which malignant cells produce a chemical substance that acts on normal cells causing them to assume distinct malignant characteristics as well as inducing inherited changes or mutations that lead to cancerous growths.[14] In their review of the chicken tumor work, they also suggested that the agent was similar to the chemical substance responsible for transforming pneumococcal types. Work on this substance in Oswald Avery's laboratory at the Rockefeller Institute eventually led to the identification of DNA as the genetic material.[15]

About this time, Simon Flexner intervened. Drawing on his expertise with the polio virus and his knowledge of other virus research at Rockefeller Institute, he concluded Murphy was working with a virus and insisted that he adopt techniques proven useful in other Institute laboratories. These included finding a chemist who could produce larger amounts of crude material as John Northrop did before crystallizing enzymes, and someone who could grow the agent in culture media like Thomas Rivers did for several viruses.[16]

Murphy resisted for a while until the chemical analyses of the tumor agent became confusing and the concentrated active material too limited for accurate testing. Then, he and Claude turned from chemical to physical methods, whereupon the centrifuge became the first critical instrument in nascent cell biology.

Claude chose an ordinary high-speed laboratory centrifuge. That may seem puzzling when ultracentrifuges of much higher performance were being developed simultaneously at the Rockefeller Institute by an independent group, the International Health Division (IHD) of the Rockefeller Foundation. Although the ultracentrifuge was for use in the IHD's own virus laboratory, many Institute scientists, including virologists, quickly adopted the new instrument.

Early ultracentrifuges of Theodor Svedberg in Sweden and Edward Pickels of the IHD at Rockefeller Institute were analytical instruments used to determine particle size, shape, and weight.[17] In contrast, Claude used a centrifuge as a preparative instrument to concentrate and purify the tumor agent, working with a small electrically driven table top International Equipment Model B centrifuge. He could increase its speed from a normal rate of 4,000 rpm to 17,000 rpm by connecting a small rotor to the main shaft, reaching a speed at the low end of what ultracentrifuges could obtain. Although not described here, Claude did not use a custom-made version of an ultracentrifuge until the mid-1940s.

Claude probably did not use the more powerful ultracentrifuge because he did not believe he was extracting a virus and he was handling tissues he thought too fragile for great centrifugal force. To break open the cells and extract a vulnerable part, Claude established a process called differential centrifugation that resulted in four separate, albeit crude, fractions. The first fraction to be spun down contained tissue debris and the nuclei. The middle two fractions were granular and differed in particle size. The supernatant fluid that remained after the final spinning contained the tumor agent.[18]

He eventually obtained a 2,800-fold increase in the infectivity of the agent over the original filtrate. Soon enough, Claude decided he had a purified tumor agent and determined that it contained "a nucleic acid of the ribose type." To the outside world, this finding strongly hinted that a virus was at work, but for Claude and Murphy it led directly to a different look at normal cells.[19]

1937, New Trends in Cancer Research

In 1937, two events generated excitement in cancer research: one affecting the general public, and the other affecting progress in the laboratory. Murphy's advocacy of cancer research outside the Rockefeller Institute was becoming fruitful. He was a long-standing member of both the American Association of Cancer Research and the American Society for the Control of Cancer. Both organizations were instrumental in getting the federal government to fund cancer research.

The National Cancer Act of 1937 signed by President Franklin D. Roosevelt opened a concerted effort to control the disease and seek a cure.

As part of creating the National Cancer Institute, Murphy headed a committee of well-known scientists charged to formulate "the fundamental aspects of the cancer problem and to suggest various lines of work which merit investigation."[20]Among their conclusions was that malignancy is "the result of a fundamental change in cell physiology," regardless of the chemical, biological, or physical agent that stimulates malignancy. Once altered, the cell process becomes automatic and this new property "becomes a fixed character, and is transmitted to its descendants. It gives evidence of being a somatic mutation."[21] The committee recommended against further research into the *causal genesis* of cancer, for which they gave a formidable list of known agents, including viruses and hereditary factors. Instead, they recommended new research objectives focused on the *formal genesis* of cancer inside the cell. The core of the cancer problem, as they presented it, lay in understanding the structure, composition, and function of the cell itself.

Although not a member of Murphy's committee, Rous was coming to agree with this evolving view of cancer. Although he maintained that viruses are "nearer causes of cancer," he also began to urge a cellular approach to the cancer problem. He suggested that "one must look to some factor accompanying the cells, or to an intrinsic alteration in them, in accounting for their new state."[22]

Concurrently in 1937, Claude used the simple centrifuge to compare particles spun down from sarcoma tissues with those from normal chicken embryos. Strictly speaking, this was not designed as a control experiment. Murphy assumed the comparison would replicate results from his experiments a decade earlier pointing to a natural ferment in healthy tissues that could cause cancer.[23] So, as planned and expected, these new tests with sedimented fractions showed that normal tissue resembled tumor tissue in its physical and chemical characteristics. Claude found the fractions from both types of tissues contained lipids and nucleoproteins in comparable amounts and chemical composition, and estimated them to be 70–200 μm in size. This new data fit remarkably with their transmissible mutagen hypothesis that normal tissues contain a factor that can be "mutagenized" into a tumor factor.[24] In retrospect, he was perhaps overconfident in the expected similarity between normal and tumor fractions, because there is no evidence that he tested whether the fractions from normal tissues produced tumors in animals.

The cancer committee's report was reflected in three new investigations in Murphy's laboratory. A physical approach was extending Claude's centrifugation of cells as he shifted to the new discovery of novel invisible particles of cytoplasmic origin that he sedimented from normal and cancerous tissues. He coined the name "microsomes" for these highly refringent submicroscopic bodies.[25] Furthermore, he compared them to the self-perpetuating units in viruses that also depend on "ribose nucleic acid" for their activity. However, this microsomal theory of cancer causation collapsed when Claude saw electron micrographs showing the difference between microsomes and viruses. The nature of microsomes did not become known until a decade after these micrographs were taken when George Palade and Philip Siekevitz identified them as vesicular fragments of the endoplasmic reticulum that in some cases carries ribonucleoprotein particles, or ribosomes, active in a cell's protein synthesis.[26]

A chemical approach involved making enzymatic analyses of the cell parts and particles that Claude obtained after spinning the cells in the centrifuge. This work was performed initially by biochemists Rollin Hotchkiss from Oswald Avery's laboratory and by George Hogeboom, an MD whom Murphy brought from Johns Hopkins. Claude indulged in another speculation that malignancy might "consist in some aberration in the functioning of the mitochondria," one of the fractions he identified.[27] He was thinking along Murphy's lines of the abnormal nature and function of normal subcellular organelles. The first success of a biochemical approach to subcellular components came a few years later when Claude's mitochondrial fraction was linked to cell energy.

A biological approach dealt with mechanisms that engender, promote, or inhibit cell growth. Murphy believed the microsomes that Claude was extracting from both normal tissues and tumors played a role in normal development—the elements were also known as the induction factor in embryology. This research project was assigned to a new laboratory member, embryologist Keith Porter. After devising inventive and dexterous methods to cultivate a variety of cells, Porter was asked to expose cultured cells to the microsomes with the expectation they would become malignant. Just as Porter began to immerse himself in learning to culture cancerous cells, the laboratory's routine was interrupted by a serendipitous letter.

1945, Revolutionary Electron Micrographs

In 1945, the electron microscope swiftly changed everything by opening views of the vast wilderness inside the cell.[28] The suspicion that the microsomes might be the elusive sarcoma agent led Claude and Porter to the electron microscope after Henry Green, a physicist at Interchemical Corporation, read Claude's description of microsomes in a 1943 *Science* article.[29] He wrote to Claude suggesting that their RCA model B electron microscope "could handle the submicroscopic particles in the cell plasm with great ease and might, therefore, reveal structure of interest."[30] Interchemical used Manhattan's first electron microscope primarily to examine pigment particles. In addition, Albert Gessler, head of Interchemical's research laboratories, had grant funds to examine biological materials and pursue cancer research. The invitation launched an eighteen-month collaboration of Interchemical's microscopist Ernest Fullam with Claude and Porter.

Three different preparations of biological tissues were visualized in the microscope. Claude prepared isolated subcellular fractions (mitochondria and microsomes) of rat sarcoma cells and sectioned slices of normal guinea pig liver tissues. The resulting micrographs showed distorted, muddy particles as well as artificial holes produced by a crude microtome. Porter prepared the most successful specimens of whole cells by culturing fibroblasts from a chicken embryo that spread out in a thin layer on a plasticized film. His delicate innovations of a hanging drop culture method, a roller flask, and a novel fixation produced diaphanous cells suitable for the harsh conditions of the microscope and they related directly to the quality of the micrographs. The difficulty and frustration in reproducing these aseptic techniques also stimulated Porter to found the Tissue Culture Association in 1946.[31]

The lone cell in the landmark micrograph shown in Fig. 1 was actually a montage of five individual pictures joined into a single image. Taken at the surprisingly low magnification of 1,600, the image revealed much more structural information than these scientists expected or knew how to interpret or describe. Among the new subcellular terrain, they had the first glimpses of Claude's microsomes and a novel lacework of what eventually came to be known

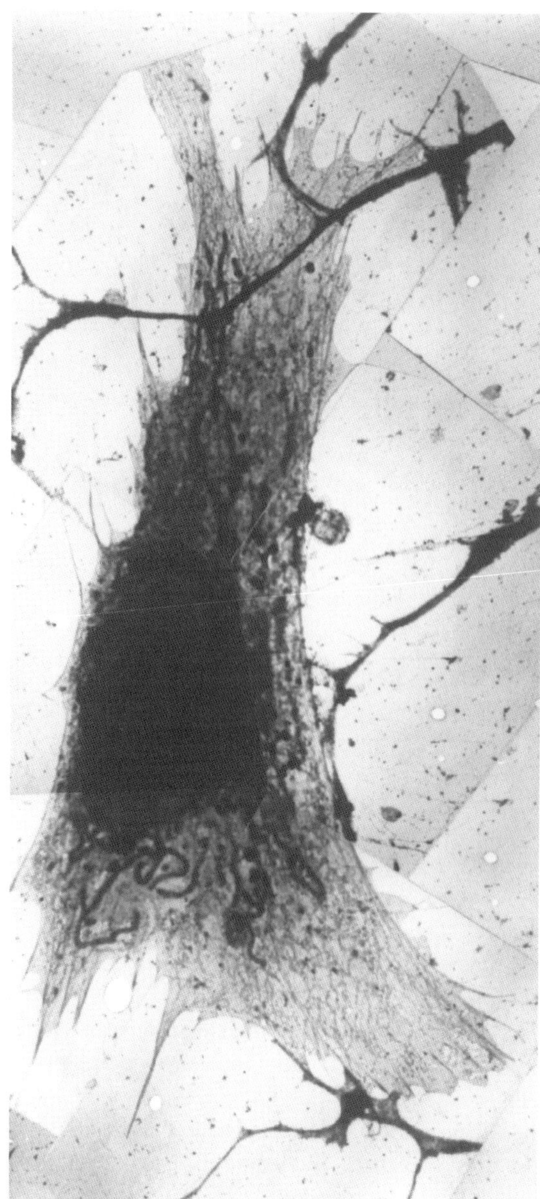

Figure 1. The first electron micrograph of an intact cell, a fibroblast from a chicken embryo, appeared as Fig. 1 in the 1945 paper by Porter et al.[2] The micrograph was taken on July 6, 1944 with an RCA electron microscope, type B. The image shown here was rephotographed in 1994 by Lee D. Peachey from the original montage of five micrographs.

as the endoplasmic reticulum. Going beyond the resolving power of an ordinary light microscope, the electron microscope was the second critical new instrument in cell biology.

Within a year of publishing this micrograph of a normal cell, Claude and Porter took the next step in the laboratory's long-standing goal to identify and locate the agent of Chicken Tumor I in a malignant cell. This time they had the use of a newer model electron microscope, the RCA-EMU, that was purchased by the Rockefeller Foundation's IHD for its virus laboratory and was installed in the basement of Flexner Hall. Pickels, the designer of the ultracentrifuge, was the IHD's microscopist charged with applying this new tool to examine viruses. Other

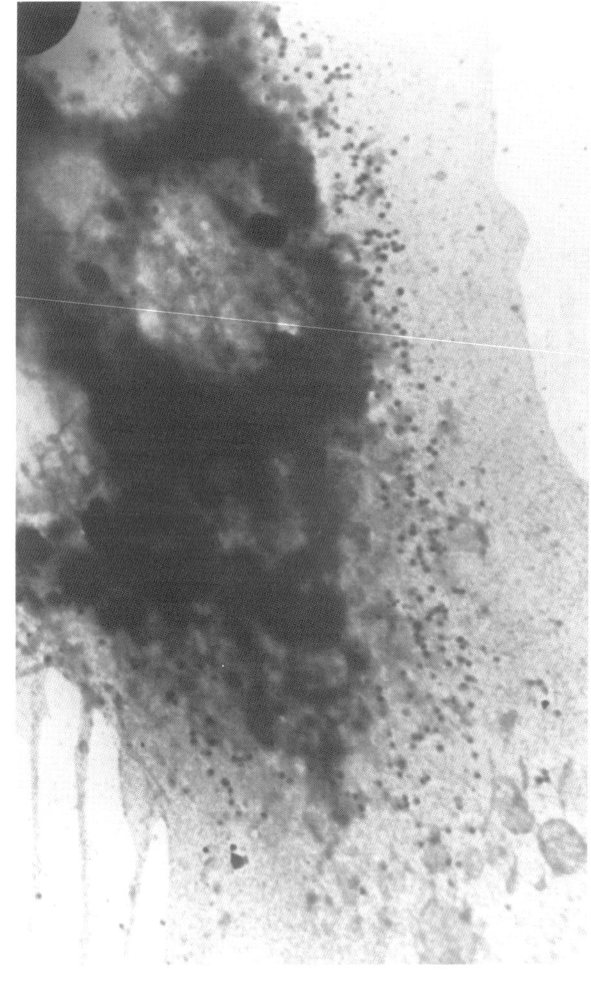

Figure 2. The first electron micrograph of an intact cell infected with Chicken Tumor I, the causative agent of the Rous chicken breast sarcoma, is also a fibroblast from a chicken embryo. The micrograph was published as Fig. 3 in the 1947 paper of Claude et al.[32] Reprinted with permission of *Cancer Research.*

scientists outside the Institute had imaged isolated virus particles in the electron microscope, but Pickels took the first micrograph of a cell infected with a virus. In many aspects it was more revolutionary than the first one.

The micrograph shown in Fig. 2 was taken in late 1945 or early 1946 but not published until 1947. The numerous viruslike bodies seen on the surface and inside cultured tumor cells gave enhanced but not convincing evidence of a viral cause for tumors. To prove the particles were not artifacts, Porter took over the microscope and went on to take micrographs of cells infected with a mammary carcinoma (the Bittner agent) and a rat sarcoma. Both sets of micrographs showed viruslike particles of uniform size inside the cancer cells that were not present in uninfected cells.[32]

Within the laboratory, the comparison of normal and tumor cells created more questions than answers. The careful, cautious interpretations of so many new details in the micrographs took place in a vacuum. These scientists, of course, had no previous knowledge to draw on, no experience with this kind of virus research, and no one to guide or review their scrutiny. Nevertheless, the micrographs quickly set the course of research.

Claude's microsomes appeared in both types of cells and they were distinctly different from the viruslike particles; consequently, this ended the theory that microsomes were the chicken tumor agent. Furthermore, except for the presence of these viruslike particles, the normal and sarcoma cells otherwise looked the same. This suggested there was still more to find; in other words, the formal genesis of cancer was still invisible. And, while the particles in the micrographs pointed to a difference between normal and malignant cells, seeing structures was not enough. The new morphological studies needed additional bridges that would lead to determining biochemical composition and measuring biological activities of cells.

Outside the laboratory and the Rockefeller Institute, there was general disbelief that Porter had actually cultivated and preserved viruses in the cells and showed them in micrographs. Neither the electron microscope nor the cultured cell was fully accepted by most scientists as reliable biological research tools. Moreover, tools to make definitive identification of viruses were still missing. There was no way to test whether these microbodies were the cause of cancer. The micrographs were so novel and advanced in cancer science that they were years away from being confirmed by other scientists. Based on abundantly clear frustrations, this micrograph of Chicken Tumor I was the last experiment on this sarcoma at the Rockefeller Institute until the arrival of Hidesaburo Hanafusa in 1973.

However, the micrograph of malignant cells that ended one long phase of cancer research had started a new science. The question propelled by the electron microscope was now what, if anything, could scientists possibly see in a cancer cell when they still did not know what the inside of a normal cell looked like. Even before Murphy retired a few years later, the laboratory changed its course. Claude continued with centrifugation and biochemical studies of his fractions, Porter progressed with the microscope and tissue culture, and George Palade joined the laboratory to begin studies combining structure and function of normal cells.

The laboratory once again renewed Murphy's persistent vision that any attack on cancer had to come from first understanding the anatomy and chemistry of normal cells. Before techniques and instruments were perfected, this vision was advanced considerably by the Institute's Scientific Director Herbert Gasser. In the aftermath of the 1945 micrograph, he became a significant force by bringing physics to biology; five years, later he created a laboratory under Porter and Palade initially called cytology. "Work in Murphy's laboratory," Gasser commented, "is integrated by the general proposition that whatever contributes to an understanding of intracellular mechanisms also contributes to the cancer problem."[33] Therein lay the challenges that shaped modern cell biology.

This essay is extracted from a history in preparation about modern cell biology. I am thankful for the interest and aid from Frederick Seitz, Ralph Steinman, Philip Siekevitz, Philippa Claude, James S. Murphy, Lee D. Peachey, and Keith R. Porter. Renee Mastrocco at the Rockefeller University Archives, Marty Covey and Bruce Montgomery at the University of Colorado, Beth Carroll-Horrocks and Scott DeHaven at the American Philosophical Society, and John Beck at the University of Maryland expedited searches in their archival collections. I am happy to acknowledge the support provided by the American Philosophical Society for research on this project.

Endnotes

1. Herbert George Wells, *Meanwhile: The Picture of a Lady* (London, 1927).
2. Carol L. Moberg, "The Electron Microscope Enters the Realm of the Intact Cell," *Journal of*

Experimental Medicine 181 (1995): 829–37; Keith R. Porter, Albert Claude, and Ernest F. Fullam, "A Study of Tissue Culture Cells by Electron Microscopy," *Journal of Experimental Medicine* 81 (1945): 233–46; George E. Palade, "The American Cradle" (speech delivered at symposium *"Journey into the Cell: Celebrating 50 Years of Electron Microscopy and Modern Cell Biology*, March 16, 1995).

3. George W. Corner, *A History of the Rockefeller Institute, 1901–1953* (New York, 1964).
4. Ibid., 109; Clarence C. Little, "James Bumgardner Murphy," *Biographical Memoirs of the National Academy of Sciences* 34 (1960): 182–203, quotation on 190–1.
5. James B. Murphy and Peyton Rous, "The Behavior of Chicken Sarcoma Implanted in the Developing Embryo," *Journal of Experimental Medicine* 15 (1912): 119–32; Peyton Rous, "A Sarcoma of the Fowl Transmissible by an Agent Separable from the Tumor Cells," *Journal of Experimental Medicine* 13 (1911): 397–411.
6. D. Ivanovski, "Ueber die Mosaikkrankheit der Tabakspflanze," *Bulletin de l'Académie Impériale des Sciences de St. Pétersbourg* 3 (1894): 67–70; Martinus W. Beijerinck, "Ueber ein Contagium vivum fluidum als Ursache der Fleckenkrankheit der Tabaksblätter," *Centralblatt für Bacteriologie und Parasitenkunde, Part II* 5 (1899): 27–33.
7. Rous, "Sarcoma of the Fowl" (n. 5 above), 397–411.
8. Peyton Rous and James B. Murphy, "On the Causation by Filterable Agents of Three Distinct Chicken Tumors," *Journal of Experimental Medicine* 14 (1914): 52–69.
9. Charles Oberling, "In Honor of Peyton Rous," *Perspectives in Virology* II (1961): 1–4; Peyton Rous and T. Mitchell Prudden, interview for an early history of Rockefeller Institute, box 1, Record Group 400, Rockefeller University Archives, Rockefeller Archive Center, Sleepy Hollow, NY (hereafter RAC); Peyton Rous to T. Mitchell Prudden, 14 October 1922, box 1, RG 199.72 Prudden Papers, Rockefeller University Archives, RAC.
10. Peyton Rous to James B. Murphy, 27 September 1929, Murphy Papers, American Philosophical Society, Philadelphia, PA (hereafter APS).
11. Henry J. James Jr., 22 July 1915, Henry Rutherford Bequest for Cancer Research, folder 1913–1949, box 5, Endowment 1913–1949, RG 216.3, Rockefeller University Archives, RAC.
12. William E. Gye, "The Aetiology of Malignant New Growths," *Lancet* 2 (1925): 109–17.
13. James B. Murphy, "Observations on the Etiology of Tumors as Evidenced by Experiments with a Chicken Sarcoma," *Journal of the American Medical Association* 86 (1926): 1270–1.
14. Albert Claude and James B. Murphy, "Transmissible Tumors of the Fowl," *Physiological Reviews* 13 (1933): 246–75.
15. Ralph M. Steinman and Carol L. Moberg, "The Experiment That Transformed Biology: Discovering the Genetic Role of DNA," *Journal of Experimental Medicine* 179 (1994): 381–4; Maclyn McCarty, "A Retrospective Look: How We Identified the Pneumococcal Transforming Substance as DNA," *Journal of Experimental Medicine* 179 (1994): 385–94.
16. Simon Flexner to James B. Murphy, 30 March 1933, Murphy Papers, APS.
17. Theodor Svedberg and Kai O. Pedersen, *The Ultracentrifuge* (Oxford, 1940); Edward G. Pickels, "Centrifugation," in *Biophysical Research Methods*, ed. Fred M. Uber (New York, 1950), 67–105; Boelie Elzen, *Scientists and Rotors: The Development of Biochemical Ultracentrifuges* (Enschede, Netherlands, 1988).
18. Albert Claude, "Particulate Components of Cytoplasm," *Cold Spring Harbor Symposia on Quantitative Biology* 9 (1941): 263–70.
19. Albert Claude, "Properties of the Causative Agent of a Chicken Tumor. 13. Sedimentation of the Tumor Agent, and Separation from the Associated Inhibitor," *Journal of Experimental Medicine* 66 (1937): 59–72; Albert Claude, "Concentration and Purification of Chicken Tumor I Agent," *Science* 87 (1938): 467–8.
20. J. R. Heller, "The National Cancer Institute: A Twenty-Year Retrospect," *Journal of the National Cancer Institute* 19 (1957): 147–90.
21. Stanhope Bayne-Jones, Ross G. Harrison, Clarence C. Little, John Northrop, and James B. Murphy, "Fundamental Cancer Research," *Public Health Reports* 53 (1938): 2121–30.
22. Peyton Rous, "The Nearer Causes of Cancer," *Journal of the American Medical Association* 122 (1943): 573–81.

23. James B. Murphy, "The Nature of the Filtrable Agent in Chicken Tumours," in *International Conference on Cancer, London 1928* (Bristol, England, 1928), 33–7.
24. Albert Claude, "A Fraction from Normal Chick Embryo Similar to the Tumor-Producing Fraction of Chicken Tumor I," *Proceedings of the Society for Experimental Biology and Medicine* 39 (1938), 398–403; Albert Claude, "Particulate Components of Normal and Tumor Cells," *Science* 91 (1940): 77–8.
25. Albert Claude, "The Constitution of Protoplasm," *Science* 97 (1943): 451–6.
26. George E. Palade and Philip Siekevitz, "Liver Microsomes: An Integrated Morphological and Biochemical Study," *Journal of Biophysical and Biochemical Cytology* 2 (1956): 171–200.
27. Albert Claude, Rockefeller Institute Staff Meeting, 1940, private papers of Albert Claude, courtesy of Philippa Claude (hereafter Claude Papers).
28. Carol L. Moberg, "The Electron Microscope" (no. 2 above), 834; Nicolas Rasmussen, *Picture Control: The Electron Microscope and the Transformation of Biology in America, 1940–1960* (Stanford, 1997); Carol Moberg, "Review of *Picture Control,*" *American Zoologist* 38 (1998): 793.
29. Claude, "Constitution" (n. 25 above), 451–6.
30. Henry Green to Albert Claude, 28 May 1943, Claude Papers.
31. Carol L. Moberg, "Keith Porter and the Founding of the Tissue Culture Association," *In Vitro Cellular and Developmental Biology, Animal* 32 (1996): 663–9.
32. Albert Claude, Keith R. Porter, and Edward G. Pickels, "Electron Microscope Study of Chicken Tumor Cells," *Cancer Research* 7 (1947): 421–30; Keith R. Porter and Helen P. Thompson, "A Particulate Body Associated with Epithelial Cells Cultured from Mammary Carcinomas of Mice of a Milk-Factor Strain," *Journal of Experimental Medicine* 88 (1948): 15–24; Keith R. Porter and Helen P. Thompson, "Some Morphological Features of Cultured Rat Sarcoma Cells as Revealed by the Electron Microscope," *Cancer Research* 7 (1947): 431–8.
33. Herbert S. Gasser, Report to the Corporation, October 1946, *Annual Scientific Reports to the Board of Scientific Directors of the Rockefeller Institute for Medical Research*, 34, RG 439, Rockefeller University Archives, RAC.

Chapter 14

The Rockefeller University and the Molecular Revolution in Biology

Robert Olby

Research Professor, Department of History and Philosophy of Science, University of Pittsburgh, PA

It is no small challenge to consider the role of the Rockefeller University in the molecular revolution in biology, but in this essay I will not attempt to assess the contribution of the Rockefeller to this revolution. Rather I shall look at the portrayal of the university in accounts of the molecular revolution, critique them, and offer some explanation for the form they take. This will lead us to address the question: Did the Rockefeller University lose its way in the 1950s?

I start by defining the molecular revolution, and continue by briefly outlining how molecular biology achieved such visibility. Next, I reconstruct the Rockefeller's place in the molecular revolution. Finally, I focus on the chemical basis of biological specificity, a theme of much of the work at the Rockefeller in the 1930s and 1940s, and a central theme of molecular biology today. This discussion will lead to an attempt to identify some of the reasons that have obscured or hidden from the public eye the significance of this work and its relation to biological information as it was understood in the molecular biology of the 1950s and 1960s.

The Molecular Revolution

The term "molecular biology" achieved headline status by the 1970s through such instruments as the launch of the *Journal of Molecular Biology* by Academic Press in 1959; such repackaging as the renaming of the as the MRC Laboratory of Molecular Biology in Cambridge in1956; the award of the 1962 Nobel Prize in Physiology and Medicine to James Watson, Francis Crick, and Maurice Wilkins; and the publication of Watson's *The Molecular Biology of the Gene* in 1965. A year later, the Delbrück festschrift, *Phage and the Origins of Molecular Biology* (1966), pointed, as its title prominently suggested, to the work of the Phage Group centered around Delbrück in the 1950s as the source of molecular biology. As the volume's lead article, the editors selected their leader's 1949 address: "A Physicist Looks at Biology." John Kendrew responded in the *Scientific American* that the Phage Group was one source, but not the only one; in fact, he noted that the tradition of the structural X-ray crystallography of the proteins was the other. He dubbed the former the informational school, and the latter the structural school. By the time Watson's enormously influential semi-autobiographical book, *The Double Helix*, appeared in 1968, the three elements—phage, structural chemistry, and the move of physicists to biology —had become the distinguishing constituents of the popular history of molecular biology. Horace Judson's book, *The Eighth Day of Creation* (1979), did not alter the popular perception of the subject, although at the end of the book the author rightly pointed to the fundamental importance of what he called "the working out of the idea of specificity."[1]

As a historian and not a legislator of disciplinary terminology or a philosopher of conceptual analysis, I define molecular biology as the customs, organizational arrangements, and intellectual commitments of the scientific community. The problem, as we will see, is which scientific community? Of course, the study of living things and their molecules (i.e., molecular biology) has a long history because everything living is constituted of molecules and involves molecular reactions. In contrast, molecular morphology has a shorter history: in terms of protein conformation, it goes back to the 1930s; of carbohydrates, to the 1920s. But the foundations of the modern molecular relationship between proteins and nucleic acids were only laid in the 1950s. They gave rise to our current understanding of the machinery of gene expression and its control, viral replication, bacterial transformation, and so much more. Indeed, our understanding of this relationship has now enriched and informed almost all branches of biology. Nevertheless, it is an approach, not a discipline, a set of tools, and—what is often left out—a manual. This manual still teaches the central dogma and the sequence hypothesis of 1958, despite the alleged exceptions to the former and the established exceptions to the latter. They are the conceptual elements of the subject.

In 1977, David Baltimore wrote a foreword to the Nobel Foundation collection, *Nobel Lectures in Molecular Biology: 1933–1975*, where he defined the subject as ". . . the study of how DNA, RNA, and protein[s] are interrelated."[2] However, this task has involved much more than the study of three-dimensional structure, phage replication, and the activities of émigré physicists. Thus, a very prominent feature of molecular biology is the sequence of subunits composing the macromolecular chains of proteins and nucleic acids. Biological "information" as defined by Crick is the sequence. But it was the protein chemists in the biochemical community—including Rockefeller scientists—who supplied sequence data based on their creative development of separation techniques. This effort was because of the concern within the Rockefeller to establish the chemical basis to biological specificity; a concern that was expressed in the research of three of its laboratories: those of Karl Landsteiner, Oswald T. Avery, and Max Bergmann.

The Portrayal of the Rockefeller University's Contribution

Where does Rockefeller figure in these accounts? *The Double Helix* mentions Avery twice, and we learn simply that he worked at Rockefeller.[3] *The Eighth Day* devotes eight pages to Avery, but all we learn about the Rockefeller Institute is that therein "opposition to any identification of DNA as the stuff of the gene was peculiarly concentrated";[4] instead, the Rockefeller's research had concentrated on demonstrating the enzymatic properties of the proteins. Phoebus Levene, the nucleic acid authority, had worked at Rockefeller, but was the foremost upholder of the tetranucleotide hypothesis of the structure of nucleic acids. Later, we learn how Mirsky and Allfrey, "biochemists at the Rockefeller, had detected protein synthesis in the nucleus, an 'irreverent illustration—like the bit of eggshell on the head of the eagle chick—of how the tatters of an old idea can cling to Rockefeller."[5] Rockefeller is mentioned once in connection with the sequencing of myoglobin,[6] and once in a derogatory tone on the numerological sequence rule of protein structure put forward in the 1930s by Max Bergmann and Carl Niemann.[7] You may have expected that Landsteiner's work would have been detailed favorably somewhere in these accounts; however, for even a mention of his work, we have to turn elsewhere.

Lily Kay, in *The Molecular Vision of Life*, described Landsteiner's influence upon Linus Pauling, leading him to advance a theory of antibody formation based on the erroneous instructional theory of Stuart Mudd, Felix Haurowitz, and Jerome Alexander, and thereby wasting time and considerable funds to no avail in his efforts to achieve a method for the laboratory—and hopefully in the future—commercial synthesis of antibodies."[8] Of Landsteiner, she wrote that he studied antibodies in isolation from their cellular milieu

> . . . focusing primarily on chemical mechanisms, an approach reflecting the Institute's emphasis on the physiochemical aspects of life phenomena. From the start, Landsteiner's conceptualization of the problem ignored the biological complexities inherent in the production of antibodies, questions that had occupied physicians and bacteriologists for decades. It glossed over such unexplained phenomena as the persistence of antibody production in the apparent absence of antigen and failed to account for an enhanced response on a second exposure to the same antigen. No attention was given to the biological riddle of how the organism distinguished self from nonself in terms of antigenic response.[9]

If we turn to the work of Bronfenbrenner and John Northrop on bacteriophage do we find a more favorable reportage? Gunther Stent's book *The Molecular Biology of Bacterial Viruses* contrasts their autocatalytic theory of phage multiplication with the bacteriological explanation supplied by Felix d'Hérelle and by Emory Ellis, Salvador Luria, and Max Delbrück. The autocatalytic theory was vanquished. If the Rockefeller's contribution to the earlier picture of biological specificity was, as Judson judged it, "lacking that entire set of meanings—those distinct dimensions—it was to acquire by 1970," can we write off the Rockefeller's contributions, save for the remarkable work of Oswald T. Avery, Colin MacLeod, and Maclyn McCarty, which the Rockefeller's leading biochemist opposed anyway and which senior members of Rockefeller made no effort to promote?[10] I do not think so. To explain why requires first that we look at Landsteiner's work more closely. Second, we turn to Max Bergmann on protein specificity leading to the studies of William Stein and Stanford Moore; and third, we examine the policy of Rockefeller towards biophysics and the impact of its closure of the Princeton laboratories.

The Chemical Basis of Biological Specificity

For a scholarly and authoritative secondary source on Landsteiner's work I have turned to the work of Pauline Mazumdar[11] and to Landsteiner's classic, *The Specificity of Serological Reactions.* Mazumdar has charted Landsteiner's shift from a colloidal interpretation of the antibody–antigen reaction to an approach towards the interpretation of Paul Ehrlich in orthodox chemical terms, followed by a partial return to a transformed colloidal view under the influence of Pauling's views on noncovalent attractions (e.g., hydrogen bonds). The fifth chapter of Landsteiner's book, entitled "Artificial Conjugated Antigens, Serological Reactions with Simple Chemical Compounds," opens by tracing the history from 1906 when the idea of making derivatives of protein antigens by combining the antigens with specifically reacting components of known chemical constitution, "chosen at will" was introduced.[12] Beginning in 1917 in Vienna and continuing in New York at Rockefeller, Landsteiner used a variety of such derivatives, called by him *Azoproteins*, to demonstrate a change in the specificity of the original protein, and "in addition the various products were serologically clearly differentiated. . . ."[13] Not only was the presence of certain groups particularly influential in determining specificity, but their "relative position" had a "pronounced effect." The latter was strikingly demonstrated in the case of ortho-, meta-, and parasubstitutions on the benzene ring. Using the stereoisomers of tartaric acid, he furnished evidence of the specificity of different spatial arrangements of the same atoms. Further studies enabled him to make some assessment of the contribution to specificity made by particular groups, and the contribution made by the "spatial structure." Both were important.

Using a range of peptides (from dipeptides to pentapeptides), he established that the specificity was not just the result of the nature of the end group of the chain. The "mere shifting of the position of one amino acid," he noted "induced a marked change in the specificity. . . ."[14] He continued, stating that the many amino acids present in a protein "permit the synthesis of a very large number of serologically different peptides. . . ." This he contrasted with "the indifferent specificity of long fatty acid chains."[15]

Although these remarkable studies brought the determination of specificity within the realm of experimental analysis for Landsteiner, his contact with Linus Pauling exposed him to the conception of the limited specificity of the hydrogen bond. The essay that Pauling wrote for Landsteiner to include in the third edition of his book expounded Pauling's view of the nature of weak inter-atomic forces—not as specific and strong as covalent or ionic bonds, but "of greater stereochemical significance than is shown by the electric van der Waals attractions." This, Pauling explained, is due to what he called "steric restriction and the limitation of the class of atoms capable of forming good hydrogen bonds. . . ."[16] Hence, given appropriate spatial configuration and sufficient positively and negatively charged groups, two molecules can attract each other in a specific manner. Thus, if "two molecules possessed such mutually complementary configurations that the surface of one conformed closely to the surface of the other" and hydrogen bond–forming groups were also "so placed as to form the maximum number of hydrogen bonds, the total energy of interaction would be very great, and the two molecules would attract one another very strongly."[17]

The correspondence between Landsteiner and Pauling regarding this essay shows clearly that Landsteiner had read it most carefully and recommended a number of clarifications.[18] But the book containing the essay did not appear until two years after Landsteiner's death in 1943. There was, to be sure, a very important concept missing—what is the relationship between the chemical sequence (arrangement) and the three-dimensional folded structure? As we know, the remarkable diversity of the immune system suggested no strict one-to-one relationship between them. Furthermore, Landsteiner and his Rockefeller colleague, Alexandre Rothen, were among those who suggested that the same polypeptide chain could be folded in a variety of ways.[19] However, we can conclude that through support of Landsteiner's work and of his association with Pauling, the Rockefeller Institute contributed by directing attention to the question of the relationship between chemical structure and biological specificity.

Nowhere was structure considered more significant than in the case of the proteins. Protein structure and specificity was the subject of research in the laboratory of the German chemist, Max Bergmann. He was an inspiring and charismatic figure under whose spell came a group of young biochemists, three of whom were to win Nobel prizes—namely, William Stein, Stanford Moore, and Paul Zamecnik. Another, Joseph Fruton, was to become the eminent historian of biochemistry. Their work at Rockefeller together with that of Carl Niemann and Emil Smith is shown in Table I.

As Stein has emphasized, their development of analytical methods for the proteins arose out of the need to ascertain accurately "the amino acid composition of proteins" in order to discover the sequence of ribonuclease and to learn "what made it an enzyme."[20] This concern with sequence dates back to 1935 when Bergmann and Niemann published their hypothesis of repeating sequences based on the assumption that proteins consist of polypeptide chains, the members of which are distributed along the chains in a repeating fashion with a frequency that is reflected in their respective contributions to the composition of the protein. The classic

Table I. **Bergmann and His School**

Researcher	Years at RI/RU	War work
Max Bergmann	1934–1944	1942–1944
Joseph Fruton	1934–1945	1942–1945
Carl Niemann	1935–1937	
William Stein	1938–1980	1942–1945
Stanford Moore	1939–1949, 1952–1982	1942–1945
Paul Zamecnik	1941–1942	None
Emil Smith	1940–1942	None

example was and is silk fibroin. Its sequence as established by modern methods is not far from the kind of repeating sequence that Bergmann proposed. Although this notion of a repeating sequence was strongly criticized, Bergmann held to the view that the innumerable variety of arrangements of the amino acids was adequate to account for the diversity of known proteins. He expressed his vision of the basis of their variety and specificity in the following passage in his Scientific Report to the Director for the year 1941–42:

> There are about as many different amino acids as there are letters of the alphabet, and the number of different proteins that can be theoretically built by different arrangements of these amino acids is as infinite as the number of words that can be made from the alphabet. Hence comes the unlimited variety of the proteins . . . Because the same twenty odd amino acids in different proportions and arrangement form all the thousands of proteins.[21]

For Bergmann, this was not a new theme. Six years earlier, in his Harvey Lecture he asked,

> What is the basis for the fact that the protein pepsin possesses enzymic properties while other proteins, composed of the same amino acids, lack these enzymic characteristics? The same question may be posed in regard to the hormone character of insulin. All evidence points to the fact that the enzymic properties of pepsin, as well as the hormonic properties of insulin, are due to particular arrangements of amino acids in these proteins. Or let us take another example, the sharply defined specificity of the serological reactions of proteins and protein constituents. The well-known experiments of Landsteiner leave no doubt that in these reactions the arrangement of the amino acids in the peptide chain is of great significance.[22]

By 1939, Bergmann had already been forced to give up the assumption that there was a stoichiometric rule or periodicity in the patterns of sequences of amino acids in proteins,[23] but his advocacy of this idea has cast a shadow over his positive influence. This concerns his focus on the chemical basis for specificity. What features, he asked, determine the specificity of action of enzymes? By exposing them to a variety of substrates, chemically modified in known ways, he explored the relation between substrate and enzyme. Realizing that more accurate quantitative methods were needed to establish sequence Bergmann, with Stein and Moore, developed a modification and refinement of the gravimetric method for which they claimed improved results. But their method was applied only to glycine and leucine and they still had to confess,

> we cannot write today the empirical formula for the amino acid composition of even the simplest protein, and among many of the more complex proteins 40% or more of the amino acids in the molecule remain completely unaccounted for.

Prophetically they remarked,

> . . . the history of this field for the past fifty years seems to point to the conclusion that a major advance in the *quantitative* knowledge of protein structure (complete analysis) can be expected only through the introduction of some fundamentally new approach.[24]

The importance of the periodicity hypothesis lay in the stimulus it gave to protein chemists to refute it by establishing accurate quantitative data on amino acid composition. The resulting effort led by the British investigators, Archer Martin, A. H. Gordon, and Richard Synge, resulted in 95% recovery of protein nitrogen in the amino acids enzymatically liberated, chromatographically separated, recovered, and measured. On such data are based the sequence information that form so prominent a feature of modern molecular biology. *This development was not a product of military objectives, not a revolution in concepts, but a logical development for the protein chemists to pursue.* As I have chronicled elsewhere, the breakthrough that came with the chromatography of the amino acids was nurtured in an industrial setting—the result of the desire of the wool industry to respond to the commercial challenge of synthetic fibers.[25] The industry formed the International Wool Secretariat (IWS), and allotted funds for research into the chemistry of wool. Sir Charles Martin, former director of the Lister Institute in London, advised the IWS on this research, and supported Synge's work with Archer Martin, at the Wool Industries Research Association, on developing a chromatographic method for the separation of amino acids, subsequently called "partition chromatography," because of its use of two liquid phases.[26]

The unexpected aspect of this story is that while the British researchers, being conscientious objectors, continued their work through World War II, the Americans in Bergmann's laboratory were diverted for four years to conduct research into mustard gas—only returning to protein research at the end of the war, by which time Bergmann was dead. What followed was a story of restitution of the pre-war program based on the new methods—their refinement and automation—directed to β-lactoglobulin, bovine serum albumin, and the enzyme, ribonuclease. The latter is a story of collaborative research between the Rockefeller and British scientists, marked by open exchange of information, instrumentation, and of personnel. Soraya de Chadarevian has described this collaboration from the British end, where Stanford Moore spent six months in 1951 working in Frederick Sanger's laboratory in Cambridge; four years later John Kendrew, needing sequence data to aid his interpretation of the X-ray crystallographic data of myoglobin, appealed to Stein and Moore at the Rockefeller University to undertake the work.[27] When funds from the Rockefeller Foundation became available for doctoral students to work at Rockefeller, Moore and Stein were able in 1956 to appoint Allen Edmunson to sequence myoglobin. This research led to his doctorate in 1960 and his move to Cambridge that fall. There, with the automated amino acid analyser shipped over by Stein and Moore, a provisional sequence for myoglobin was produced.[28] Then, Kendrew could compare his electron density maps of myoglobin to a resolution of 2 Å with these sequence data, recognizing the value of the latter in determining the three-dimensional structure. A similar story can be told of ribonuclease, where the sequence was established at the Rockefeller in 1963 and compared with the electron density maps of ribonuclease-A and ribonuclease-S.[29] These achievements in sequence analysis were not those of émigré physicists, but of protein chemists with a deep knowledge of physical chemistry and innovative in the design of equipment, extending in the case of Stein and Moore to automation—a significant catalyst to the solution of protein structures.

Biophysics at the Rockefeller Institute

In 1927, Ralph Wyckoff was appointed to head a subdivision of biophysics at Rockefeller, with the mission to study the biological applications of X-ray crystallography. As the foremost young American specialist in this new field, Wyckoff was a wise appointment for Simon Flexner. Little did Wyckoff know that five years later the same director would be warning him that the future of his subdivision was not certain, and a decision would await the appointment of Flexner's successor. This uncertainty caused Wyckoff to reply that his own "personal interests, and the interests of the things" he wanted "to see done would be injured" in the event that the new director, Herbert Gasser, did not renew Wyckoff's contract.[30] However, in his ten years at Rockefeller, Wyckoff made a substantial contribution not just to the establishment of X-ray crystallography but also to instrumentation in several areas. He set up the instrument-making shop, he and Pickels built an air-driven analytical ultracentrifuge, and he suggested that Wendell Stanley use this instrument to purify the plant viruses he studied, and used it to measure the molecular magnitudes of several plant and animal viruses.

Wyckoff's application of X-ray crystallography may have been viewed within Rockefeller as too cautious. In his five-page report on the history and work of the biophysics department, given to Gasser in January 1936, he described the simple structures advanced by Kurt Meyer, Hermann Mark, and William Astbury for biological fibers as convincing by their simplicity to the lay person; but, he cautioned, they

> . . . offer serious difficulties if taken too literally. I have always felt that a sound opinion of their value would be possible only after we knew whether the X-ray data upon which they were based are themselves complete. Our work in this field has accordingly been directed towards the development of ways of recording the large spacing reflections to be expected from true crystals with very large molecules. . . . within the last year, Bernal in England and Corey and myself here have obtained the first X-ray pictures from unaltered soluble proteins. All these patterns are what one should expect from truly crystalline (i.e., three-dimensionally regular) arrangements of very large molecules . . . These new developments . . . open up to X-ray attack a large group of problems bearing on the nature of macromolecular substances. We are studying several of these.[31]

According to Wyckoff, Gasser considered his work "medically inappropriate," which was rather a strange judgment; only two years after Wyckoff began preparing to leave, Gasser stated the need to bring in "disciplines not now represented," and he described two at some length: biophysics and genetics![32] Politics and personalities within Rockefeller seem to have had more to do with Wyckoff's departure than the scientific merits of the decision.[33] The benefit for science was that Corey departed to Caltech to work with Linus Pauling, taking the X-ray diffraction data on glycine with him, and from this grew the extended study of the three-dimensional structure of the amino acids at Caltech. But, assessing his research at Rockefeller, Wyckoff recalled,

> The last years, culminating in my enforced leaving seemed at the time tragic for they meant the abrupt loss of what had been built up for the future and led to the cessation of the crystal structure studies that had been the basis of my career.[34]

The Closure of the Princeton Laboratories

Financial concerns in the immediate post-war period led the chairman of the Rockefeller's board of trustees, John D. Rockefeller Jr., to suggest transferring research at the Department of Animal and Plant Pathology in Princeton (New Jersey) to New York and closing the laboratories. The capital investment had cost some two million dollars, and was valued at twice that figure in 1947. Princeton University finally bought it for one-and-a-half million dollars. The members and associate members of Rockefeller in New Jersey numbered eleven: five were due to retire in six years or less. Gasser wanted to keep John H. Northrop, Wendell M. Stanley, and Richard Shope by transferring them to New York. However, only Northrop moved to the New York campus.

It is easy in retrospect to criticize this important decision, the reasons for which go beyond purely financial considerations. Among those who expressed interest in the Princeton laboratories was the Office of Naval Research. Their Advisory Panel in Biochemistry had suggested funding a protein institute, but the Office could not buy the labs and found the institute; it could fund only its research.[35] This suggestion was deemed fruitless as the aim of the Rockefeller trustees was clearly to raise capital to add to the Rockefeller's investments and to cut costs. The combination of the Princeton closure in 1950 and the earlier closure of the biophysics department laboratory meant the loss of Wyckoff, Corey, Stanley, and Shope—though Shope returned in 1952.

Did the Rockefeller Institute Lose its Way?

With the advantage of hindsight one can imagine an alternative scenario in which Wyckoff's X-ray crystallographic study of hemoglobin was not terminated by the decision to close his laboratory. The ribonuclease enzyme discovered by René Dubos, crystallized by Moses Kunitz, and sequenced by Stein and Moore, all at Rockefeller, could have been the subject of a structural study by the biophysics laboratory. Then, the solution of the three-dimensional structure, as well as the sequence, might well have been a Rockefeller achievement, making ribonuclease even more than it already is, a Rockefeller achievement. But this is mere fantasy. It is not clear that Wyckoff's heart was in the tedious and long, drawn-out study of complicated large molecules like hemoglobin. To his family he explained that solving the structure of such compounds was very different from the kind of work he had undertaken hitherto.

> Calculations became much more time-consuming as more complex crystals were studied and it became clear that new mathematical procedures were needed. Their application is now leading to the successful analysis of the huge molecules of proteins but this is a type of research that appeals to a very different kind of person from those of us who were active in the early stages of crystal analysis.[36]

Why did Gasser not act on his need for biophysics and genetics? He rightly considered that biophysics was being practiced in Rockefeller within physiology—in particular there was his own line of work, the biophysics of the nerve impulse. But the fine analysis of cell structure down to the molecular level, he stated, required X-ray crystallography. Clearly, he recognized the contribution that Wyckoff had made to the improvement in techniques, but the main occupation of a laboratory of biophysics, he asserted, would be biology, and its merits "would have to be judged on the basis of the significance of its contributions to that subject." With veiled reference to Wyckoff he added

> From this fact it follows that the head of the laboratory would have to be a biologist as well as a physicist—a rare combination and one difficult to find. But, after all, the important partner in biophysics is biology. And it would be far better never to start the laboratory than to foredoom it to failure through the appointment of a physicist unable to judge whether or not a biological problem was significant.[37]

Gasser did not underestimate the importance of genetics. He rated the gene as "one of the greatest facts, if not the greatest fact, added to biology in this century." Discovering the structure of the gene and the chromosome was fundamental to the study of constitutional diseases, an area to which more attention would rightly be devoted by Rockefeller in the future. But to analyze the gene's structure would require the aid of the Rockefeller's defunct biophysics laboratory. And he judged the stage reached by genetics did not yet give geneticists "a clear idea of what should be done. Until that stage is reached," he reckoned, "the medical problem with respect to constitution will be to learn how to compensate for what the genes fail to do."[38]

Little did Gasser know that within another three years McCarty would establish that the transforming principle upon which Avery, MacLeod, and he had been working was composed almost exclusively of DNA, and that Avery would interpret the function of DNA as genetic. Avery's report to Gasser for the fiscal year 1942–43 contains a discussion of this result that is remarkable because, in contrast to the published paper, the *only* interpretation offered is the genetic one. Hence, it is not surprising that when Macfarlane Burnet visited Avery's lab in 1943 he wrote to his wife describing Avery's discovery as "the isolation of a pure gene in the form of deoxyribonucleic acid."[39] Avery's 1943 report also contains the paragraph that the editor of the *Journal of Experimental Medicine,* Avery's Rockefeller colleague, Peyton Rous, requested Avery and his colleagues delete from the published paper. It reads,

> Leathes has pointed out that in the chemical make up of protoplasm, proteins are not the only essential substances. Among other constituents he ranks the nucleic acids as preeminent, and referring to their occurrence as major components of nuclear chromosomes he raises the question "whether the virtues of nucleic acids may not rival the amino acid chains in their vital importance."[40]

Unfortunately, Rockefeller's only geneticist, John Gowen, had left the Princeton laboratories in 1937 for a professorship at Iowa State College. If Rockefeller had a resident geneticist at that time, would the outcome have been any different? Many geneticists, H. J. Muller included, suggested the transforming DNA was a mutagen, rather than being the substance of the gene, and their commitment to the protein or nucleoprotein gene was still strong. In truth, supportive evidence was needed for an alternative explanation. It came from two directions: examples of transformation involving other hereditary traits, and analytical data demonstrating chemical diversity among DNAs of different origin. In 1948, Rollin Hotchkiss at Rockefeller published preliminary evidence of the latter; and in 1951, he reported an example of another hereditary trait acquired by transformation—penicillin resistance. Meanwhile MacLeod, who had moved to New York University in 1941, described three independently transmitted traits acquired by transformation.[41] Nevertheless, until Hotchkiss took up the subject in 1948, no staff at Rockefeller had sought to extend Avery's work in these directions.

In popular accounts the rather negative impression of Rockefeller regarding this episode has more to do with the attitude of senior staff members than with Rockefeller as a whole. This assessment is in part justified. Gasser seems not to have appreciated the significance of Avery's work, perhaps because his senior biochemist, Alfred Mirsky, was so highly critical. Thomas Rivers, head of the Rockefeller hospital where Avery's work was performed, was very preoccupied with his duties for the Navy both at the Rockefeller Hospital and overseas. The needs of war affected the hospital, focusing attention upon pathogens of relevance to military theaters abroad. At the same time, the increasing availability of the sulfonamide drugs reduced interest in studies of the kind pursued by Avery on the type changes in the causal agent of lobar pneumonia.

In any case, nothing suggests that Rockefeller lost its way. If anything, remaining true to its medical mission kept its focus on subjects and fields that seemed more promising at the time than molecular structure.

Conclusion

The discovery of the identity of the transforming substance was made in wartime, when scientific communication was suboptimal, and fundamental research worldwide was limited. The location of the work in the hospital of an institute devoted to medical research, limited its appeal within that institution. Yet the same institute had from the beginning promoted chemical studies fundamental to medical questions. Avery and his colleagues had, in George Corner's words, "gone far beyond the practical aim of finding means to control" the causal agent of lobar pneumonia, "and had built up a great structure of fundamental immunochemistry."[42] As has been documented here, both Landsteiner and Bergmann raised and attempted to answer the question of the nature of the chemical construction of protein and peptide molecules that confers upon them their specificity of action. As Kay has emphasized, the model for protein synthesis provided by the immune reaction proved misleading,[43] and the importance of Bergmann's contribution has been brushed aside because of his initial support of the erroneous frequency hypothesis. But by no means do all advances in science come from appropriate models and correct hypotheses! The history of the development of a science comprises the errors, the misleading, and sometimes the false, as well as the correct, the reliable, and the true. Nor should the Rockefeller's place in the history of molecular biology be assessed only in terms of the impact within the institution of relevant work performed there. The work of Avery and his colleagues ultimately had worldwide impact. Landsteiner's and Alfred Mirsky's influence on Pauling played a decisive part in drawing him into the study of protein structure and specificity, work which led to the α helix.

In any history of the molecular revolution in biology, the Rockefeller University's scientists and laboratories should to be accorded a significant role.

Endnotes

1. Horace F. Judson, *The Eighth Day: Makers of the Revolution in Biology* (New York, 1979), 582.
2. See p. viii in William Stein, ed., *Nobel Lectures in Molecular Biology: 1933–1975* (Baltimore, 1972).
3. See pp. xiv and 12 in James D. Watson, *The Double Helix: A Personal Account of the Discovery of the Structure of DNA* (New York, 1968).
4. Judson, *Eighth Day* (n. 1 above), 40.

5. Ibid., 293.
6. Ibid., 564.
7. Ibid., 608–9.
8. Lily Kay, *The Molecular Vision of Life: Caltech, the Rockefeller Foundation, and the Rise of the New Biology* (New York, 1993), 293.
9. Ibid., 166.
10. Judson, *Eighth Day* (n. 1 above), 582.
11. Pauline Mazumdar, *Species and Specificity: An Interpretation of the History of Immunology* (Cambridge, 1995).
12. Friedrich Obermayer and Ernst P. Pick, "Überdie Chemische Grundlagen der Arteigenschacten der Eiweisskörper," *Wiener klinische Wochenschrift* 19 (1906): 327–34; Karl Landsteiner, *The Specificity of Serological Reactions*, 2d. ed. (Cambridge, 1945), 156.
13. Landsteiner, 157.
14. Ibid., 179.
15. Ibid. See specifically Landsteiner's footnote 44.
16. Ibid., 285.
17. Ibid., 292.
18. Karl Landsteiner to Linus Pauling, April 28, 1942, Ava Helen and Linus Pauling Papers, Oregon State University Library, Corvallis, Oregon.
19. A. Rothen and K. Landsteiner, "Adsorption of Antibodies by Egg Albumin Films," *Science* 90 (1939): 65–6.
20. Stein, *Nobel Lectures* (n. 3 above), 441.
21. Max Bergmann, Scientific Report to the Director, 1942, box 5, RG 439, Rockefeller University Archives, Rockefeller Archive Center, Sleepy Hollow, New York (hereafter RAC).
22. Max Bergmann, "Proteins and Proteolytic Enzymes," in *Harvey Lectures* (1935–36), 21–2.
23. Joseph Fruton, *Proteins, Enzymes, Genes: The Interplay of Chemistry and Biology* (New Haven, 1999). See page 212 for this quote.
24. Stanford Moore, William Stein, and Max Bergmann, "Protein Constitutent Analysis by the Solubility Method," *Journal of Biological Chemistry* 30 (1942): 423–32.
25. Robert Olby, "The Recasting of the Sciences: The Case of Molecular Biology," in *La ristrutturazione delle scienze tra le due guerre mondiali*, ed. G. Battimeli, M. de Maria, and A. Rossi (Rome, 1986).
26. Archer J. Martin and Richard Synge, "A New Form of Chromatogram Employing Two Liquid Phases," *Biochemistry Journal* 35 (1941): 1358–68.
27. John Kendrew to Stanford Moore and William Stein, November 2, 1955, folder C.273, John Kendrew Papers, Bodleian Library, Oxford, England. Cited in Soraya De Chadarevian, "Sequences, Conformations, Information: Biochemists and Molecular Biologists in the 1950s," *Journal of the History of Biology* 29 (1996): 371–3.
28. Allen Edmunson and Christophe H. W. Hirs, "The Amino-Acid Sequence of Sperm Whale Myoglobin," *Nature* 190 (1961): 663–5.
29. Derek G. Smyth, William H. Stein, and Stanford Moore, "The Sequence of Amino Acid Residues of Bovine Pancreatic Ribonuclease: Revisions and Confirmations," *Journal of Biological Chemistry* 238 (1963): 227–34; G. Kartha, J. Bello, and D. Harker, "Tertiary Structure of Ribonuclease," *Nature* 213 (1967): 862–5; H. W. Wyckoff, K. D. Hardman, N. M. Allewell, T. Inagami, N. Johnson, and F. M. Richards, "The Structure of Ribonuclease-S at 3.5 Å Resolution," *Journal of Biological Chemistry* 242 (1967): 3984–8.
30. Ralph Wyckoff to Simon Flexner, April 3, 1935, Ralph W. G. Wyckoff folder 5, reel 127, Simon Flexner Papers (microfilm), Rockefeller University Archives, RAC.
31. Ralph Wyckoff, "Future of Biophysics," report to Herbert Gasser, January 17, 1936, folder 2, box 1, Ralph W. G. Wyckoff Papers, RG 450 W972, Rockefeller University Archives, RAC.
32. Herbert Gasser, "Future Directions. Report on the Activities and Problems of the Rockefeller Institute," 1940, box 5, RG 439, Rockefeller University Archives, RAC.
33. Ralph Wyckoff to Joshua Lederberg, January 10, 1983, with extract of biographical notes, National Library of Medicine, Profiles in Science, available at http://profiles.nlm.nih.gov/BB/A/G/G/C.
34. Ibid.

35. Rear Admiral Lee to Dr. Kimball, April 8, 1949, folder 14, box 1, RG 302.4, Rockefeller University Archives, RAC. See also supportive letter from the Dean of the Graduate School (Princeton), Hugh S. Taylor to Rear Admiral Lee, April 12, 1948, folder 12, box 1, RG 302.4, Rockefeller University Archives, RAC.
36. Wyckoff (n. 30 above).
37. Gasser, (n. 31 above), 71.
38. Ibid., 37.
39. M. Burnett to Mrs. Burnett, in *Changing Patterns: An Atypical Biography* (Melbourne, 1968), 81.
40. Oswald T. Avery, Scientific Report to the Director, 1943, p. 152, box 5, RG 439, Rockefeller University Archives, RAC.
41. Robert Austrian and Colin M. MacLeod, "Acquisition of M Protein by Pneumococci through Transformation Reactions," *Journal of Experimental Medicine* 89 (1948): 451–60.
42. George W. Corner, *A History of the Rockefeller Institute 1901-1953: Origins and Growth* (New York, 1964), 460.
43. Kay, (n. 8 above).

Chapter 15

Paul A. Weiss, 1898–1989: The Cell Engineer

Sabine Brauckmann

Research Fellow, Konrad Lorenz Institute for Evolution and Cognition Research, Altenberg, Austria

> ***We must treat all cells as physical systems in space and time, endowed with definable properties which are subject to the limitations of all physical bodies and their laws of behavior.***[1]

When writing about Paul Alfred Weiss, a former member and professor of the Rockefeller University, it is important to discuss how his experimental work on developmental, cell, and neurobiology influenced the scientific environment at that time. However, literature from 1954, when he became the director of the newly established Laboratory for Developmental Biology, to 1978, when he left Rockefeller, marginalizes Weiss's contribution to and influence on the rise of these biological disciplines at the university. Yet, by carefully examining his articles, lectures, reports, and grant applications that contained the protocols, data, and theories, his expertise on cell contact and cell locomotion becomes apparent, and one can identify his impact. In neurobiology, Weiss discovered the axonal flow of peripheral nerves; in neurosurgery, he developed a new technique for bridging cut nerves without sutures; and in cell biology, he explained the mechanisms of cell contact with immunological and morphological models. Moreover, modern medical technology uses his patent for welded tantalum tubes to pin together broken bones.

Given these contributions, it is astonishing that the historiography of biology has barely recognized the significant role Weiss played in American biology of the twentieth century.[2] There are numerous reasons that one might suggest for this neglect. Although some called him respectfully "dean of growth," he was not unanimously liked by his fellow biologists. Paul Weiss's nickname, given when he worked at the University of Chicago, was "Herr Geheimrat" —a term of exaggerated distinction suggesting to Americans a self-important German professor. No doubt, Weiss sometimes behaved like a version of it, especially in his strong penchant for theorizing, which discouraged and annoyed many of his American colleagues. But these reasons are in themselves too simple to explain the neglect or marginalization of Weiss.

Instead, one should look to the specific discipline of developmental biology on which Weiss worked over some decades. Because of the rise of cell biology and molecular genetics, his field faded around the late 1960s or early 1970s—or so it is said. With developmental biology's eclipse, its founding fathers disappeared from the historical narrative, and their scientific achievements were marginalized. Further possible answers will be left to the yet-to-be-written scientific biography of Paul Weiss that will portray an individual climbing up the ivory tower of pure research. As in every tower, this one also consists of steps impeding the rise of this *homo scientificus*, and partly preventing his advancement. Each floor in this tower matches the experimental fields of developmental, cell, and neurobiology, offering him some rest until his yearning for acceptance and certitude drives him forward again.

Therefore, the objective of this essay is to reconstruct a nearly forgotten chapter of theoretical cell biology. The following will chronologically discuss a cell model of the 1950s that describes how contact and locomotion affect growth and differentiation. From a more theoretical point of view, it means walking on surfaces, interfaces, and extracellular matrices, all which are permanently contacted by cell systems. The main argument being addressed here is how the Weissian model of cell adhesion and cell motility fits into his framework of topochemistry, or cytophysics, as he called his model of cell biology in an article on cellular differentiation.[3] Both terms, whether one speaks of topochemistry or cytophysics, were used to investigate the physical properties of cell boundaries and the physico-chemical mechanisms triggering cell contact, cell orientation, and cell locomotion. With this new discipline of biochemical morphology, Weiss wanted to build a bridge linking cell behavior to the molecular level, and conversely molecular structure to cell movements, without reducing the living cell completely to a model system of biochemistry.

This essay begins with a brief portrayal of the academic life of Paul Weiss before he came to Rockefeller. It is followed by a more theoretical treatise on molecular ecology and the contact guidance theory, on which his cell dynamics was based. With them he explicated the cellular specificity that he and Cecil Taylor investigated in a series of experiments at the University of Chicago and the Rockefeller Institute from 1950 to 1960. Their main objective was to study the fate of single cell suspensions that were obtained by mechanical dissociation of embryonic chick tissues into their constituent cells.[4] Weiss and Taylor followed up an experiment originally performed by H. V. Wilson in 1907 and repeated with tissue culture by P. S. Galtsoff nearly twenty years later.[5] Their joint work culminated in the famous finding that single cell suspensions from embryonic organs could reconstitute the original type of organs (e.g., liver and kidneys) from which they had been derived; i.e., they underwent organotypic differentiation.[6] As this famous experiment is well known, the essay will end shortly before they reported the finding to the National Academy of Sciences in October 1960. Instead of a conclusion, the essay ends with a rough outline of the relevance of the Weissian cell model to more recent approaches.

Biographical Sketch

Paul Weiss was born in Vienna on March 21, 1898, and studied biology, engineering, and physics at the University of Vienna. In 1922, he finished his studies with a thesis about the movements of butterfly wings that sharply criticized the mechanistic tropism theory formulated by Jacques Loeb. In the same year, he presented a paper at the centennial of the "Gesellschaft Deutscher Naturforscher und Ärzte" about the controversial resonance principle by which he interpreted the data of his transplantation experiments. Weiss's first contact with the Rockefeller philanthropic network occurred in 1928 when he was awarded an International Education Board travel grant to conduct his research on tissue culture and nerve–muscle reinnervation at the Oceanographic Institute in Monaco, the Sorbonne in Paris, and the Kaiser-Wilhelm Institute for Biology in Berlin-Dahlem.

In September 1931, he started his American career as a Sterling Fellow of Yale University by working in the laboratory of Ross G. Harrison, the doyen of American embryology and master of the tissue culture technics. At Yale, Weiss reexamined whether his earlier results on the orientation of a mixture of coagulated blood plasma and embryonic extract that was affected by mechanical tension would also hold for the outgrowth of nerve fibers. Based on the new data, he formulated a general rule of "contact guidance" for protoplasmic movement that he later refined to "selective contact affinity" between cell and substratum in the 1940s. After the Sterling Fellowship ended in 1934, the University of Chicago appointed him assistant professor to succeed Benjamin Willier; and after eight struggling years, he was promoted to professor.

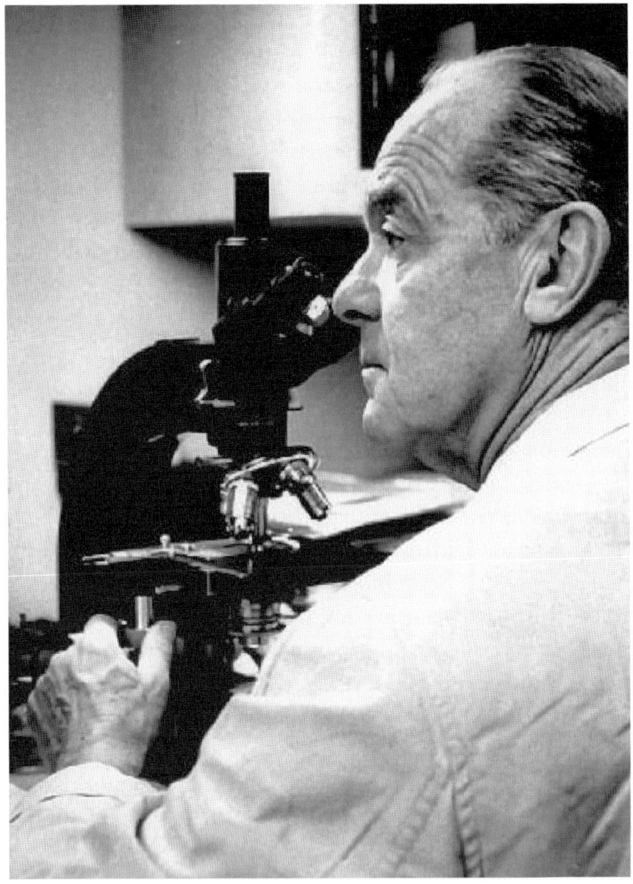

Figure 1. Portrait of Paul Weiss (circa 1960), courtesy of the Rockefeller Archive Center, Sleepy Hollow, NY.

In 1935, Weiss met Detlev W. Bronk when studying nerve action potentials at the Eldridge Reeves Johnson Foundation for Medical Physics in Philadelphia that Bronk headed.[7] The research program that Weiss continued there centered on his dual interest in growth and development of embryonic and nerve cells. For example, he demonstrated the reality of neurofibrils in vertebrate nerve cells and further investigated the mechanical stress in cartilage. Moreover, he took up a new experimental approach of neurosurgery derived from the discovery of nerve fasciculation, which led to the reunion of small nerves by tubulation. By serendipity, he also discovered that spontaneous rhythmic nerve discharge is a fundamental property of motor nerve pools. This basic finding led the way for Weiss's work on peristaltic waves pulsating on the surface of neurons and on contractile movements of the nerve sheaths in the 1960s. The tubulation technique became of great importance when Weiss was the principal investigator for governmental research on nerve repairs during World War II, when he and his group also tried to establish the first nerve banks of frozen-dried tissues.

His findings also included a correction of his programmatic article on cell orientation.[8] Now Weiss confirmed that nerve fibers are oriented by protein not tension. Furthermore, he and his collaborators detected the role of colloidal exudates in tissue organization and how the caliber of nerve cells is established. Using radioactive tracers, his group, which included his former student Roger W. Sperry, measured the steady proximo-distal flow of fluid among nerve fibers that later resulted in the important discovery of the axonal transport of peripheral nerves by Weiss and his doctoral student Helen Hiscoe in 1948. It corroborated the theory that growth of nerve fibers occurs from nerve centers in their nucleated cell bodies.[9] Among the many works he published in that period, the textbook *Principles of Development* (1939) stands out, even if it was over ten years until his fellow biologists comprehended this masterpiece of "experimental embryology."

Animated by the success of his neurosurgical method, Weiss proposed to Alan Gregg, director of the Medical Sciences of the Rockefeller Foundation, the establishment of an "Institute of Genetic Neurology" at the University of Chicago, which he would direct with Ralph W. Gerard and George W. Bartelmez. His main goal was to extend the research program on the systematic experimentation of the regeneration of peripheral nerves. Gregg, who very much disliked Weiss's personality, rejected the project after he had discussed the case with William Taliaferro and Ronald W. Harrison, dean of Chicago's Division of Biological Sciences. Neither Gregg nor the two physicians had the imagination to recognize the importance and the far-reaching consequences of this neurobiological research project. Weiss's ambitious project was condemned to fail from its planning for several reasons. Clinical medicine resented a trained biologist who was very successful in a medical specialty, particularly if the biologist's name was Paul Weiss. In addition, biology was afraid to share the grants that were meager compared with those of the well-to-do medicine. Weiss was very disappointed about the setback, but it did not affect his commitment to neurobiology.[10]

In 1948, the International Union of the Biological Sciences authorized him to organize a conference at the University of Chicago exploring the various aspects of the nervous system. Some of the participants were Francis O. Schmitt (Massachusetts Institute of Technology [MIT]), Viktor Hamburger (Washington University), Roger Sperry (University of Chicago), Holger Hyden (University of Stockholm), Rita Levi-Montalcini (Washington University), Jan Boeke (University of Utrecht), and John Z. Young (Cambridge University). This time Weiss, who had learned his lesson about Gregg's lack of enthusiasm, requested financial support from Warren Weaver, director of the Natural Sciences Program of the Rockefeller Foundation. Although the Division of Medical Sciences did not support the application, Weaver nonetheless granted it. Simultaneously, the most fruitful period of Weiss's research began, as he himself stated in a biographical addendum sent to the National Academy of Sciences that had elected him to membership in 1947.[11]

In 1950, as chairman of the National Research Council's Division of Biology and Agriculture, Weiss sent a questionnaire to his colleagues regarding the possible institutionalization of developmental biology by splitting up the experimental embryology specialty into developmental and (molecular) cell biology. One year later, Weiss chaired a symposium organized by the Committee on Growth of the National Research Council. There, he enumerated the issue of the morphogenetic field, or pattern formation, and the role of molecular structure and how it controls growth and differentiation as important developmental problems needing further exploration. To push the topic of developmental biology, he arranged a series of conferences that occupied him for nearly three years. In 1956, for example, an international community of anatomists, biochemists and biophysicists, histologists, cytologists, endocrinologists, geneticists, and immunologists met at various sites in the United States to discuss how growth and cell differentiation is connected to immunology and genetics.

In March 1954, when Bronk offered Weiss the opportunity to join the Rockefeller Institute as member and director of the newly founded Laboratory of Developmental Biology with a starting budget of $50,000, he accepted the position and wrote very enthusiastically,

> My desire to spend what active life is left to me in effective service to the field of developmental biology is matched by my intent to serve you personally in your striving towards ideals of scientific and humanistic attainment which I know to be our common goal.[12]

To furnish his laboratory and staff it with personnel, Weiss traveled extensively throughout Europe in the summer of 1954. In addition, he wanted firsthand knowledge of the newest research done at European universities and research institutes in order to correlate his developmental biology research program with other research data in cytology, genetics, histology, pathology, and endocrinology. Therefore, Weiss visited several research institutions in Switzerland, Germany, Sweden, and the United Kingdom where he was mainly interested in seeing the newest findings of adaptive enzyme formation, immunogenetic analysis of embryonic proteins and cytochemistry, and new methods like the electron microscopy or in vitro tissue culturing. Because his laboratories in Flexner Hall were not available until January 1955, he conducted his research on epidermal cell suspension and the effects of vitamin A on cellular differentiation in the Chicago lab.[13]

After Weiss came to Rockefeller, many distinguished European scientists worked as visiting investigators in Weiss's laboratory, including Wulf Emmo Ankel (Giessen, Germany), Jean Brachet (Brussels, Belgium), Fritz Lehmann (Bern, Switzerland), Trygve Gustafson (Stockholm, Sweden), Silvia F. Jackson (Cambridge, UK), and Sir John T. Randall (London, UK). Among his co-workers and graduate students, besides Cecil Taylor, the master in microphotograpy, were Michael Corner, who later succeeded Ariens Kappers as director of the Netherlands Central Institute for Brain Research; Lee Kavanau, a former assistant of Francis O. Schmitt at MIT, who developed a mathematical theory of growth; Alexander Matoltsy from Harvard Medical School experimenting with eye and skin tissue; Aron A. Moscona who succeeded Weiss at the University of Chicago; and Murray Rosenberg, trained in physics at Harvard, who spent over seven years in Weiss's laboratory researching cultural cells. Rosenberg later became one of the outstanding investigators in cellular and molecular biophysics when he was appointed director of the Cell Biology Program of the University of Minnesota.

In the fall semester of 1956, Weiss became visiting professor of biology at MIT, where he lectured on growth and cell differentiation. The lectures were primarily designed for graduate students in biochemistry and biophysics and were jointly given at the Rockefeller campus and MIT. The University of Giessen feted Weiss in the following year, awarding him his second honorary degree of doctor of science at the university's 350th anniversary celebration in June 1957. A few months later, he became the first American to receive the 500,000th Leitz microscope, an award whose predecessors included Paul Ehrlich and Gerhard Domagk. Beginning in the fall of 1956, and continuing over the next several years at the Rockefeller campus, Weiss taught a course on contemporary biology and related physical sciences—including the molecular basis of cellular differentiation—and once gave a series of lectures with Jean Brachet on genetics, biochemistry, and developmental biology. In their experiments, he and his co-workers could corroborate for the first time that cell suspensions, to which the enzyme trypsin was applied to strip the cells of any memory or previous association, reaggregate to their initial organs. The United Cerebral Palsy Association credited Weiss for his contributions in the field of neuroembryology with the Max-Weinstein Award in 1959.

In 1964, Weiss left Rockefeller Institute to accept the deanship of the Graduate School of Biomedical Sciences at the University of Houston (GSBS). Although he was more than hesitant, Weiss finally agreed to the offer, and in turn rejected an offer from Indiana University in Bloomington. What Weiss did not know was that when the University of Texas received state authority to establish the GSBS in 1963, the enterprise was largely contingent on the transfer of governmental grants from the M.D. Anderson Cancer Center to the new biomedical faculty. Unfortunately, the University of Texas was unsuccessful in that gambit, and GSBS was degraded to an academic accessory; as a result, the dean's position became essentially meaningless. Weiss was not willing to accept this loss of prestige and resigned in September 1965, after only 11 months in Texas. He never recovered from this experience, particularly because his position at the University was now lost and his reputation was damaged. After a mental breakdown, he was hospitalized in White Plains, New York in 1978. Paul Alfred Weiss died there on September 8, 1989.

From Topochemistry to Cytophysics

In 1928, when studying the impact of the matrix structure on cellular growth and shaping at the Kaiser-Wilhelm Institute in Berlin Dahlem, Weiss realized that organ formation is basically a cooperative product of cells and the ground substance in which they are embedded.[14] As a visiting scientist in Albert Fischer's tissue culture laboratory, he tried to impose form by mechanical tension on shapeless cell masses cultured in a colloidal medium. In so doing, he found that the shape and motility of cells depend on the physical and chemical constitution of the culture medium, a coagulated mixture of blood plasma and embryonic extract. Later, he confirmed this finding in a series of experiments at Harrison's laboratory at Yale, and took up the topic again at the University of Chicago in the 1940s. His results about the mechanism of wound healing contributed to improved methods of peripheral nerve repair.

Shortly after his war research on neuromuscular connections, Weiss concentrated his experimental work on the enigma of cell migration in general. Weiss's basic statement at that time was that the position of the molecules inside a cell determines the development.[15] Here, "position" refers to the concept that cellular components coadaptated to certain physical and chemical conditions prevailing at that particular location. Consequently, he interpreted development as the sorting and segregation of biochemically distinct entities into definite locations. If the hypothesis of positional effect proved true, the organization and growth of the embryo would be regulated by the ever-changing physical environment surrounding the newly multiplied cells. Even the first cells formed after fertilization of the egg experience different environments. Thus, two cells with similar components could develop and mature differently, depending on which molecules were situated on the inside and which on the outside.

As the original similar cells come in contact with different environments consisting of other cells and their products, the differences in surface conditions cause their membranes to become occupied by different molecular species. When the cell divides, its environment continues to change, so that the outer cells must adapt to other conditions than those established for the inner ones. Weiss's approach to cellular development presupposes the spatial conditions of solid state systems as, for example, all surfaces and interfaces in the cell demonstrate them. These systems are the physical bases for the selective localization and the traffic management in the chemical machinery of the cell. The new biological discipline focusing on these structures was named *cytophysics.*[16]

In a famous lecture at Yale Medical School that he delivered in 1946, Weiss used the model of serological specificities to translate the purely descriptive concepts of embryology to its molecular equivalents.[17] First, he coined the term "molecular ecology" as merely another term for the more symbolic one of the cell, describing a cell as a bounded and mixed population of molecules the surface of which conditions the developmental fate of the surrounding cells. Thus, cells of a particular type lodge in specific *niches* of a closely defined space to which they are physically, chemically, and physiologically adapted.

Weiss construed cellular movements within the principle of steric molecular interlocking across cell boundaries as a possible mechanism although there was not yet any direct experimental confirmation of such a selective lodging of cells. In effect, he applied Ehrlich's key–lock model and Pauling's templates, which are both based on spatial correspondences. However, Weiss reformulated the latter: in his model, master populations that are specifically configured macromolecules serve as templates or as intracellular specific catalysts forcing surrounding molecules to assume a complementary structure and to trigger specific growth. That means that they act precisely like antigen–antibody systems. The postulated cell-specific diversity of compounds was thought of as the chemical correlate of the differentiation of cell strains, and the growth rate as proportional to the concentration of these intracellular specific catalysts (or templates) in the active state. Furthermore, each cell also produces antitemplates that can inhibit the former species by combining with them and forming inactive complexes. The antitemplates have to enter the extracellular space by carrying the specific label of their producer cell type which endows them with selective affinity for any cell of the same type. In other words, the key compounds in the cytoplasm become gauges that reshape or convert more complex structures, furnished from the genic space, into conforming patterns. Consequently, the new surface populations occupy a position such that they can initiate transient changes in the appearance and distribution of compounds inside a cell. With the function of membranes, they control the selective transfer of substances and energy between the molecular realms they divide. The modulations, as Weiss called the transient processes, merely regroup the existing molecular species without basically changing their structure, whereas differentiation irreversibly transforms the composition of a cell population.

In 1945, Weiss—with Dan Campbell and Robert Petzold, who both had worked under Alfred Sturtevant and Linus Pauling on immunogenetics at Caltech—started a series of experiments using isotope-tagged antibodies. The aim was to demonstrate the selective absorption directly and to confirm homologous growth interactions. Although the series of experiments was performed over a period of five years and they even used aided isotope assays, they did not produce the expected results.[18] At that time, it was not possible to corroborate the Weissian suggestion that the complementary systems of growth-catalyzing and growth-repressing compounds are of the antigen–antibody class, mainly because experimental tools such as monoclonal antibodies and recombinant DNA were lacking. Nevertheless, Weiss was convinced that his concept of a selective chemical communication among cells had proven its value as a guide for further research. In the early 1950s, Weiss baptized the new experimental field, which used immunological techniques for investigating cellular differentiation and growth, immunoembryology or topochemistry.[19]

To summarize, Weiss had formulated a molecular theory of mutual recognition between cells of identical types on surface contact and translated the cytological problems of growth, development and cell behavior to a molecular vocabulary. Experimentally, this endeavor led to a study of inductive interactions between cells and tissues as contact agents, and to the further investigation of organ-specific antibodies, or rather the nonimmunological demonstration of cell type–specific regulatory effects by homologous cell constituents, as possible catalysts in growth and differentiation of the respective organs.

As an illustration, the following roughly outlines a series of experiments started at the University of Chicago in 1949 originally to test chicken feathers, and later extended to test higher animals and embryonic stages. The "chicken feathers" research program stimulated further research that studied the fate of single cell suspensions. These experiments established that embryonic cells, reunited after random dispersal, underwent organotypic differentiation. Why had Weiss and his collaborators selected feathers of all the experimental systems that they could have used? A very pragmatic answer is that in the 1950s, it was difficult to trace injected cells that had to be tagged. At that time, tracing had been achieved only for pigment cells because the ability to produce donor-specific pigment is genetically fixed.

Weiss and his collaborators took eggs from White Leghorns, Barred Plymouth Rocks, and Brown Leghorns. White Leghorns owe their white color to the death of pigment cells after their immigration into the tissues. In the Barred Plymouth Rock, the shape of the pigment granules and the distribution of the pigment cell population correspond essentially to those of the dark pigment cells of the Brown Leghorn. The embryonic material of three-day-old White Leghorns was incorporated into three pooled two-day-old embryos of Barred Rocks and Brown Leghorns. The main questions they wanted to answer were whether the dissociated embryonic cells will survive, whether they will retain their developmental capacities in the blood stream, and where they will settle. His group observed thousands of pigment cells, but never saw a single one that was ever out of place. Therefore, they concluded that the cells were selectively coalesced at their type-specific destinations, confirming Johannes Holtfreter's tissue affinity theory. Interestingly, Holtfreter also stated in his seminal article that gestalt locomotion results in pattern formation, whereas cellular differentiation and migrations affect the shaping process first at a later stage of development.[20]

How did Weiss now explain contact guidance, the biological translation of molecular ecology, in his behavioral model? For him, contact guidance of cells along an extracellular matrix that ultimately determines cell morphology, means a dual operation. First, each cell, according to its type of differentiation, acquires specific surface properties that enable it to apply itself to, or detach itself from, matching and nonmatching surfaces; and, second, adjoining surfaces—composed either of other cell surfaces or of cellular products—have chemical constitutions that can act as selective guides for the differential application of cell types.

Weiss could demonstrate this framework of interlocking chemical sensitivities for nerve fibers by the early 1940s and ten years later for the screening out of embryonic cells from the bloodstream by their appropriate sites as well.[21] Furthermore, his collaborators confirmed it for the selective coalescence of homologous or complementary tissues in wound healing and for the self-sorting according to tissue types of scrambled epithelial cells from single cell suspensions.[22] As homotypic cells are swarming about one another without forming rigid connections, Weiss assumed that the phenomenon of selective association could not be explained in terms of complementary molecular films acting as permanent cements between identical cell surfaces, as he had suggested earlier.[23]

Research had suggested that cells get in touch with each other because they possess a specific surface composition, and because a medium guides and controls their outgrowth and motility. However, how does the medium (i.e., the extracellular matrix) push the cell to move and to differentiate on its way? For the answer, Weiss applied the anisotropic field of engineering conduction to his model of cell locomotion:

> Since the formation of a feather requires a complicated and strictly coordinated pattern of movements and growth of the tributary cells, our experiment had proved that a random assortment of cells can, as a group, set up conditions de novo—a "field"—which will cause the members of the group to move and grow . . .[24]

The field that surrounds the cell disturbs the pressure–tension configuration of the embryonic cell.[25] By doing so, it forces the embryonic cells to deform themselves and to lose the spherical shape of their initial state. Starting from a planar pattern, the embryonic cell extends itself into a spatial grid as peristaltic waves sweep from the epidermal surface downward to coordinate the random population of fibrous elements to a three-dimensional structure. Although he could not explain the underlying dynamics, for Weiss, rhythmic oscillations synchronize phases that regulate the chemical activities of cell surfaces. The rhythmic activity orients the cellular locomotion along the extracellular matrix, thereby offering a cell-binding framework to the migrating cells and lining their pathways.[26] Both conditions, the deformation and the changing of the spherical shape, are prerequisites of cellular locomotion.

However, what does the field really mean? How does it function? And, most importantly, is the field the force of orientation pressing the moving cell to develop? Weiss would probably answer these questions as he did in his discussion at the symposium on the "Biochemical and Structural Basis of Morphogenesis" in Utrecht in 1952 and in a theoretical paper, published with his doctoral student Beatrice Garber in 1952. The article, which discussed the shape and movement of mesenchyme cells, aimed at correlating quantitatively the organic form, and its shaping, to the underlying mechanism.

Fig. 2 illustrates the fate of an embryonic blood island in the chick embryo where a group of equipotential cells (top) undergo divergent differentiation (bottom). The outer cells form a vascular endothelium and the inner ones form free blood cells. The whole cell cluster is activated in producing metabolites that can diffuse into the outer medium, but will be most concentrated in the center. Thus, some cells along the free surface will spread inward with a gradient from their source (Fig. 2 b, top). The cell net can react to a particular constellation or combination of such factors by a differentiating step whereby the threshold for their reaction lies at the level of the dashed line **t**. Then in the central area, all cells will be switched into the altered course. This case demonstrates the response to a graded field of partly self-generating stimuli. In the transition zone near the threshold level, the prospective response of a given individual cell will be unpredictable, but the steeper the gradient, the sharper the line of demarcation will be.

In turn, a new chain of responses can be activated in the central cell net (Fig. 2 b, dots). This may contract the central group from the broken to the solid contour, and the outer cells attached to the shrinking core will be subject to centripetal tension. As a result they become radially elongated (Fig. 2 c) which in turn may facilitate the outward diffusion or transmission

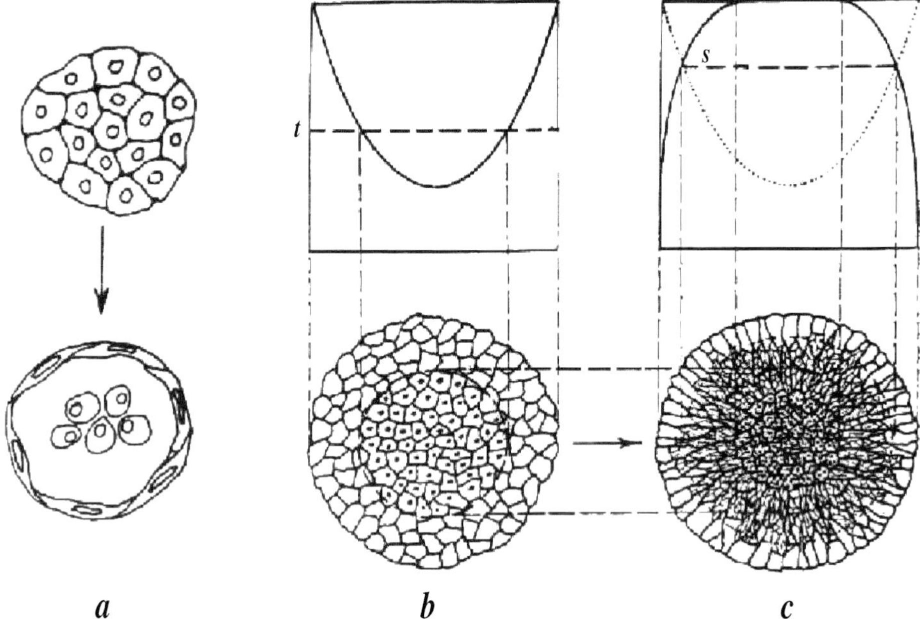

Figure 2. An illustration of the cellular field. From Paul A. Weiss, "Some Introductory Remarks on the Cellular Basis of Differentiation," *Journal of Embryology and Experimental Morphology* 1 (1953): 208. Reprinted with permission of The Company of Biologists.

of the newly produced agent. (Its emergent diffusion field is represented by the solid curve in Fig. 2 c.) The earlier substance gradient will have persisted (dotted line) and interacted with the new centrifugal factor derived from the rotating nucleus that at the same time will stop further diffusion by a precipitate. This happens in the area where the concentrations of the two agents are about equal, as indicated by the intersection of the two curves at the level **s** (dashed line). Hence, a new zone intermediate between the original core and a new barrier will arise with new influences, activating in the constituent cells the next step of their differentiation repertory.

To recall the hypothesis of the position effect, a cascade of developmental fields determines the fate of a cell that occupies a specific position within the cellular group as he stated in a lecture on "The Cellular Basis of Differentiation" at the Zoology Club of the University of Chicago in 1953.[27] In 1959, Weiss explicated these questions again in his grant report to the NIH. However, he did not answer it with the field concept, but referred to an inherent polarity of cells that can be experimentally investigated; i.e., the so-called two-center effect. This effect implicitly refers to contact guidance. In a short and critical response to an article by Allan Katzberg published in *Science* in 1951, Weiss precisely elaborated on the means of avoiding the misinterpretation of a mysterious force that attracts cellular tissue over distance. In his approach that categorically rejected distance actions, a cell needs a medium to guide its outgrowth and motility. In a seminar on connective tissue held at the University of Wisconsin in 1955, he further illustrated his model of cell behavior with his transplantation experiments of cut nerves.[28] In Weiss's view, the expansion of a cell could be understood only when thinking of a competition between two opposing set of forces such as cohesion and surface tension shaping a minimal surface, ideally a sphere.

When his collaborator Taylor observed that glass slides scored with microgrooves had similar effects on cells as tissues—the physical medium they had used before—they took moving pictures of the act of orientation. They deposited single cell suspensions obtained by trypsinization of embryonic organs on such a slide and showed how the initial spherical cells first spread, flattened along the slide, and gradually elongated to slender spindle shapes oriented in the direction of the microgrooves. Thus, they could resolve the morphological polarization of the cell into a problem of adhesivity of different parts of the cell border according to differences in the physical substratum.

Furthermore, they discovered that after its polar elongation, a single cell retained an active motility at its two free ends even if it did not move forward. The reason was that these two ends counteracted each other forcing the cell to shuttle back and forth about a stationary position. When two mesenchymal cells contact each other with their free motile ends by chance, they produce a mutual paralysis of the colliding tips. The two remaining, nonconfronting ends of the two colliding cells that were not affected, dragged the bodies apart in opposite directions. The paralysis consisted of an active detachment from the substratum followed by a contractile wave. After nearly an hour, the paralyzed ends move, attach themselves again on the substratum, and hold the cells once more arrested at a greater distance from each other. Weiss and Taylor here construed the phenomenon of "cell repulsion."[29]

Instead of a Conclusion

In general, Weiss's research program focused on solving some puzzles of cell biology, namely, how cells move, how they translocate themselves or how they glide over an extracellular matrix, and how they are oriented at interfaces. In other words, explicitly recalling his self-assessment as a morphological biologist, Weiss investigated cell–cell interactions and the self-sorting of cells as they shape organic form. Of main importance for the research project on the life and works of Paul Weiss is that his theories on cells in the 1950s can be traced back to the concept of the morphogenetic field of the 1920s when he started his scientific career in Vienna and Berlin.

The conservative developmental biologists of that time not only rejected Weiss's highly sophisticated model but they also did not even appreciate its possibilities. The same negative attitude holds true for molecular biology and the burgeoning field of cell biology—whose meteoric rise in the 1980s was due to the new technique of immunofluorescence. Although he more or less suggested schematic representations of the cellular interface phenomena always relating to a surface forming the boundary between two bodies or chemical phases, and of cell behavior in general, his proposal that surface reorientations could result in transient breaches of the plasma membranes was confirmed by more elaborate electron microscopic research on the interface between some erythroblasts. Furthermore, Weiss's hypotheses were consistent with contemporary theories of membrane structure and function as exemplified by the fluid mosaic model of Seymour J. Singer and Garth Nicholson in 1972, particularly with the dynamic aspect of membranes emphasized by the property of translational mobility of the intercalated proteins.

Instead of the case of interfaces and surfaces, one could also refer to the well-established model of positional information or to the vast field of topobiology.[30] The working hypothesis for the cytophysical research program was Weiss's conviction that biology had accumulated data concerning biochemical processes within cells in an impressive way. However, information regarding the physical and structural mechanisms which permit, enhance, inhibit or modify these specific chemical operations, as well as the mechanisms of intracellular and transcellular substance transport, were lacking. To counteract the molecularization of biology, he renamed *topochemistry* of 1953 to *cytophysics* in 1960—both describing the investigation of the physical properties of cell surfaces and the mechanisms involved in cell contact, orientation, and locomotion. To this end, he emphasized the importance of engineering principles for growth and differentiation of cells, characterized as a physical body undergoing displacement in space. Thus, it is ironic that the Weissian cytodynamics finally resulted in a field like molecular embryology or topobiology.

No doubt, Paul Weiss influenced the institutionalization of cell and neurobiology just as the cell engineer researching the contact mechanisms of neural and embryonic cells did nearly 50 years ago. In general, he was recognized as one of the leading biologists whose scientific contributions to developmental biology in that period was acknowledged as of outstanding eminence comparable with that of E. B. Wilson and Harrison in an earlier generation. However, what distinguished him from many of his contemporaries was the emphasis he laid on an integrated approach towards the living cell that he comprehended as an organismic entity.[31] With his terminology of system behavior, resonance principle, contact guidance, homologous reaction, molecular ecology, and axonal transport, he dominated the communication of biological scientists over a decade—even if his fellow biologists rather disliked his concepts and approaches, or sharply criticized them.

To close this introduction to Weissian cytodynamics, I quote a more poetic Paul Weiss. In a lecture, held at Columbia Teachers College in New York City in 1959, he speculated about the outlook of the life sciences in 1970 and concluded by offering a metaphor that exemplifies his view of cell engineering:

> Who is the cell? . . . a cell is simply another community. . . . We can say that a city, like a protoplasm, is composed of people, of trolley cars, automobiles, and dogs. . . .[32]

Among the many scientists and colleagues who have helped me comprehend the scientist and the person Paul Weiss, I would like to thank Georg W. Kreutzberg for supporting my concept of the title "Cell Engineer"; Bernice Grafstein for her patience when talking time and again on Paul Alfred Weiss; Sybil and Howard Holtzer for commenting on the essay; and Aron A. Moscona for critically reading it. However, I am particularly indebted to the Rockefeller Archive Center and all its staff members for their help, assistance, and the perfect working atmosphere that I could share as Scholar-in-Residence for five months in 2000.

Endnotes

1. See p. 239 in Paul A. Weiss, "The Problem of Specificity in Growth and Development," Yale *Journal of Biology and Medicine* 19 (1947) 235–78.
2. Obviously, there are some exceptions, e.g., Scott F. Gilbert and J. P. Greenberg "Intellectual Traditions in the Life Sciences. II. Stereocomplementarity," *Perspectives in Biology and Medicine* 28 (1984): 18–34; Bernice Grafstein, "Half a Century of Regeneration Research," in *Regeneration in the Central Nervous System*, eds. Nicholas A. Ingoglia and Marion Murray (New York, 2000); E. B. Grunewald, "The conceptual and experimental foundations of vertebrate embryonic cell adhesion research," in *A*

Conceptual History of Modern Embryology, ed. Scott F. Gilbert (Baltimore, 1991), 129–158; Georg W. Kreutzberg, "Paul A. Weiss. 21.3.1898–8.9.1989," *Max-Planck-Gesellschaft (München). Berichte und Mitteilungen*, Heft 4/90 (1990): 114–16; Jane Overton, "Paul Alfred Weiss. March 21, 1898–September 8, 1989," *Biographical Memoirs, National Academy of Sciences* 72 (1997): 372–86; Sabine Brauckmann, *The homo scientificus Paul A. Weiss. A Life Along the Cell* [forthcoming].

3. Paul A. Weiss, "Some Introductory Remarks on the Cellular Basis of Differentiation," *Journal of Embryology and Experimental Morphology* 1 (1953): 181–211.
4. A letter that Weiss wrote to his friend Sir John T. Randall (King's College, London) on January 4, 1960, illustrates the program: "We have, therefore, embarked on a systematic program of study, with all possible methods including electron microscopy, Langmuir films, ellipsometry, fluorescence microscopy . . . of the adhesiveness of cells and the spreading of cells on different inorganic and organic substrate in relation to molecular constitution and spacing . . .": Weiss to Randall, January 4, 1960, folder 5, box 34, Record Group 450W436 Paul A. Weiss Papers (hereafter Weiss Papers), Rockefeller University Archives, Rockefeller Archive Center, Sleepy Hollow, NY (hereafter RAC).
5. Henry V. Wilson, "Development of Sponges from Dissociated Tissue Cells," *Bulletin of the Bureau of Fisheries* 30 (1911): 1–30; Paul S. Galtsoff, "Heteroagglutination of Dissociated Sponge Cells," *Biological Bulletin* 57 (1925): 250–60.
6. Paul A. Weiss and A. Cecil Taylor, "Reconstitution of Complete Organs from Single-Cell Suspensions of Chick Embryos in Advanced Stages of Differentiation," *Proceedings of the National Academy of Sciences* 46 (1960): 1177–85.
7. Detlev Bronk to Paul A. Weiss, 20 February 1935, folder 11, box 17, RG 303.1 Detlev W. Bronk Papers, Rockefeller University Archives, RAC.
8. Paul A. Weiss, "Methodik der Functionellen Extremitätentransplantation," in *Handbuch der Biologischen Arbeitsmethoden*, ed. Emil Abderhalden (Berlin, 1929), 5 (part 2:2):1335–56.
9. The article became a classic of neurobiology in the late 1960s, compare with Paul A. Weiss and Helen Hiscoe, "Experiments on the Mechanism of Nerve Growth," *Journal of Experimental Zoology* 107 (1948): 315–95.
10. For a further information about Weiss's trial to establish a new discipline of neurobiology, see Sabine Brauckmann, "Paul A. Weiss and the Intellectual and Institutional Framework of Science," *Research Reports from the Rockefeller Archive Center* (Spring 2000), 6–9.
11. "Developments Since Deposition of Biography with the National Academy of Science (1947–1957)," c. 1957, folder 3, box 1, Weiss Papers, Rockefeller University Archives, RAC.
12. Paul Weiss to Detlev Bronk, March 11, 1954, folder 4, box 10, Weiss Papers, Rockefeller University Archives, RAC.
13. Catherine Overton to Johan J. P. Zaaijer, May 21, 1954, folder 2, box 95, Weiss Papers, Rockefeller University Archives, RAC.
14. In 1932, the German hydrobiologist Richard Woltereck first applied the histological term *matrix* to developmental biology stating that the matrix conditions the specific constitution of an organism. Weiss had already adopted the approach in the late 1920s.
15. This statement heavily relies on the concept of the equipotential system, as Hans Driesch (1908/1921) characterized the embryo.
16. In a lecture on cellular dynamics, held at the University of Miami in 1960, Weiss referred in this context to a newly emerging discipline and called it *cytophysics*. See folder 2, box 60, Weiss Papers, Rockefeller University Archives, RAC.
17. "Differential Growth," Yale University Medical School, 1946, folder 12, box 57, Weiss Papers, Rockefeller University Archives, RAC.
18. Gert Andres, "Experiments on the Fate of Dissociated Embryonic Cells (Chick) Disseminated by the Vascular Route. Part II. Teratomas," *Journal of Experimental Zoology* 122 (1953): 507–40; Howard Holtzer, "Reconstitution of the Urodele Spinal Cord following Unilateral Ablation. Part I. Chronology of Neuron Regulation," *Journal of Experimental Zoology* 117 (1951): 523–57; Howard Holtzer, "Reconstitution of the Urodele Spinal Cord following Unilateral Ablation. Part II. Regeneration of the Longitudinal Tracts and Ectopic Synaptic Unions of the Mauthner's Fiber," *Journal of Experimental Zoology* 119 (1952): 263–301; James W. Lash, "Studies on Wound Closure in Urodeles," *Journal of*

Experimental Zoology 128 (1955): 13–28.
19. Paul A. Weiss, "Specificity in Growth Control," in Biological Specificity and Growth, ed. Elmer G. Butler (Princeton, NJ, 1955), 195–206. For the first time, Weiss circumscribed chemical morphology with *topochemistry* in a lecture on cellular differentiation held at the Zoology Club of the University of Chicago in 1953. See folder 22, box 66, and folder 12, box 57, Weiss Papers, Rockefeller University Archives, RAC.
20. Grunewald, *Conceptual History* (n. 2 above), 136: "Holtfreter interpreted these cell and tissue rearrangements to reflect attractions and repulsions between cells which were, unlike those proposed earlier by Roux, contact-dependent."
21. On the issue, whether the reinnervation of nerves to their motor muscles is controlled by the resonance principle as Weiss claimed, or whether it is caused by chemical specificities as Roger W. Sperry has stated, Weiss and Sperry had a lifelong controversy. Paul A. Weiss, "Nerve Patterns: The Mechanics of Nerve Growth," *Growth* 5 (1941): 163–203.
22. Aron A. Moscana, "Development of Heterotypic Combinations of Dissociated Embryonic Chick Cells," *Proceedings of the Society for Experimental Biology and Medicine* 92 (1956): 410–6.
23. "Cinemicrography of Cell Interactions in Culture," 1959, folder 1, box 70, Weiss Papers, Rockefeller University Archives, RAC.
24. Paul A. Weiss, "The Compounding of Complex Macromolecular and Cellular Units into Tissue Fabrics," *Proceedings of the National Academy of Sciences* 42 (1956): 819–30.
25. From the 1920s, Weiss emphasized the existence of pattern principles (fields) that arrange the cellular system to a whole. (See Paul A. Weiss, "Unabhängigkeit der Extremitätenregeneration vom Skelett bei *Triton Rouxs cristatus*," *Rouxs Archiv für Entwicklungsmechanik der Organismen* 104 [1925]: 359–94; Paul A. Weiss, "Regeneration der Urodelenextremität als Selbstdifferenzierung des Organrestes," *Die Naturwissenschaften* 11 [1923]: 669–77.) He had deduced the field concept from the equipotential system of the biologist Hans Driesch, the gestalt theory of the psychologist Wolfgang Köhler and the mathematical model of the Russian histologist Alexander Gurwitsch. For further discussion, see Sabine Brauckmann, "The Morphogenetic Field and the Epigenetic Landscape" (presentation, William Bennett Munro Memorial Seminar, California Institute of Technology, Pasadena, CA, February 27, 2004).
26. Paul Weiss, "Summary Comments at the Conclusion of the Symposium," *Proceedings of the Symposium on the Biochemical and Structural Basis of Morphogenesis,* supplement to *Archives Néerlandaises de Zoologie* 10 (1953): 165–76, reprint no. 190, box 108, Weiss Papers, Rockefeller University Archives, RAC.
27. Paul A. Weiss, "The Cellular Basis of Differentiation," January 14, 1953, folder 13, box 57, Weiss Papers.
28. Lecture Book III, 1951–1954, folder 13, box 57, Weiss Papers, Rockefeller University Archives, RAC.
29. "Cinemicrography," 1959 (n. 23 above).
30. In the introduction of his monograph on molecular biology, Edelman defined topobiology as "those place-dependent interactions of cell surfaces with other cell surfaces or with substrates that result in changes in cell regulation . . . [which] can lead to regulation of the primary processes of embryological development and thus to change in morphology." Gerald M. Edelman, *Topobiology: An Introduction to Molecular Biology* (New York, 1988), xii.
31. For a further elaboration of his holistic thinking compare with Sabine Brauckmann, "Paul Alfred Weiss (1898–1989): The Factory of the Cell and Molecular Ecology," in *From Symbiosis to Eukaryotism—Endocytobiology VII.*, eds. Edgar Wagner et al. (Geneva, 1999), 707–17.
32. Paul Weiss, "The World of 1970," December 3, 1959, folder 2, box 58, Weiss Papers, Rockefeller University Archives, RAC.

Index